KNOW YOUR WOODS

TO THE WAYFARER

Although the beauty of trees
has been praised by many poets,
the utility of trees and wood
has rarely been better expressed
than in the following
inscription, which has been
posted on timber trees in
Portugal. The English translation
forms a fitting preamble
to this book.

Ye who pass by and would raise your hand
against me, hearken ere you harm me.
I am the heat of your hearth on the
cold winter nights, the friendly shade
screening you from the summer sun, and
my fruits are refreshing draughts
quenching your thirst as you journey on.
I am the beam that holds your house,
the board of your table,
the bed on which you lie, and
the timber that builds your boat.

I am the handle of your hoe, the door
of your homestead, the wood of your cradle,
the shell of your coffin.
I am the bread of kindness and
the flower of beauty. Ye who pass by,
listen to my prayer; harm me not!

United States Department of Agriculture photo of bur oak

THE HOME CRAFTSMAN
SERIES OF
WOODWORKING MANUALS

•

KNOW
YOUR
WOODS

Their identification, properties and
uses from the standpoint of craftsmen,
cabinetmakers, carpenters, dealers and
students . . . lumber and veneers . . . unusual,
curious and fabulous woods . . . and detailed
descriptions of 423 individual woods . . . with
profuse illustrations and a full-color
identification plate

By ALBERT CONSTANTINE, Jr.

HOME CRAFTSMAN PUBLISHING CORPORATION

NEW YORK

PRINTED IN
THE UNITED STATES OF AMERICA

To the memory of my father

ALBERT CONSTANTINE

1862-1948

who shared his extraordinary knowledge
of woods with me and encouraged me in the
studies that led to the writing of this book

preface

EVERY PERSON interested in the broad subject of woods—their identification, characteristics and uses—will find this book a revelation. The
information is presented in a clear, nontechnical style for enjoyable and
informative reading. So many facts, including some that are unusual or
little known, have never before been assembled in a volume of this kind
and skillfully organized for ready reference. In particular, the descriptions
of individual woods should be useful to the student as well as to the
general reader. This volume will be a much sought reference by craftsmen
engaged in dealing with woods.

William L. Stern   B.S., M.S., Ph.D.
Assistant Professor of Wood Anatomy,
Curator, Samuel James Record Memorial
Collection of Woods, and Editor of
Tropical Woods, School of Forestry,
Yale University

A NOTE ABOUT THE ILLUSTRATIONS

IN ADDITION TO PHOTOGRAPHS from the author's collection and drawings made especially for this book by Howard R. Berry and Arthur Collani, a number of illustrations from other sources are being used by permission. Acknowledgments for the photographs and drawings which have so generously been made available are as follows:

American Museum of Natural History, New York—Figs. 3-7 in Chap. 1; eucalyptus and cinchona in Chap. 9; citrus and fig trees in Chap. 10; Fig. 10 in Chap. 12; and photos of the following trees in Part 2: ailanthus, apple, quaking aspen, bamboo, banana, basswood, American beech, paper birch, butternut, cherry, chestnut, cottonwood, hackberry, hickory, dogwood, kauri, locust, sugar maple, monkey pod, sour orange, pawpaw, pear, European plane, sassafras, sweetgum, sycamore, yellow poplar, black walnut and black willow; also drawings of maple and oak leaves in Part 2.

Armstrong Cork Company, Lancaster, Pa. —Harvesting cork in Part 2.

Birds Eye Veneer Co., Escanaba, Mich.— Figs. 2, 4 and 5 in Chap. 5; Curly maple, red oak in Part 2.

Capital Machine Co., Indianapolis, Ind.— Fig. 3 in Chap. 5.

Coe Manufacturing Co., Painesville, Ohio— Fig. 6 in Chap. 5.

Fine Hardwoods Association, Chicago — Figs. 2, 3, 9, 10 in Chap. 6. Photos showing grain and figure of ash, aspen, avodiré, ayous, basswood, birch, bubinga, butternut, cedar, cherry, ebony, elm, faux satine, gum, harewood, imbuya, iroko, limba, maidou, makoré, maple, myrtle, narra, oak, olive, oriental wood, paldao, peroba, primavera, purpleheart, redwood, rosewood, satinwood, sycamore, teak, walnut, white lauan, yew in Part 2.

Hedrich-Blessing, Chicago—Photos showing grain and figure of lovoa and water tupelo in Part 2.

Home Craftsman Magazine, New York — Photos of cedar, fir, larch, pine, spruce in Part 2 (from Western Pine Association, Portland, Ore.).

Mahogany Association, Inc., Chicago — Figs. 1 and 3-5 in Chap. 4 and Figs. 4-8 in Chap. 6. Photos showing grain and figure of mahogany in Part 2.

McGraw-Hill Book Co., Inc., New York, by permission from **Textbook of Wood Technology,** Vol. 1, Brown and Panshin, copyright 1940, McGraw-Hill Book Co., Inc.— Figs. 1 and 2 in Chap. 2.

United Nations, New York—Fig. 8 in Chap. 1; Figs. 2 and 7-9 in Chap. 4; also, in Part 2, photos of a log depot in Turkey; pulpwood in Finland; rolling logs in Haiti, logging in the Philippines; rubber trees; sawing cedar in Brazil.

United States Department of Agriculture, Washington, D. C.—Frontispiece. Figs. 1 and 2 in Chap. 1 and Fig. 1 in Chap. 8. Leaves and needles of numerous species, as well as maps showing distribution of various trees, from **Trees—The Yearbook of Agriculture, 1949,** U. S. Government Printing Office, in Part 2, as well as photos of various fir, hemlock, juniper, maple, oak, pine, poplar and spruce trees, and a photo of each of the following: ash, blackgum, blue paloverde, cabbage palmetto, catalpa, cedar, coffeetree, crabapple, cypress, dogwood, downy serviceberry, elm, holly, laurel, locust, magnolia, myrtle, redwood, sassafras, smoketree and tamarack. The Liberian pine photo in Part 2 is from the Forest Products Laboratory.

X

acknowledgments

I AM PARTICULARLY GRATEFUL to Dr. William L. Stern, Assistant Professor of Wood Anatomy, Curator of the Samuel J. Record Collection of Woods at Yale University, and Editor of the magazine, Tropical Woods. Dr. Stern's vast scientific knowledge of woods and the many hours of his time which he so generously contributed to the preparation of this manuscript have added a great deal of value to the book.

Grateful acknowledgment is also made to E. Howard Gatewood, Executive Vice-President of the Fine Hardwoods Association, the members of which represent the country's largest manufacturers of the world's fine hardwoods. Mr. Gatewood's kind co-operation in furnishing many photographs showing various figures in wood has been of inestimable assistance to me in illustrating this book.

And my personal thanks go to the publisher's staff members, particularly to Harry J. Hobbs, Arthur Wakeling and E. Mary Trow for their capable devotion to the publishing of this book.

Albert Constantine, Jr.

contents

contents

introduction

MUCH OF THE MATERIAL in this book is based on information gathered during almost forty years of active participation in the fine cabinet-wood business. The Constantine family has been connected with the fine wood trade in New York since 1812—from its early history to the present. For many years, Constantine & Company acted as the official measurers, weighers and inspectors of all foreign timbers entering the port of New York. At an early age, therefore, the author acquired a love for woods which led to many years of research in this field.

Many people find beauty and pleasure in trees and the craft objects which can be produced from their timbers. Because of this, there are no doubt some who would like to know a bit more about these plants to help increase their interest and enjoyment. Wood is pleasant and friendly; it is nice to look at; it is warm in winter, cool in summer and always comfortable to live with. I feel sure, therefore, that many people share with me this close attachment to wood and that they will gain from this modest introduction to the study of wood. I have tried to present a general, readable, nontechnical story about trees and woods, their characteristics and uses, and some of the fascinating facts not ordinarily encountered by the lover of woods.

Trees producing timber grow in practically all regions of the globe. There is little doubt that wood was one of the earliest materials employed by ancient man in his fabrications. Even today, with the tremendous emphasis on steel, concrete, glass and plastics in construction and manufacture of all kinds, wood still maintains its importance as an essential commodity. The concrete building is constructed by employing re-usable plywood forms; the plastic in radio and television cabinets is strengthened with wood-fiber filler; wood is still uppermost as a construction material for small homes. More wood is being used today than ever before. Trees also provide us with many intangibles: they improve the appearance of our homes and other buildings, they shade us from the hot sun and keep the strong winds from buffeting our dwellings. Trees are effective in flood control, they clothe the watersheds of our reservoirs and rivers and provide refuge for wildlife. Our recreational areas are more useful and enjoyable when surrounded by trees. Briefly then, besides the material things, the value of trees and tree-covered lands is not measurable in a monetary way.

In order to understand woods and the trees producing them, it is essential that we know something of tree growth, how trees are named and the methods used in collecting and identifying woods. Therefore, I have included sections on these subjects written in nontechnical language. Chapters on medicinal trees, food and beverage trees, poisonous trees, unusual woods, and woods mentioned in the Bible are also among those in this volume. The major part of the text is, however, concerned with the woods themselves.

The largest collection of woods in the world is Yale University's Samuel James Record Memorial Collection. Here are housed over 52,000 specimens of wood. More than 240 plant families are represented in this collection, each possessing some woody species. It is certainly beyond the scope of this book to include even a small fraction of this vast array of woods; rather, I have chosen the species described later because some are commercially important, others are interesting historically, a number produce valuable fruits, and some are of a curious nature. For the most part, however, I have selected trees which are producers of lumber and veneer. The descriptions are brief and are for the most part confined to some of the more interesting facts, including some technical information. Among the subjects considered are the appearance of the wood itself, the texture, figure, weight, seasoning characteristics and strength data where available. For the craftsman, I have tried to include the working qualities of woods; which can be used with power or hand tools, which woods finish easily and which require special care. With common trees, a more detailed description of the flowers and leaves is presented; with trees growing in remote areas, descriptions are mostly limited to wood characteristics. Detailed information on the bark has been omitted except where the bark is of striking appearance.

In general, the information given has been selected to provide the craftsman and layman with a broad, practical knowledge of woods. Some references are cited at the ends of chapters and in the bibliography for those who wish to delve more deeply into a given subject. Illustrations have been liberally employed to provide a vivid, visual supplement to the text. I have tried to approach the subject personally, to convey to readers my own thrill and fascination in this living subject. I hope that I can also make woods live for them.

Albert Constantine, Jr.

PART 1
THE WONDERFUL STORY OF WOODS

a tree lives

FROM THE SEED THAT CHANCES TO LODGE in a suitable niche, the seedling emerges. Surely the seed is a thing at which to marvel. When conditions for sprouting are favorable, when the soil is moist and warm, deep changes begin to take place in the dormant seed. The embryo "feeds" upon the stored food in the seed, water is absorbed and the latent plantlet begins to grow. Normally the embryo grows fast, swelling with vigor and splitting the seed coat. The seedling emerges to greet the sunlight. The upper portion or shoot elongates skyward; the rootlet plumbs the earth to perform its function of anchorage, support, food storage and absorption of water and soil nutrients. Unlike animals, most plants remain stationary throughout their lives.

The seedling tree is tender. Its first leaves may remain within the seed beneath the ground as in the oak, or they may be carried upwards as in maple. At the tip of the little shoot, tucked in between the seed leaves, is the terminal bud which contains the growing point *(apical meristem).* The growing point is responsible for the growth in length of the shoot. Theoretically, the tree is capable of indefinite growth, and we know that there are trees now living which are in excess of 4,000 years. Root tips also possess a growing point, the action of which elongates the roots (Fig. 1).

Most trees can be classified into one of two groups as far as their root systems are concerned, either the fibrous-root system or the taproot. Trees with fibrous-root systems, to which the firs, various types of maples, beeches and many others belong, have many horizontal roots and a maze of smaller rootlets, all close to the level of the ground. Trees with the taproot system have a principal vertical root which in a large tree may go the depth of from 14 to 18 ft., from

21

TREES INCREASE EACH YEAR IN HEIGHT AND SPREAD OF BRANCHES BY ADDING ON A NEW GROWTH OF TWIGS

1961
1960
1959

LIGHT AND HEAT ARE REQUIRED BY THE LEAVES IN THE PREPARATION OF FOOD OBTAINED FROM THE AIR AND SOIL. THE LEAVES GIVE OFF MOISTURE BY TRANSPIRATION

PART OF A LEAF
(VERTICAL CROSS-SECTION)

CO_2 AND O_2 CO_2 AND O_2

H_2O

CROWN

HEARTWOOD (INACTIVE) GIVES STRENGTH

SAPWOOD CARRIES SAP FROM ROOT TO LEAVES

TRUNK

CAMBIUM (LAYER OF CELLS WHERE GROWTH IN DIAMETER OCCURS) BUILDS TISSUES— WOOD INSIDE AND BARK OUTSIDE

INNER BARK CARRIES FOOD MADE IN THE LEAVES DOWN TO THE BRANCHES, TRUNK AND ROOTS

OUTER BARK PROTECTS TREE FROM INJURIES

ROOTS

ROOT HAIRS TAKE UP WATER CONTAINING SMALL QUANTITY OF MINERALS IN SOLUTION

TAPROOT

① THE SHOOT TIPS, ROOT TIPS AND CAMBIAL LAYER ARE THE GROWING PARTS. THE TREE TAKES IN OXYGEN OVER ITS ENTIRE SURFACE THROUGH PORES ON LEAVES, TWIGS, BRANCHES, TRUNK AND ROOTS

Fig. 1.   How a tree lives

22

A= CAMBIAL ZONE
B= INNER BARK
C= OUTER BARK

D= SAPWOOD
E= HEARTWOOD
F= PITH
G= VASCULAR RAY

H= LATEWOOD
I = EARLYWOOD
J = ANNUAL RING

Fig. 2. Cross section of tree trunk

which smaller separate lateral root systems extend. A few of the more common trees that belong to this group are pines, various hickories and the oaks.

Sometime during its first year of life, another growth tissue is formed as an internal sheath surrounding the stem and root. This sheath is called the *vascular cambium*. It causes the tree to increase in diameter and produces layers of wood toward the inside, and layers of bark toward the outside. In regions where growth is interrupted at some time during the year as in temperate climates, distinguishable layers are produced each growing season in the wood. These layers are called *growth rings,* or *annual rings* where they correspond to yearly increments of wood (Fig. 2). Therefore, by

23

counting these rings, a fairly good estimate of a tree's age can be made. In the tropics, where growth is continuous throughout the year, rings, if formed, are ordinarily not indicative of age. Tree rings can often tell stories: a year of poor rainfall is indicated by narrow annual rings; conversely, years of abundant rainfall are reflected in wide annual rings. Employing this method, scientists can estimate, on a section of an old tree, the climatic conditions of the past. This technique is embodied in the science of dendrochronology.

Using a lens, one can see minute pores on the cross section of a hardwood. These pores are in reality sections of tubes or vessels which transport water and dissolved minerals through the stem and its branches to the leaves. In softwoods, no such vessels are present and the water must move through fiberlike cells. In hardwoods, most of the wood is composed of narrow, elongated cells called fibers. In softwoods, too, the wood is composed almost exclusively of fiberlike cells called *tracheids*. Both the fibers of hardwoods and the fiberlike cells of softwoods serve to strengthen the tree. However, in softwoods the fiberlike cells have the additional function of water conduction.

As stated previously, one of the main functions of roots is anchorage. About 10 per cent of the wood mass of a tree is found in the root system. The root system of a large tree is enormous, and the combined length of the roots of a spreading oak amounts to many hundreds of miles. Especially in dry areas, root systems are very well developed; in more moist environments, the growth of roots is curtailed. It is important to remember that roots are an integral part of the living organism that is the tree. They require air, food and water for growth and in order that they may perform their functions of anchorage, support, storage and absorption.

Like other green plants, trees manufacture food in leaves *(photosynthesis)* in the presence of sunlight, from the carbon dioxide of the air, and the water from the soil (Fig. 1). The simple food thereby produced combines in complex ways with minerals brought up by the water stream, through the trunk from the soil, to produce the living substances of which the tree is built. Most of the solid matter of trees is wood, a chemical compound made up mainly of *cellulose* and *lignin*. It is the latter compound which, in greater or lesser amounts contributes to the hardness of wood. When wood is burned, the elements of which it is composed are dispersed; the carbon, hydrogen, nitrogen and oxygen are dissipated in the smoke; the phosphorous, some carbon and other elements make up the ash. All in all, 27 elements, including silver, titanium and nickel, are found in the ashes of white pine wood.

24

Fig. 3. This log was cut from the Mark Twain tree, a giant sequoia 1,341 years old that grew in Fresno County, California. The tree was 332 ft. tall and 90 ft. in circumference at the base, and there were no limbs up to the height of 200 ft. Its fibrous root system covered three acres

25

Water is contained in all the tissues of a tree, both dead and alive. Young leaves or tips of roots contain up to 90 per cent water. Tree trunks may contain as much as 50 per cent. Water is indispensable to the tree, as all living processes take place in this medium. As explained previously, mineral nutrients are carried from the soil to the top of the tree in a stream of water. In the spring, the organic material in the form of sugars and amino acids is rushed in a stream of water from its place of winter storage to the bursting buds. Water is absorbed by the roots, pushed into the sapwood and then pulled up to the leaves—in redwood, as high as 350 ft. above the ground.

Reproduction occurs when the tree reaches maturity. The sexual reproduction of trees is basically similar to that of animals. In flowering plants, reproduction manifests itself by the appearance of flowers. Male and female reproductive parts may be borne in a single flower, or they may occur in separate flowers. Male and female flowers may occur on the same tree or on separate trees as in cottonwood. The male germ cell is carried in the pollen to the receptive portion of the female sexual apparatus. The sperms fertilize the eggs, which then mature into embryos. The process of reproduction differs in the hardwoods or flowering plants from that in the softwoods or cone-bearing plants.

Sexual reproduction in trees is responsible for the development of diversity. In the germ cells of male and female are located the bearers of hereditary traits, the chromosomes. By combining characters of the pollen parent with those of the seed parent, new combinations may be formed, some of which may be very valuable. But sexual reproduction is not absolutely necessary for the propagation of trees. Many of them can be reproduced by vegetative means such as by cuttings, grafting and budding. These methods enable the grower to maintain stocks of young trees exactly the same as their parents.

Old age comes to trees as to all other living organisms. As noted above, theoretically the life span of a tree is indefinite; however, we find that certain species are longer-lived than others. The gray birch is old at 40; sugar maple lives longer, up to 500 years. Some oaks may live 1,500 years, junipers in excess of 2,000 years. Some of the giant sequoias (Fig. 3) are believed to have been on earth in Christ's time. Recently, a bristlecone pine has been reported from California over 4,000 years old. Old trees are like old people. The infirmities of age come upon them (Figs. 4-6). They have difficulty with respiration and their recuperative capacity is impaired; wounds do not heal so easily as before. The leaves become smaller and their moisture content decreases. It becomes more and more difficult for the tree to

Fig. 4. The effect of competition on a tree's growth is seen from this cross section of loblolly pine. Germinating with hundreds of others in an abandoned field, it grew at an average rate for 17 years. Then, neighboring pines began to rob it of light at the top, water and minerals at roots. After 64 years of slower growth in the crowded stand, the pine was released from this competition by the felling of many of its neighbors. Thereafter, the tree grew rapidly

provide water for its vital functions (Fig. 7). Soon the tree decays, little by little, until it is entirely consumed. The elements from which it was composed have been released into the environment, to be used again and again by new life, just developing.

Scientific forestry is being practiced in many countries to improve the growth of trees. One of the first steps taken in connection with a natural forest is to clear away the heavy undergrowth (Fig. 8) and leave only useful species standing so that they may attain maximum growth.

The way a forest modifies temperature and humidity has been noticed by all who spend a good deal of time in the heavy woods, but the precise effect is realized by few, so a brief reference to these changes should be of interest. The changes in temperature vary a great deal in the same forest, depending upon the level between the

27

Fig. 5. Annual rings can also record such events as landslides, windstorms and other disturbances that tip trees. The growth rings of leaning trees are abnormally wide toward one side. Here, a red spruce shows two such upheavals. The first, occurring at age 24 (recorded by normally shaped rings in center), tipped the tree toward the upper right. The second, six years later, pushed it in the opposite direction, and the spruce kept leaning that way 43 years more

floor of the forest and the level of the tree tops. The few figures given are of the two extremes—weather at the level of the tree tops and on the ground. These figures are the result of study in an average forest in the northern United States.

Light. On summer afternoons with bright sunlight, less than 1 per cent of the light reaches the floor of the forest, but on overcast, cloudy days, 3 per cent of the light measured at the top of the trees reaches the ground.

Wind. In midsummer, trees in full bloom will, at the level of the ground, reduce a wind of 50 miles an hour to approximately 4 miles. Even during the winter, when the trees and branches are bare of foliage, they will reduce the velocity of the air more than 50 per cent.

Temperature. During the summer there is practically no variation from the forest floor to the tree tops during the night or on rainy days, but in the hours of bright sunlight, in midsummer, the floor

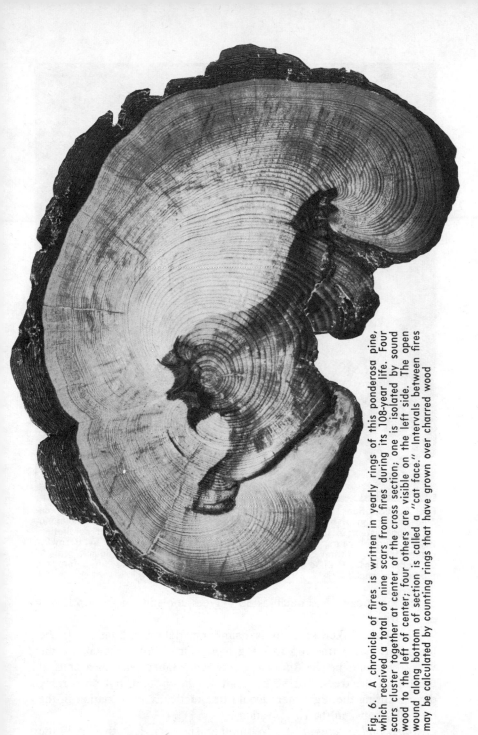

Fig. 6. A chronicle of fires is written in yearly rings of this ponderosa pine, which received a total of nine scars from fires during its 108-year life. Four scars cluster together at center of the cross section; one is isolated by sound wood to the left of center; four others are visible on the left side. The open wound along bottom of section is called a "cat face." Intervals between fires may be calculated by counting rings that have grown over charred wood

29

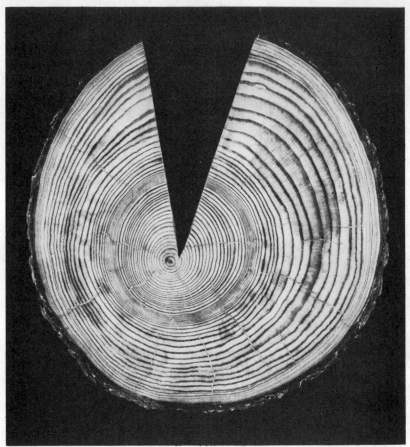

Fig. 7. Variations in growth are seen in varying width of rings. Width decrease is a sign of hindrance to water-absorbing system in roots or food-manufacturing system in leaves, through factors like drought or insect defoliation. Healthy for 24 years, this eastern larch was stripped of leaves by a sawfly-caterpillar plague (first band of narrow rings). The end of the epidemic brought 20 wider rings. Then, a second plague struck. The tree was cut before the plague had ended

of the forest can be as much as 30 degrees cooler than the top leaves of the trees.

Humidity. Likewise, there is a similar variation in humidity in the forests from the tree top to the ground. On a hot summer day the variation could be the difference between 28 per cent, measured at the top of the trees, and 80 per cent on the ground, but on a rainy day or during the night there would be practically no variation in the humidity between the two positions.

Rains and Evaporation. In summer showers, less than half the

Fig. 8. To leave only useful species, the heavy undergrowth in this Brazilian forest has been cleared away—an example of the scientific forestry practiced in many countries

31

amount of the rain reaches the level of the ground, but in a continuous steady rain, the percentage is higher. However, each acre of woodland on a summer day returns to the air over 2,000 gallons of water through the process known as transpiration.

Insects are extremely important members of the forest community. Their most vital roles are as pollinators of the flowering plants and as scavengers that feed on waste matter and organic remains. The most typical forest insects are those that feed on trees.

The greatest variety of insects is of the leaf-chewing type, attracted to the highly nutritious and extremely accessible leaves rather than to any other part of the tree. These are divided into seven broad groups:

Leaf-Mining Insects. The larvae of a number of very small leaf-eating insects feed within the leaf tissues of the leaves.

Gall-Making Insects. Many insects possess the ability to cause plants to produce abnormal growth called "galls." Most of these gall insects are wasps, flies and sawflies.

Twig-Boring Insects. The larvae of a few insects, all of which are beetles, bore through the tender twigs and small branches of the trees. At times large portions of a tree's crown may be killed. Such damage is especially serious on young trees.

Seed-Eating Insects. The abundant and nutritious food stored in tree seeds presents a lavish feeding and spawning ground for insects.

Cambium-Eating Insects. Many species of insects feed on the highly nutritious cambium and the adjacent layers beneath the bark. Under normal conditions, healthy trees are able to combat the insects by surrounding them with pitch.

Wood-Eating Insects. The woody trunk is the most characteristic organ of the tree. However, the wood is so well protected, so tough and relatively so low in food value that comparatively few insects have become adapted to feeding on it. The majority of wood eaters are attracted to weak or dead trees.

Sap-Sucking Insects. The rich sap of the trees is normally contained beneath the bark or wood to protect the tissues. When these tissues are injured and the sap escapes, a great variety of insects may gather to feed upon it. The injury caused by sap-sucking insects is ordinarily insignificant. Occasionally, a great number of sap suckers remove sufficient volumes of food and water and inject large amounts of poisonous saliva to cause serious injury or even the death of trees.

To most people the surface of dead leaves and the thin layer of top soil that forms the forest floor seem to be a lifeless trash heap. In reality, the floor is the most densely populated stratum of the forest. The number of organisms that live in every square foot may be four times as great as the human population of the world. Most of these organisms are microscopic bacteria, fungi, algae and Protozoa. Each year about two tons of leaves, flowers, wood cuttings and twigs, fall on every acre of forest floor.

the identification of woods

"The Staple of the Stuff is so exquisitely fine, that no Silkworm is able to draw anything near so fine a Thread. So that one who walks about with the meanest stick, holds a piece of Nature's Handicraft, which far surpasses the most elaborate Woof or Needle Work in the World."

Description of wood from Nehemiah Grew, 1682, in his *The anatomy of plants begun,* which contains one of the first treatises on wood structure.

THE COMPLEXITIES OF WOOD STRUCTURE have been recognized for several centuries. Man is a curious creature, and he has pondered, investigated and communicated his ideas regarding the objects of his curiosity. The structure of wood has not been exempt from this inquisitiveness. Indeed, there is hardly a person who exists or has existed on this earth who has not thought to some extent about wood, its kinds, colors, textures and uses. Such a ubiquitously used material is certainly deserving of interest.

That we may know something of how woods are characterized and identified, we must know something of wood itself, of what chemical substances it is composed, of how these substances form the ultimate particles of wood (cells) and of how the organization of the cells and the compounds they contain impart character to wood.

Our story begins with the *vascular cambium,* that sheath of generative cells which surrounds the tree between the bark and the wood. It is the production of new cells by this sheath that gives rise to wood on the inside, and bark on the outside. As mentioned in another chapter, wherever there are climatic periods during the year which are not conducive to growth (cold winters, periodic droughts), the formation of wood is discontinuous. Because of this, successive layers of wood are visible on the cross section of a log. Where the period of growth and production of wood occurs once a year, these layers correspond to the year. Therefore, we can term such annual layers *annual rings*. This is the condition in most temperate lands. In certain climates, several interrupted periods of growth occur during the year; several layers of wood are produced, and these layers do not correspond to an annual cycle. It is best here to call such layers by a general term as *growth rings*. In the tropics where growth and wood formation are more or less continuous, growth layers are not formed for the most part, and the wood appears quite homogeneous from the pith to the bark.

An annual ring is frequently divisible into two closely applied layers, one formed during the beginning of the growing season and another toward the end. These are termed *springwood* or *earlywood* and *summerwood* or *latewood*. Cells in springwood are generally larger, and thinner-walled than those in summerwood. The distinctness of these layers is at times important in identification (Fig. 1).

When looking at a cross section of a log, we are frequently impressed by the fact that the wood in the center is of a darker or different color than the wood toward the outside. This inner darker layer is the *heartwood;* the outer layer is the *sapwood*.

The heartwood is physiologically inactive; its cells are dead and frequently clogged with dark-colored waste materials which give it a characteristic color. Heartwood serves as the main structural element of the trunk. It is more resistant to decay than the sapwood. The sapwood is physiologically active; it contains living cells and is responsible for conducting water and dissolved minerals from the roots to the crown of the tree. Normally there is less sapwood than heartwood. Heartwood is more valuable commercially and most timbers with which we are familiar come from this colored, denser wood. The characteristic purple-brown of black walnut *(Juglans nigra)* occurs only in the heartwood; the sapwood is almost white. Purpleheart, a beautiful tropical American timber, exhibits bright purple heartwood; the sapwood is creamy white. The heartwood is commercially valuable; the sapwood is discarded.

Lumber is commonly divided into two main categories: *softwoods* and *hardwoods*. These two groups correspond roughly to conifers or cone-bearing trees and flowering trees. All commercial species of trees belong to one or the other of these groups. This division, based on hardness of wood, has its shortcomings, as there are softwoods (conifers) with harder woods than certain hardwoods (flowering trees). For example, any one of the southern pines (U.S.A.) has harder wood than balsa. Yet, according to this classification, the southern pines are softwoods and balsa is a hardwood. Regardless

Fig. 1. Schematic three-plane drawing of the wood of eastern white pine or northern white pine *(Pinus strobus)* from *Textbook of Wood Technology* by Brown and Panshin

Surface *A*. 1-1ᵃ, portion of an annual ring; 2, resin canal; 3-3ᵃ, wood ray; *a-a'*, longitudinal tracheids; *b*, epithelial cells; *c*, ray cells; *d*, pit pair in median sectional view; *e*, bordered pits in the back walls of longitudinal tracheids, in surface view; *f*, pit pair in sectional view, showing the margin of the torus, but so cut that the pit apertures are not included in the plane of section; *g*, pit pair in which neither the pit aperture nor the torus shows; *h*, windowlike pit pairs between longitudinal tracheids and ray parenchyma.

Surface *B*. 4-4ᵃ, portions of longitudinal tracheids in radial aspect (the ends are blunt); 5-5ᵃ, upper part of uniseriate ray; *i*, bordered pits on the radial walls of longitudinal springwood tracheids (the base of the pit is toward the observer); *j*, small bordered pits on the radial walls of longitudinal summerwood tracheids, in the same view as in *i*; *k*, ray tracheids; *l*, cells of ray parenchyma.

Surface *C*. 6-6ᵃ, portions of longitudinal tracheids in tangential aspect; 7-7ᵃ, portion of a xylary ray; *m*, tapering ends of longitudinal tracheids; *n*, a small bordered pit on the tangential wall of a longitudinal summerwood tracheid; *p*, cells of ray parenchyma; *r*, transverse resin canal.

Fig. 2. Schematic three-plane drawing of the wood of sweetgum or redgum
(Liquidambar styraciflua)

Surface *A*. 1-1ᵃ, boundary between two annual rings (growth proceeded from right to left); 2-2ᵃ, wood ray consisting of procumbent cells; 2ᵇ-2ᶜ, wood ray consisting of upright cells; a-aᵟ, inclusive, pores (vessels in transverse section); b-bᵗ, inclusive, fiber tracheids; c-c³, inclusive, cells of longitudinal parenchyma; e, procumbent ray cell.

Surface *B*. *f, f¹*, portions of vessel segments; *g, g¹*, portions of fiber tracheids in lateral surface aspect; *h,* a strand of longitudinal parenchyma in lateral surface aspect; 3-3ᵃ, upper portion of a heterogeneous wood ray in lateral sectional aspect; *i*, a marginal row of upright cells; *j*, two rows of horizontal cells.

Surface *C*. *k*, portion of a vessel segment in tangential surface aspect; *k¹, k²*, overlapping vessel segments in tangential surface asnect; *l*, fiber tracheids in tangential surface aspect; 4-4ᵃ, portion of a wood ray in tangential sectional view; *m*, an upright cell in the lower margin; *n*, procumbent cells in the body of the ray.

37

of the exceptions, this system is in common use and should be understood by the wood enthusiast. There are, however, more fundamental ways of classifying woods, subject to fewer exceptions. These will be considered when we take up wood structure below.

Chemically, wood is not a single substance; rather, it is a complex aggregate of compounds, the nature of which is still inadequately understood by wood chemists even today. About 99 per cent of the dry weight of wood consists of cellulose and related substances, and of lignin. Cellulose is a carbohydrate, as are sugar and starch; it contains the chemical elements carbon, hydrogen and oxygen, the hydrogen and oxygen being present in the same proportions as in water, namely, two of hydrogen for one of oxygen.

The chemical structure of lignin is still poorly known. We do know that there are several kinds of lignins in wood, each designated by the name of the chemist who synthesized them, as Braun's lignin, Klason's lignin and Bjorkman's lignin. Since lignin is the substance that makes wood woody (cotton fibers are pure cellulose), the following facts should be noted: 1) Lignin is composed of carbon (61-65 per cent, hydrogen (5-6 per cent) and oxygen (30 per cent). It is the manner in which these three elements are chemically united, and their proportions, that makes lignin differ from cellulose. 2) Lignin is the major constituent remaining in woody tissues after the cellulose has been removed.

Wood also contains minerals. These chemicals are present in varying amounts and kinds. The principal components of ash (minerals) are calcium, potassium and magnesium; some sodium, manganese, iron and aluminum are also usually present. Other minerals may occur in trace amounts. Numerous other substances may be found in wood, for instance: crystals of calcium oxalate, starch grains, sugars, essential oils (as in camphorwood), fats, fatty oils, resins (in pines), latex, tannins, dyestuffs (in heartwood of fustic) and various alkaloids (caffeine is an alkaloid).

The identification of woods is largely based on the kinds of cells (Figs. 1 and 2), the arrangement of these cells into tissues, and the gross appearance these tissues present to the eye. Wood cells are microscopic and can be observed on slivers cut so that light will pass through them (about 15/25,000 of an inch thick). Such slivers may need to be dyed to make the cells more easily visible.

In general, wood serves the tree in two ways: it supports the tree (main function of heartwood) and carries water from the roots to the leaves (sapwood). The cells of which wood is composed are specialized to perform these two functions. Thus we have cells which are largely supportive, cells which are supportive and conductive, and cells which are largely conductive. Supportive cells generally have thick, minutely pitted walls, are long, and are sharply tapered at either end. Such cells are classified as *fibers*. Cells which function both in support and conduction have thinner, conspicuously pitted walls, and have blunter tips. These cells are called *tracheids*. *Vessels* are tubes composed of short cells which can be called *vessel cells*. The vessel is much like a long pipe made up of shorter lengths of pipe (vessel cells, Fig. 2). Vessel cells are functional largely in conduction. They are thin walled and open at the ends much as the lengths of pipe. A cross section of a vessel is called a pore. All of the elements of wood just described are oriented parallel to the axis of the stem. Fibers and vessels are characteristic of hardwoods (flowering trees), the vessels being embedded in a matrix of fibers. Tracheids (Fig. 1) compose most of the wood mass of softwoods (conifers). Thus, based on the wood, the major difference between hardwoods and softwoods is that in the former, vessels (pores) are present. Softwoods do not contain any vessels (pores). Hardwoods are sometimes referred to as *pored* or *porous* timbers and softwoods as *non-pored* or *non-porous* timbers.

In hardwoods, when pores are larger or more abundant in one portion of a growth ring than in another, we say that the wood is *ring porous*. The northern oaks *(Quercus),* ash *(Fraxinus),* and hickory *(Carya)* are examples of ring-porous woods. If the pores, on the other hand, are of fairly even sizes and are well distributed throughout the growth ring, the wood is diffuse porous. The woods of magnolia, maple *(Acer),* birch *(Betula),* and beech *(Fagus)* are diffuse porous. This classification does not apply to softwoods since they do not have pores.

Other kinds of cells and tissues occur in the woods of hardwoods and softwoods. One category is mostly concerned with the storage of foods. These tissues are the co-called soft tissues or *parenchyma* (pa-ren'chy-ma). The *vascular rays,* or the tissue which radiates from the pith through the bark, are composed of soft tissue. Vascular rays occur in hardwoods and softwoods. Hardwoods contain vertical strands, grouped in various ways, of soft tissue. Softwoods generally lack such vertical soft tissue. Certain softwoods as the pines, larches, spruces and Douglas fir possess *resin ducts* (Fig. 1). These are channels in the wood surrounded by special secretory parenchyma cells which exude resin into the canal.

An exhaustive treatment of the kinds of cells and their modifications is beyond the scope of this work, but we should now be able

Fig. 3A. EASTERN HOPHORNBEAM *(Ostrya virginiana)*

Fig. 3. Magnification of the end grains of nine woods 3A-3I on this and follow-ing pages. Like a person's fingerprints, there are no two alike in all the 25,000 species of woods. The examination of the end grains, either by magnifying glass or photographs taken through a microscope, is one of the scientist's main helps in identifying wood

to understand what the trained wood anatomist must consider when identifying woods. He must examine the various facets of wood, the cross section, the tangential-longitudinal and radial-longitudinal sections. He must ascertain the cells present, their relationship to each other, the modifications of their cell walls, their arrangement, their number and distribution. As the external portions of trees differ from species to species, so does the wood differ. However, we find that closely related woods are often so similar that it is impossible to distinguish among them. For example, it is not possible to tell one oak *(Quercus)* from another on the basis of wood structure. Although the wood of eastern white pine is distinguishable from that of the southern pines, woods of the latter group of pine species are not dis-tinguishable from each other. The hard and soft maples are only distinguishable with difficulty; hemlock and true fir are accurately distinguishable only with the aid of the microscope. In general prac-tice, nevertheless, it is possible to identify accurately a whole host of commercial timber tree species by the wood alone. Thus, by and large, the best aid in identifying wood is the micro-structure of the wood (Fig. 3). This may be observed with the use of a compound microscope as is done in the laboratory, or by an ordinary 10-power

Fig. 3B.   MAHOGANY
(*Swietenia mahagoni*)

Fig. 3C.   BLACK LOCUST
(*Robinia pseudoacacia*)

Fig. 3D.   TEAK
(*Tectona grandis*)

Fig. 3E.   YELLOW POPLAR
(*Liriodendron tulipifera*)

41

Fig. 3F. SWEETGUM
(*Liquidambar styraciflua*)

Fig. 3G. AMERICAN HOLLY
(*Ilex opaca*)

Fig. 3H. PERSIMMON
(*Diospyros virginiana*)

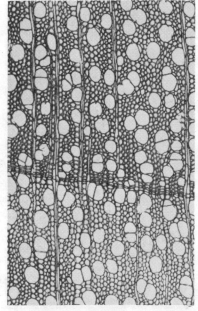

Fig. 3I. MAGNOLIA
(*Magnolia acuminata*)

42

Fig. 4. An excellent 20-power wide-field magnifier of the self-illuminated type, manufactured by E. W. Pike & Co., Elizabeth, N. J.

magnifying lens. Many woods are identifiable with such a simple lens. A 20-power wide-field magnifier is shown in Fig. 4.

Other guides to the identification of wood include the color, odor, texture, grain, character of the ash, presence or absence of growth rings, presence or absence of colored heartwood and presence or absence of resin ducts. In short, any stable feature in wood may be employed as a key to identification.

Practically, to identify a timber, the layman needs a sharp knife, a 10- or 12-power magnifying lens and good light. Much can be seen on the cross section and a clean cut will reveal in sharp detail the pattern of cells exposed in this view. Sometimes, by moistening the cut surface, the structural detail will be seen to better advantage. After examining the cut surface, recourse must be made to a "key." A key is a written deductive device by which woods (or plants, or rocks) can be identified by the process of elimination. One examines a statement in the key and either accepts or rejects it. If he accepts a statement, he proceeds to the next closest statement until the wood is identified. Below is a sample of a simple key to woods, based on gross features, extracted from *Trees—The Yearbook of Agriculture, 1949*.

A. Rays comparatively broad and conspicuous
   1. Rays crowded on the end grain............................Sycamore
   2. Rays not crowded on the end grain............................Beech
B. Rays not broad but distinctly visible
   1. Heartwood deep, rich, reddish brown. Annual rings clearly defined ....Black cherry
   2. Heartwood dingy, reddish brown, often streaked darker. Annual rings not sharply defined........................Sweetgum

An example of a more detailed, complex key is as follows:

A. Resin canals present
   1. Resin canals invisible to naked eye
     a. Wood with a somewhat greasy or oily feeling......Larch
     b. Wood with a dry feeling.....................................Spruce
   2. Resin canals visible to the naked eye
     a. Ray to tracheid pits pinoid, ray tracheids dentate
        Loblolly pine
     b. Ray to tracheid pits fenestriform, ray tracheids smooth
        Eastern white pine
B. Resin canals absent
   1. Wood aromatic ....Eastern red cedar
   2. Wood odorless
     a. Heartwood red ....Redwood
     b. Heartwood pale brown to dark brown........Baldcypress

It should be borne in mind that not all woods are identifiable. This is especially true of noncommercial woods and woods collected from remote areas. Such woods may never have been studied and described and probably do not occur in any keys. Another point of interest is that keys to woods are restrictive in some manner, as is indicated in their title: a key to common commercial American woods, a key to Indian woods used for railway ties, a key to coniferous woods of Europe, a key to woods with pores arranged in flame-like fashion, and so on. Therefore, keys, if available, are not panaceas for identification. The key must fit the lock!

REFERENCES

Brown, H. P., A. J. Panshin, and C. C. Forsaith. 1949. Textbook of wood technology. Vol. I. McGraw-Hill. New York.
Jane, F. W. 1956. The structure of wood. Macmillan. New York.

how a tree
is named

IN ORDER TO DEAL INTELLIGENTLY WITH TREES, in order to be able
to refer to them accurately in writing or in conversation, they must
have names. Generally speaking, there are two classes of names
applied to trees: the scientific or botanical names, and common
names. The botanical name is usually of Latin or Greek derivation,
whereas common names may be in many languages. The botanical
name for a species is always the same, regardless of the country in
which it is used; the common name may vary from place to place.
Botanical nomenclature is governed by a strict, international set of
rules, *The international code of botanical nomenclature.* Common
names are not subject to international regulation. It is important to
remember that every tree (or other plant) has a scientific, botanical
name, but it may or may not have a common name. Therefore, the
most important name is the scientific name, but common names may
have more or less importance, depending upon their standardization,
general acceptability and frequency of use. The science of naming
trees and other plants is called *taxonomy* or *systematic botany.* One
who names plants is a taxonomist or systematic botanist.

A plant is named when, in the opinion of taxonomists, it represents
a new species. A species can be defined simply as a kind or sort. In
other words, when a newly collected plant is different in certain
respects from all other closely related plants, it represents a new kind
of plant. So that we may refer to this plant, we need to name it.
Not only must we name it, we must also describe it so that others
will know to just what kind of plant the name applies. According to
The international code of botanical nomenclature, descriptions of
new species of flowering plants and conifers must be in Latin. Thus,

45

the description will be intelligible to all systematic botanists, regardless of their native tongue. Each new species is given two names (the binomial). It is assigned to a *genus* and allotted a *specific epithet*. Thus we find the red maple is known botanically as *Acer rubrum; Acer* is the genus of maples, and *rubrum,* the specific epithet, refers to the red maple. Another example is eastern white pine—*Pinus strobus; Pinus* is the genus of pines, and *strobus* pertains to a particular pine, eastern white pine. Scientific names are always set in italic type or underlined when typewritten. The generic name is capitalized; the specific epithet may or may not be capitalized.

When a botanist names a plant, his name is placed after it. It is possible then to know who was responsible for naming and describing a particular species. The individual is known as the author of the name. Frequently authors' names are abbreviated in a set manner. However, extremely well-known taxonomists' names are often represented by only a letter or two. For example: L. for Linnaeus; DC. for de Candolle; H.B.K. for von Humboldt, Bonpland and Kunth; Sieb. & Zucc. for Siebold and Zuccarini, and Benth. for Bentham. Names of one syllable are usually spelled out.

It is admitted that botanical names at first sight appear formidable. However, is *Fagus grandifolia* (American beech) any more frightening than "thermonuclear," "hydroelectric" or "superheterodyne"? Words such as these appear every day in newspapers and magazines. Furthermore, without knowing it, many of us use common plant names which are identical to the generic names of plants, e.g., chrysanthemum, begonia, geranium, amaryllis, anemone, hydrangea, iris and lotus. Many common names are clearly derived from scientific names or vice versa: the rose is *Rosa,* lavender is *Lavendula,* the violet is *Viola,* the juniper is *Juniperus,* the pine is *Pinus,* the larch is *Larix,* a genus of orchids is *Orchis,* the true laurel is *Laurus* and the true cedar (of Lebanon) is *Cedrus.*

Many times, if we were to know the Latin and Greek roots used to make botanical names, we would find that these names are not just so much gibberish, but actually mean something. Sometimes they are descriptive of the plant, sometimes they honor a man's name and at other times they note the locality of collection or the native geographic habitat of the species. For example, *Gossweilerodendron balsamiferum* is an African timber tree commonly known as agba. Let us parse this mouthful: Gossweiler/o/dendron, balsam/i/ferum. "Gossweiler" honors the name of John Gossweiler, a collector in Portuguese West Africa; "dendron" is derived from the Greek for tree; "balsam" refers to the Latin *balsamum* or the Greek *balsamon* for the gummy substance called balsam; "ferum" is from the Latin

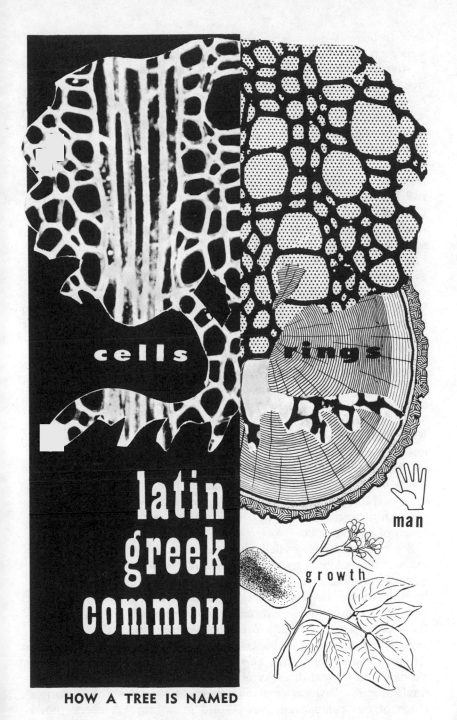

cells

rings

man

growth

latin
greek
common

HOW A TREE IS NAMED

fero, to bear. We can see now that our tongue twister means Gossweiler's tree that bears or produces balsam.

Another, more familiar case is that of the yellow poplar or tuliptree, *Liriodendron tulipifera.* "Lirio" comes from the Greek for lily, *leiron;* "dendron" we already know means tree; "tulip" refers to the scientific name for the tulip or *Tulipa;* and "ferum," of course, means to bear. Thus we have the lily tree which bears tulips, a reference to the lovely tuliplike flowers of this stately native tree. The name for our eastern hemlock is *Tsuga canadensis.* "Tsuga" is derived from the Japanese name for the local hemlocks of Japan; "canadensis" is Latin for of Canada. Eastern hemlock then is the tsuga from Canada. The magnificent redwood of the West is *Sequoia sempervirens.* The generic name "Sequoia" commemorates Sequoyah (also spelled Sequoia), or George Guess (1770?-1843), American Indian inventor of the Cherokee alphabet; "semper" is Latin for forever, ever or always; "virens" is from the Latin *vireo,* to be green or verdant. The redwood is Sequoyah's (tree) which is always green. We can see from these few examples that the scientific name of a tree is not a thing to be shunned or relegated to specialists. It is usually a meaningful name, full of lore and interest which will help maximize our enjoyment of woods and strengthen our appreciation.

It is not meant here to imply that common names are not meaningful or useful. The major objection to their use is their great diversity and general lack of standardization. We find, for instance, that our conception of oak (botanically *Quercus)* is quite different from the Australian idea of oak *(Casuarina,* the silky-oak or *Grevillea,* the turkey oak). Turning to a commonly known name such as beech, we find that it refers to *Fagus,* our eastern beech; *Nothofagus,* the beech of New Zealand and Australia; *Carpinus,* the blue beech of eastern U.S.A.; *Litsea,* the soft bolly beech of Australia; *Cryptocarya,* the brown beech or jack apple of Australia; and *Myrsine,* the Cape beech of south Africa.

Some outstanding physical characteristics of a wood may prompt the use of a common name descriptive of this feature; ironwood, for instance. A great many woods of above average hardness are called by this name; however, they may be botanically very diverse: *Krugiodendron ferreum, Syncarpia subargentia, Dialium guianense, Bumelia tenax, Lophira procera, Casuarina* spp., *Eusideroxylon zwageri, Acacia peuce, Backhousia myrtifolia, Ostrya virginiana, Lyonothamnus floribundus, Olneya testosa,* and so on. Conversely, we may find a great diversity of vernacular names which apply to a single species. *Swietenia macrophylla* is the species which comprises much of our commercial, New World mahogany. A check shows that the following names apply to this species: caoba, foja pendula, zopilote de mator pescado, ciruela, cirndillo, cedro mondi, caoba mondi, Guatemala mahogany, Mexican mahogany, mahogany, aguano, Central American mahogany, black-veined mahogany, red mahogany, caoba blanca, caoba rosada, large leaf mahogany, Panama mahogany, black mahogany, cedro caoba, caobilla, cedro dulce, yulu, aguna, orura, caoba negra, caobano, sapoton, Brazilian mahogany, Peruvian mahogany, caoba liso, araputango and Honduras mahogany. This example is somewhat extreme, but is representative of the great multiplicity of names sometimes applied to one species of tree. Commercially valuable timbers suffer most from this malady.

Common names can be divided into two broad categories: vernacular and trade. Not all common names are easily placed into one or the other of these classes, and a vernacular name may also be a trade name. Furthermore, as we have seen, a common name may be derived from a scientific name. This in turn may serve as a trade name. In any event, we can define a common name as one which is not a scientific name, i.e., one not Latinized. A vernacular name is one which is in the language of the people inhabiting the region in which a tree grows. A name used in marketing timber can be termed a trade name. *Terminalia superba* is a west African timber tree. Vernacular names are various and include ka-ronko in Sierra Leone, fraké in the Ivory Coast, fram in Ghana, eji in Nigeria and djombe in Cameroons. A popular trade name for this wood is Korina. *Afrormosia elata,* a West African commercial species, is known in the trade as kokrodua. However, kokrodua is also the native Ashanti name in Ghana. In the trade, *Alstonia congensis* is called by its scientific name alstonia. Native or vernacular names are various and include bantang foro in Senegal, kaiwi in Sierra Leone, emien on the Ivory Coast, sindru in Ghana, abun in Nigeria and bokuk in Cameroons. A more common example is *Liquidambar styraciflua.* This species is known in the eastern U.S.A. as sweetgum or bilsted. On the market it is sold as redgum or sapgum. A good instance of duplicity of names is afforded by *Taxodium distichum,* usually called baldcypress. In the trade it may be listed as red cypress, white cypress or yellow cypress. Other names also applied are common baldcypress, gulf cypress, southern cypress, tidewater red cypress and cypress. An interesting sidelight is that this species is not even a true cypress; these belong to the genus *Cupressus.*

It is evident from the common names applied to trees and timbers, that they are usually descriptive or comparative. Certain trade names are fabricated to glorify a wood and charm prospective buyers. Less desirable woods are compared with more desirable—Philippine mahogany basks in glory reflected from the well known and much used New World mahoganies, although in certain respects it is inferior. Common names have an attractiveness all their own; they frequently reflect the peoples who have named them, or are quaint and graceful: *Amelanchier,* the shadbush, it blooms when the shad are spawning; *Amyris balsamifera,* the torchwood, its gum-containing wood burns as a torch; *Symphonia globulifera,* doctor gum, probably a reference to the local medicinal use of its gum; *Populus deltoides,* eastern cottonwood, the fruits bear a cottony mass which is freed at maturity; *Chionanthus virginica,* fringetree, referring to the fringelike aspect of the drooping, narrow-petaled flowers; *Cliftonia monophylla,* buckwheat-tree, a reference to the clusters of fruits resembling buckwheat cereal grains; and *Coccoloba uvifera,* the seagrape, an allusion to the grapelike clusters of edible fruits borne by this seaside tree.

Who was it who said, "What's in a name"?

REFERENCES

Benson, L. 1957. Plant classification. D. C. Heath. Boston.
Lawrence, G. H. M. 1951. Taxonomy of vascular plants. Macmillan. New York.

from the forest to you

Have you ever stopped and given a moment of thought when you held a small piece of fine cabinet wood in your hand as to where the original tree came from—how it traveled over thousands of miles of land and water finally to reach you in its present form? It is difficult perhaps to conceive that men faced hardships of primitive living, dangers of wild animals, poisonous snakes and tropical fevers in a far-distant tropical forest or jungle, so that you finally might be able to have this finished product. To appreciate fully the hardships and romance of logging, let us consider the first step in producing a fine piece of wood—the logging of the trees.

The locating of suitable trees, regardless of what kind they may be or in what country, and the process of felling the trees, converting them into logs and transporting these logs to sawmills or to market places, is all a part of that which comes under the term of logging. The problems met, the methods used, vary greatly according to the part of the world from which the trees come and the species.

It is an enterprise that requires skill (Fig. 1) and often the ability to endure hardships. The importance of this has long been recognized, as in early Biblical times when it is recorded that Solomon, in a message to the King of Tyre, said: "Command thou that they hew me cedar trees out of Lebanon; * * * for thou knowest that there is not among us any that can skill to hew timber like unto the Sidonians."

Since then the world known to man has grown and the number of new trees known to man has multiplied many times. There has been a complete evolution and improvement in the way man lives and works, but in many countries—perhaps the one from which the piece of wood came that you hold in your hand—the method of living and conditions of working are as primitive as ever.

51

Fig. 1. Axmen standing on rude pole scaffold 6 to 12 ft. from the ground to fell a mahogany tree. Typically, the tree is heavily buttressed at the base—apparently a provision of nature against the violence of tropical storms

Fig. 2. Elephants still provide the only practical transportation in removing teak logs from the forests of Thailand, where this photo was taken, and India

Books could be devoted to methods and ways of logging—how the piece of teak from India has perhaps taken six years to reach you. These trees are so very large and heavy that, before being felled, they are girdled as they stand in the forest and left to die so their weight will be greatly decreased. The elephant (Fig. 2) has been, and will be for many years to come, the principal means of transporting the teak logs. An elephant with an average working lifetime of 50 years can drag a log weighing up to four tons over rough, mountainous land.

If your piece of wood has come from Australia or tropical America (Fig. 3), oxen power most likely started the tree on its journey to you. In some cases as many as ten yoke of oxen are used to draw a single log out to the nearest waterway. Some of the logs are so heavy they will sink in water, and in these cases, other much lighter

Fig. 3. Hauling mahogany logs to streams has always been a difficult operation. For 300 years in tropical America, cattle have provided this transportation over the crudest of trails to a maximum distance of about 7 miles

54

Fig. 4. When the rains come, the mahogany logs are rolled into the flood streams to start the long, uncertain journey to the ocean. Then, having reached deep water, the logs are made up into rafts. Note the native huts on the raft

55

logs are lashed alongside heavy ones to prevent them from sinking as they are floated to the port where they are to be loaded on the steamer.

If it is a piece of tamo you are holding in your hand, it probably grew in the mountainous regions of Japan and was carried down through rugged terrain to the point of transportation on the shoulders of men.

On the west coast of Africa, large logs were felled by hand and, after being squared up with axes, were pulled to the nearest stream— sometimes by hundreds of men for a single log. The logs were laid alongside of streams until the rainy season came, and the waters carried them down to the harbors where they were put on rafts (Fig. 4), towed out to steamers and loaded. In seasons when the rains failed, logs could not be brought out of the forest. Today, mechanized power is gradually replacing hand operations in various places of the world, but it will be a long time before it replaces primitive methods in many far-distant places.

After logs have reached the port of embarkation, they still have a long way to go before they reach the final market. To what port they are shipped (Fig. 5) often depends upon the species of wood and whether it is of prime quality or not. Different ports of the world specialize in different woods and also in different qualities of wood.

For many years New York City was considered the leading market in the United States for the importation of mahogany and other woods from all parts of the world. On the East River there were the large storage yards of Constantine & Company (Fig. 6) to which foreign shippers in different ports of the world would send their logs. Going into the yard, the logs would be either measured or weighed and a measurement certificate would be issued. Importers in this country also would bring logs and have them stored in the yards of Constantine & Company where they would be inspected by manufacturers of lumber and veneers from various parts of the United States. When the logs were sold, they would be shipped to the respective mills.

Adjoining Constantine & Company were the log yards of Willard Hawes & Co., for years probably the country's largest importers of practically all the rare and exotic woods of the world, including mahogany. With the changing of time, these two yards are gone. Both were taken away to form part of the Franklin D. Roosevelt Drive along the East River in New York City. However, Constantine & Company, in a limited way, still issues inspection returns on cargoes when requested. Some logs are still brought into New York, some go into Boston, a few into Philadelphia, others into Pensacola and

Fig. 5. Steamer from the tropics unloading logs at a sawmill dock

Fig. 6. Inspection yards of Constantine & Company, 6th to 8th Streets on the East River, New York City. There were 6 million feet of mahogany logs in the yard when this photograph was taken, October 18, 1884

New Orleans. What is probably the leading port of arrival in this country today is Norfolk, Virginia, where the logs are inspected prior to purchase.

In Europe, England still maintains the position that it had for many years. Both Liverpool, which specializes in African mahogany and other African woods, and London, which has the African mahogany as well as woods from the East, have public storage yards. At regular periods, auction sales are held where all the logs are put up in separate parcels and auctioned off to the highest bidder. Buyers attend these sales from many countries of the world, and there are wood brokers, like the stock brokers in Wall Street, who execute purchase orders from clients in many different countries, using their judgment on the value of the different lots of logs offered.

At one time in New York similar public auction sales were conducted in the offices of Constantine & Company at their log yard at 7th Street and the East River.

In France, the log markets are Le Havre, Bordeaux, which specializes in African wood, and Marseilles, which specializes in wood from the East. Paris is a manufacturing market for veneers and lumbers. Logs are brought into Paris, manufactured by the mills, then offered to buyers from many places in the form of veneers and lumber.

Hamburg and Bremen in Germany are large log markets. In the Netherlands, Rotterdam and Amsterdam (Fig. 7) are the markets where logs are shipped; in Belgium, Antwerp is the large log market. From these various markets, dealers in logs and manufacturers of veneers and lumber procure much of their timber.

Some of the other larger organizations will send their buyers directly to those countries throughout the world (Figs. 8 and 9) in which the various timbers are grown and there will make local contracts to buy directly from native shippers. All this is a fascinating business. Like the diamond business with its headquarters in Holland, it is a lifetime study for those who deal in timbers from far countries.

Outside of being able to recognize and identify the various species of logs, which is relatively simple to these people, the great science lies in determining the value of the logs. In highly figured logs, each log is carefully studied on the outside and the signs are read, indicating what the interior of the log will look like after it has been opened up and cut into choice veneers. What will the color be in the logs? Will there be any extraneous strain going in from the ends of logs, which some wood is subject to? Will there be any defects in the logs—what are known as ring checks, gum pockets or

Fig. 7. Up to 50,000 tons of logs can be stored in the lumber warehouses of Amsterdam, and there is space for twice the quantity outside

Fig. 8. Crosscutting logs at a sawmill in Belem, Brazil, on the River Guama, a tributary of the Amazon. The crane is stacking logs which have floated down the river

Fig. 9.   Logs ready to be cut at a local mill in the Amazon basin. This basin covers one third of Brazil and supports about one twentieth of the population. A great part of its future weo' depends upon the scientific exploitation of the rich forests

cross-breaks—which could make a valuable log almost worthless?

What type of figure will the log contain? Will it have a stripe—a broad stripe or a fine pronounced stripe? Will it have a mottle figure or a roe figure and how strong will be the figure? Will it go through the entire log or only part of the log? The appraisal of logs of this kind is one that requires a highly specialized knowledge of woods, and most individuals more or less work with just one type of wood. One dealer may be a specialist in African mahogany, another in Honduras mahogany, another in Peruvian mahogany. One may specialize in woods from the East or only certain woods that come from the East; another may be a specialist in woods coming from the Philippines.

We recall an instance some years ago in New York where great interest was shown in a log of Ceylon satinwood. It was a fine, large log containing about 1,000 ft., and interest was very keen among all the log buyers because the log showed indication of having a finer quality bee's-wing figure than any log that had been shown. Many bids were received for this log and it was finally sold to a firm which offered $5 per foot, or approximately $5,000 for the log.

When the log was prepared for manufacturing into sliced veneers, it was found that the figure was so strong and presented such a quantity of what is called "end wood" in the log that it was impossible to cut the wood into veneers. Because of this it had very little value—almost a total loss to the buyer. On the other hand, logs are often found which have very little indication of value on the outside but when opened, prove very valuable.

Large sums of money can be made by the wood expert who can detect figures and such things as escape the eye of the other people, and can obtain the logs at a fair price. This is a great gamble, equal to that of horse racing, and the stakes are often higher. This is another phase of the log business which makes it so interesting to people who have lived with it, and the reason they find they are never able to get the love of it out of their blood.

Formerly, logs would be sold either by board measure, by a type of measurement called Liverpool sales measure, by Constantine measurement, by Scribner & Doyle measurement, but some would be sold by weight. Today practically all are sold by weight.

This, briefly, is the story behind the piece of wood you are holding in your hand. No matter how many times we handle a piece of wood, this thought of what has gone behind it always comes to us. And if the piece of wood you are holding happens to be in the form of veneer, how it was converted from the log into veneers is the story in the next chapter.

from log
to veneers

MOST OF THE WOODS that we talk about are, at some time or another and in some form or another, converted into veneers. A few veneer mills have been erected in various tropical and other distant points where the wood grows, but the great percentage of the logs is transported overseas by boat, or in our own country by rail or truck to the sawmill.

Many logs, when they arrive at the mill, are dumped overboard into a log pond where they are usually kept until wanted. Immersion in the water protects the logs from insects and fungus attacks and prevents rotting and splitting. African mahogany logs, measuring as much as 6 ft. after being squared and weighing from 10 to 15 tons, are sometimes handled by large sawmills.

SAWING THE LOG

Hoisted from the pond into the mill, the log is mounted on a car, resembling a flat railroad car, which runs on a track. The sawyer controls the powerful machinery which moves the log to the carriage, as well as the carriage itself. This is now moved slowly against a large band saw having wheels 8 ft. or more in diameter and a blade as much as 50 ft. long and 14 in. or more wide. This blade travels as a rule at the speed of from 7,500 to 8,000 ft. per minute. The first cut is generally made near the center of the log for the purpose of "opening" it and examining the wood of the interior (Fig. 1).

I spent many hours of my earlier life in sawmills watching mahogany and other logs being opened and have always been fascinated by these big saws, running at a speed of a mile and a half a minute. Occasionally one of the bandsaw blades will break and do thousands of dollars of damage. Such accidents have at times taken the lives of sawyers, who have to stand within two or three feet of the saw.

64

Fig. 1. "Opening up" a log of African mahogany

Only a small percentage of the logs has a highly figured grain suitable for veneers. Those having straight or narrow grain are sawed into flitches, which are smaller timbers, squared on all four sides. Their thickness, width and length depends upon the size of the log and the extent of the figured grain. There are four generally accepted methods of cutting veneers: These are sawing, slicing, rotary cutting and half-rounding.

SAWED VENEERS

Sawed veneers are cut from flitches mounted on a movable carriage. The type of saw used is usually the segmental circular saw, the blade of which is built up of many parts or segments molded to a cast-iron hub (Fig. 2). Although these segments are very thin, the saw wastes as much veneer as is cut in sawing veneers of, generally, $\frac{1}{24}$ in. thickness. Thicker veneers may also be sawed, in which case, of course, the waste is proportionately less.

SLICED VENEERS

Sliced veneers are cut with a knife. In this case the flitch must first be softened by steaming or "cooking" in boiling water for several hours. The *veneer slicer* is a very heavy machine consisting of two main parts: a movable bed to which the flitch is bolted, and a knife supported in a rigid frame. The bed moves up and down while the knife remains stationary (Fig. 3). By means of diagonal guide bars, the veneer is sliced with a shearing cut as it moves against the knife. After each cut, the knife is given a slight sideways movement corresponding to the thickness of the veneer so that all sheets are exactly of the same thickness. The *standard thickness* is $\frac{1}{28}$ in. or 28 pieces to an inch. This is the thickness of all the woods that you see on fine pianos, television cabinets, furniture and paneling in rooms. Veneers can be cut much thinner—as thin as $\frac{1}{100}$ in. A great deal of thin veneer is used in laminating plywood for special purposes. As in sawed veneers, the sheets are kept and piled in the order in which they were cut. Sheets cut from the same flitch are always kept together, because only veneer cut from the same log can be matched for perfect uniformity and in such ways that the grain and figure will form a decorative pattern.

ROTARY-CUT VENEERS

Rotary-cut veneers are also cut with a knife, but from a whole round log instead of a flitch (Fig. 4). Since logs are cut with a knife, they must first be softened by steaming or boiling. The bark is removed with an automatic debarking lathe (Fig. 5)—work once done with adzes. Then the log is mounted in a lathe and rotated against the knife, which

66

Fig. 2. Veneer saw in operation

Fig. 3. Slicing veneers. The bed moves up and down while the knife remains stationary

Fig. 4. Rotary veneer cutting. The veneer is shaved from the log in a long, continuous sheet by a massive blade

is held rigidly. By giving the knife a slight sideways movement in the direction of the center of the log, a continuous sheet or peeling of uniform thickness results. This is cut into suitable widths on a clipper machine. The center of the log is cut up for crating lumber. Knives as long as 10 ft. are used for the rotary cutting of veneers, and knives as long as 17 ft. are used for slicing veneers. These knives weigh several hundred pounds and require the constant attention of an expert to keep the edge in proper shape at all times. Some woods require a very sharp knife; others require a duller edge. Some woods need a great amount of steaming or boiling beforehand; others very little. Acquiring the skill to judge the necessary steps to slice each and every log to obtain the finest results is a task which demands constant and methodical study.

HALF-ROUNDED VENEERS

Half-rounded veneers are also cut on a veneer lathe. In this case half the log is bolted to the lathe and revolved against the knife. The sheets of veneers cut in this manner are slightly rounded. Walnut stumps and bird's-eye maple are examples. In cutting wood this way, an entirely different figure effect is obtained than when the log is sliced.

DRYING VENEERS

All types of veneers are dried after they are cut. This is done in various ways. Nowadays most veneers are placed in a machine (Fig. 6) which consists of a series of heated plates which move up and down like bellows, alternately squeezing and releasing the sheets of veneers placed between them. After drying, the veneers cut from the same flitch are placed in numerical order, measured and crated for shipment. Veneers keep well after manufacturing, and will remain in good shape indefinitely if they are laid flat on some flat platform with a slight weight on top of them. If veneers should become dry and buckled, they may be flattened just by sprinkling the sheets with water. A good way to do this is to use a whisk broom dipped into a pail. The damp veneers should then have a heavy weight placed on them. Soon they become perfectly flat and ready for use again.

THE ADVANTAGES OF VENEERING

It would be impossible to construct a piece of furniture of many of the highly figured woods—as an example, walnut burl—because the grain of such wood as produced is structurally weak and would split and warp all out of shape. Many of the types of figures shown in this book could not be obtained in the manufacture of lumber. Other woods, particularly tropical varieties such as ebony, are so dense that

Fig. 5. An automatic debarking lathe removing bark from a log—a speedy operation. At one time this work was done by men with adzes. In some of the larger mills, particularly in the northwestern part of the United States, debarking is done by hydraulic methods

71

Fig. 6. Two-zone direct gas-fired veneer dryer

if a piece of furniture were constructed from the solid wood, it would be so heavy as to be practically immovable.

The art of veneering has been practiced for many years though the scientific way of utilizing veneers was not developed until the beginning of the present century. The plywood industry is now a large and important one. In the furniture industry this scientific knowledge of veneering, combined with its older decorative values, has enabled the manufacturer to create a product that is greatly superior to solid wood, both structurally and artistically.

Some of the lumbers of the rare, exotic, figured woods might cost up to $10 per foot in the lumber form, whereas produced in the veneer form they can be converted into plywood, if desired, by gluing them on straight-grain lumber of the same kind of wood. By that means not only is strength obtained, but costs are kept within permissible limits.

the physical
appearance
of wood

THE GENERAL, GROSS PHYSICAL PROPERTIES OF WOOD are of prime importance to the craftsman and woodworker. No two human beings are absolutely identical. Twins appear alike but there is usually some distinguishing characteristic. Similarly, no two pieces of wood are exactly alike or have precisely the same figure. There are differences in grain, figure, texture, color and other physical properties. It is these characteristics of wood that will largely govern a woodworker's choice. Features such as color, grain, figure and texture enter into the appearance of the finished product. Colored woods are desirable for period furniture, but are shunned for use in some modern pieces; a decorative figure need not be used for a bookcase backing, but it is highly beneficial to the appearance of a table top; the wood turner will select a fine-textured wood for his work rather than one of coarse texture. In brief, the worker in wood, like any artist, should carefully choose his medium in order to achieve the best results for his efforts. Below are some of the general characteristics of wood which will be of interest to the craftsman.

The terms grain, figure and texture are frequently misused. An inaccurate application of these terms can detract from their value. Such misusage often involves the direction of sawing. Timber that is cut parallel to the rays as shown at A, Fig. 1 is termed *quarter-sawn.* That cut perpendicular to the rays (B, Fig. 1) is termed *flat-sawn* or *plain-sawn.* In quarter-sawn timber the rays are viewed *en face,* and the growth rings appear as roughly parallel vertical lines. In flat-sawn timber, the rays are viewed on end and growth rings appear as inverted V's.

quarter-
sawed

plain-sawed

A

B

Fig. 1.

Fig. 2.   Straight-grain walnut, quarter-cut

GRAIN

Grain, used in the restricted, technical sense, refers to the direction
or orientation of wood cells, particularly the fibrous elements. Thus
we may distinguish six general types of grain: 1) *Straight grain:* In
such timber, the fibers and other longitudinally oriented elements are
more or less parallel to the vertical axis of the stem · (Fig. 2).
2) *Irregular grain:* This kind of grain is produced in timber where
the fibers are at varying and irregular inclinations to the vertical axis
of a log. It is frequently restricted to limited areas in the region of
knots or swollen butts. 3) *Diagonal grain* is a milling defect and results when otherwise straight-grained timbers are not sawn parallel
to the vertical axis of the log. 4) *Spiral grain* is produced when the
fibers follow a spiral or helical course in the living tree. The twist
may be right- or left-handed. 5) *Interlocked grain* results from the

75

fibers in successive growth layers being inclined or spiraled in opposite directions. Interlocked grain is relatively uncommon in timbers from the temperate zone but is characteristic of many tropical timbers. 6) *Wavy grain* is produced when the direction of the fibers is constantly changing so that a line drawn parallel with them appears as a wavy line on a longitudinal surface.

FIGURE

The term "grain" is frequently misused in referring to the natural design or pattern seen on the surface of wood. This pattern is not the grain of the wood, but the *figure*. Figure frequently results from the interaction of several features present in the wood, for example: the presence, absence, abundance and/or conspicuousness of growth rings; the prominence and abundance of the vascular rays; the type of grain and its modification in the vicinity of knots, burls, crotches, buttresses and swollen butts; local variations in color due to uneven deposition of coloring substances in wood. The grain in wood is particularly important in its effect on figure. Different kinds of irregular grain may give rise to *blister* or *quilted figure;* interlocked grain produces *ribbon* (Fig. 3) or *striped figure;* wavy grain (Fig. 4) shows as *fiddleback figure;* and a combination of wavy grain and interlocked grain produces a broken ripple on quartered surfaces (Fig. 5) called *rope figure.* The names given to figure variations are many. Some are narrowly applied to increase the sale of a given lot of veneer; others truly reflect or characterize the pattern. Among the more popular figures we find silver "grain," mottle figure (Fig. 6), snail figure, finger-roll figure, plum-pudding figure (Fig. 7), bird's-eye figure, curly figure, swirl figure (Fig. 8), swirly knots, burl figure, crotch figure, feather crotch figure, moonshine crotch, stump-wood figure and pigment figure.

Among the most strikingly beautiful patterns are those exhibited in wood from the vicinity of crotches. A crotch is that place in a tree where the main stem (or large branch) forks to produce two smaller stems. Crotch figure is obtained from wood directly below the bifurcation and is the result of the division of the stem.

Burls are responsible for the formation of a number of interesting natural designs. A burl is an abnormal, wartlike excrescence on the trunk or branches of a tree. Examined closely, it may consist of a great mass of "eyes" or dormant buds. The surface of such a bulge may be smooth or rough. In either case the alignment of the fibers is very irregular and the burl is thus gnarled. It is because of this that many bizarre figures are derived from veneers cut from burls. Causes of burls are imperfectly understood and the following theories

Fig. 3. Ribbon-stripe figure
in African mahogany

Fig. 4. Fiddle-back figure
in Cuban mahogany

Fig. 5.   Rope figure
in African mahogany

Fig. 6.   Large block mottle figure
in African mahogany

Fig. 7. Plum-pudding figure (rare) in African mahogany

Fig. 8. Moonshine swirl in African mahogany

79

have been advanced to explain this unusual growth: injury from frost, fire or mechanical contact, irritation of the cambium by bacteria, fungi and possibly viruses. A legend states that wounds inflicted by woodpeckers cause burls. However, this is easily discredited by the fact that trees produce burls in regions where woodpeckers do not exist. Burls can and do grow on all species of trees; however, they are found more commonly on certain trees, as for example, the redwood *(Sequoia sempervirens).*

Records show that by the time the Roman Empire was at its height, decorative burls were in demand for table tops and other articles of furniture. Wealthy Romans paid high prices for particularly fancy or unusual burl patterns. Even today good burl wood commands top prices, for the percentage of trees in which burls develop is negligible, and in many of these burls the wood is unsound and defective. Burl veneer has high decorative value for inlays and overlays, as well as for matching into four- or eight-piece combinations.

BIRD'S-EYE FIGURE

The figure in a bird's-eye maple log resembles somewhat the figure in a burl. It contains a small eye like that of a burl, but it is more distinct (Fig. 9). In a burl, the eye is surrounded by a series of clusters, but in bird's-eye maple each eye stands out separately. This is one of the few woods which is laid face side down in veneering, due to the conical shape of the eye. When laid face side down, the eyes will never chip out. This maple is very popular in the musical instrument trade because of its wonderful sounding qualities. It is also a favorite in seating stock due to its durability and toughness.

There has long been a discussion as to what causes the bird's-eye figure in maple and the accepted belief today is that it is caused by a stunted growth. It is found in trees where the growth has been the slowest—always on the northeast slopes of hills and in trees that have been hemmed in on all sides in the forest, where the tree has had little light and air. Careful studies made over a period of many years in marking trees have shown that when a tree that had been among a large number of trees has been left to stand alone because of the clearing away of the other trees, and when, after 20 years or more, this tree was cut down and brought into the veneer mill and manufactured, it would yield plain veneer for the number of years it was out in the open, but during the years that it lacked space and sunshine, it had developed the bird's-eye figure. An excellent example of a large firm that for its lifetime has specialized in the manufacture and marketing of only one or two woods is the Birds Eye Veneer

80

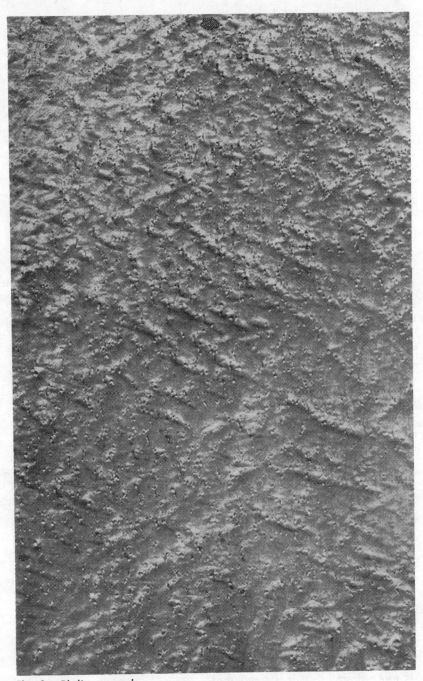

Fig. 9. Bird's-eye maple

81

Co., of Escanaba, Michigan. This firm has specialized in producing maple and birch for well over a quarter of a century and supplies many countries of the world.

The part of the log from which the butt figure (Fig. 10) is obtained is the buttressed or swollen part of the tree, just above the ground. It usually shows a crinkly, curly figure, obtainable only in relatively few woods and more commonly associated with walnut in this country. To preserve, as far as possible, this figure, a walnut tree is not sawed down, but dug out, the main roots cut, and then pulled over. Logs are sent in this condition to the mill.

TEXTURE

Another important physical aspect of wood is the *texture*. Texture pertains to the relative size and the amount of variation in the size of wood cells. It refers, if you will, to the "feel" of the wood. Texture is described as coarse, fine, even and uneven. The differentiation between coarse and fine texture is based on the dimensions of the pores and the width and abundance of the rays. Timbers in which the vessels are wide, or rays broad, are said to be of *coarse texture*. When vessels are narrow, and rays thin, the timber is of *fine texture*. Many intermediate grades also exist. For example, oak *(Quercus)* is coarse-textured; walnut *(Juglans nigra)* and mahogany *(Swietenia* spp.) are moderately coarse-textured; sycamore *(Platanus* spp.) is fine-textured, and European boxwood *(Buxus sempervirens)* is very fine-textured. Strictly speaking, all softwoods are fine- or at most only moderately coarse-textured, as their cells are of relatively small diameter. The texture of softwoods is frequently influenced by the alternation of the zones of spring- and summer-wood. When the contrast between the zones is strongly marked as in pitch pine *(Pinus rigida)* Douglas fir *(Pseudotsuga menziesii)* or larch *(Larix* spp.), the wood is said to be of *uneven* texture. In eastern white pine *(Pinus strobus),* the true firs *(Abies* spp.) and spruces *(Picea* spp.) the wood shows little or no contrast between spring- and summer-wood. Consequently, we can say these woods are *even-textured.* The same terminology can be applied to hardwoods, diffuse porous woods being even-textured, ring porous woods being uneven-textured.

THE COLOR OF WOOD

From the practical viewpoint, color is of importance in wood because it may enhance or detract from the decorative value of the timber. Ebony *(Diospyros* spp.), mahogany *(Swietenia* spp.) and walnut *(Juglans* spp.) owe their desirability at least in part to their decorative color. On the other hand, wood for toothpicks and wooden spoons is more desirable if it is uncolored.

Fig. 10.   Walnut butt or stumpwood

83

We know that color is caused largely by various infiltrates in the cell wall. Some of the infiltrates in certain timbers as logwood (*Haematoxylon* spp.) are extracted and used as dyes. Some undergo changes when timber is exposed to light, air or heat with the result that many timbers darken with age, and others fade. Mahogany fades under strong sunlight, but darkens under moderate light. African mahogany coming from one port on the west coast of Africa will have an entirely different color than mahogany coming from another port, relatively only a short distance away. A specialist in African mahogany can generally tell by the color of the logs which port they come from, as Grand Bassam or Half Assinee or Axim.

Different species of walnut will also vary greatly according to the country it comes from, whether Italy, France or the United States, and with the latter it will also vary according to the section or state it comes from. This is easily explained, because color is caused by the presence of extraneous materials in the walls of the wood and the color is dependent upon the type of soil and the content of the soil it grows in. Also, in many of the woods there are distinct differences in color between the sapwood and the heartwood.

Several timbers, as teak (*Tectona*) and Borneo white seraya (*Parashorea* spp.), exhibit quite a range of color when freshly planed, but after a short exposure to daylight the colors even out considerably. The moist heat that is employed during kiln-seasoning darkens many woods—so much so that some are steamed purposely to alter the color, as beech (*Fagus*) and walnut (*Juglans*) sapwood. Color changes are also effected by chemical means; liming lightens color and fuming with ammonia gas darkens it, removing the pink or red shades. Bleaching of wood is also feasible and produces attractive finishes.

ODOR AND TASTE IN WOOD

Many timbers have a characteristic odor, which is apparent when they are worked in a fairly fresh condition, but which usually disappears as the wood dries out. Perhaps the most outstanding examples are the characteristic resinous odors of the pines, the spicy aroma of sandalwood (*Santalum album*) and Spanish cedar (*Cedrela* spp.), and the camphorlike odor of Formosan camphorwood (*Cinnamomum camphora*). Certain Australian woods of the *Acacia* group possess an odor not unlike violets, coachwood (*Ceratopetalum apetalum*) is reminiscent of newly mown hay. Some woods, as *Viburnum lentago*, have a fetid odor.

The taste of wood is closely related to odor and can probably be traced to the same constituents. Both properties influence the utilization of timber. The choice of woods for food containers is restricted to those without pronounced odor or taste. The flavor of tobacco on the other hand is alleged to be improved when stored in boxes made of Spanish cedar *(Cedrela* spp.). Camphorwood and eastern red cedar are used to make boxes in which clothes are stored because of their reputed repellent effect on insects.

LUSTER IN WOOD

Luster depends on the ability of the cell walls to reflect light. Some timbers possess this property to a high degree, and others are comparatively dull. As a general rule, quarter-sawn surfaces are more lustrous than are flat-sawn. If stripe, fiddleback or roe figures are present, the figure is considerably enhanced in timbers possessing natural luster. Although luster is an asset in a cabinet wood, the capacity for taking a good polish is quite as important from a practical viewpoint, and the two do not necessarily occur together.

REFERENCES

See references after Chapter 2, "The Identification of Woods."

woods of
THE BIBLE

THE BIBLE IS A SOURCE of many interesting references concerning trees and woods, some of which are familiar to us today. The tree and its fruit have always been symbolic of strength and fertility.

Perhaps the most famous Bible tree in this regard is the cedar of Lebanon, *Cedrus libani*. In Psalms 92:12 we read, "The righteous shall flourish like the palm tree: he shall grow like a cedar in Lebanon." Further it is stated in Ezekiel 31:3-18, "Behold the Assyrian was a cedar in Lebanon with fair branches . . . and his top was among the thick boughs." There are almost 50 references in the Bible traceable to the cedar of Lebanon. This is most likely due to the fact that these trees were the grandest trees with which the Israelites were acquainted. They grow rapidly and attain heights of 120 ft. and trunk diameters up to 8 ft. Such magnificent specimens fill all who see them now with awe and reverence and must have in Biblical days.

Today only a pitifully small remnant of this once proud forest remains. What has become of this remnant? Lebanon has created the Cedars of Lebanon National Park and protects it as a "National Treasure." It is still known by the French name "Les Cedres." The park is near the village of Basharri or Becherre, 84 miles north of Beirut in the Lebanon Mountains. It is an easy three-hour drive from Beirut. No woodsman can now deplete these celebrated trees due to a strictly enforced national law. The grove numbers around 400 trees and a few smaller groves are known to exist elsewhere in Lebanon. The Lebanese revere the tree, have made it the national tree and the official emblem of the nation. It is used on everything from the flag to a postage stamp. Efforts are being made to propagate

Artist's rendering depicts Cedars of Lebanon grove in Biblical times

the tree from seeds, although it has been in cultivation for some time. Europe and America have many specimens. One of the most magnificent is in Portland, Ore. This tree has a straight bole 2 ft. in diameter with a height of approximately 100 ft. and is free of limbs for about half that distance.

Many other trees mentioned in the Bible were symbolic as well as practical. Among these is the myrtle *(Myrtus communis)*. Besides its use as a spice, myrtle is representative of fertility and life. This is seen in Isaiah 41:19. Isaiah is restoring the dry, barren desert and wilderness with the life-giving tree. "I will plant in the wilderness the cedar, the shittah tree and the myrtle, and the oil tree; I will set in the desert the fir tree and the pine, and the box tree together." These trees can all be found today, providing the same life-giving shade for which they were noted in Biblical times.

The olive *(Olea europea)* is mentioned in Genesis 8:11: "And the dove came in to him in the evening; and lo, in her mouth was an olive leaf pluckt off; so Noah knew that the waters were abated from off the earth." Perhaps this was the beginning of the olive branch as symbolizing peace. The same branch, which signified God's peace with Noah, has been used throughout history as a reminder of peace between nations, and can be seen today as a symbol on the flag of the United Nations.

The wood provided by trees has been turned into many decorative

The Bible, in Exodus 26, refers to shittim wood used to build the tabernacle

and useful articles. The cabinetmakers of today only follow a long tradition of a handicraft which was practiced by Jesus, a carpenter, centuries ago. Men searched the world over for rare and useful woods during Biblical times, even as they do today. We see in Ezekiel 27:15: "The men of Dedan were thy merchants; many isles were the merchandise of thine hand; they brought thee for a present horns of ivory and ebony" *(Diospyros* spp.).

Other trees, including the cedar of Lebanon, were employed during Biblical times for construction purposes. The builder and craftsman of today is no doubt interested in timbers used in these bygone days. The ark of Noah was of gopher wood, gopher being in the Hebrew. We learn that the Lord said to Noah, "Make thee an ark of gopher wood . . ." (Genesis 6:14). The gopher wood of the Bible most likely is one of the true cypresses, *Cupressus sempervirens* var. *horizontalis.* Although the walnut *(Juglans regia)* is not mentioned in the Bible as being sought for timber, the ancient Hebrews were acquainted with its fruit (Song 6:11). Probably they also employed its wood in construction of some sort.

Pinus halepensis, though referred to in the Bible as a fir, enters as a building material: In Song 1:17, "The beams of our house are cedar, and our rafters of fir," and in Ezekiel 27:5, "They have made all thy ship boards of fir trees of Senir . . ." Reference in the Bible

The sacred chest, The Ark of the Covenant, was made of acacia wood

to almug trees has been traced to *Pterocarpus santalinus.* We read in I Kings 10:11-12 that ". . . the king made of the almug trees pillars for the house of the Lord, and for the king's house, harps also and psalteries for the singers."

The oak *(Quercus* spp.) is mentioned by a variety of names in the Bible. Several species of oaks now grow in the Holy Land which may have been employed in Biblical days. A statement in Isaiah 44:14 refers to the logging of oaks: "He heweth him down cedars, and taketh the cypress and the oak . . ."

Acacia wood is known as shittim in the Bible and was commonly used in construction: Exodus 26: 15-16, 26, 32, 37, "And thou shalt make boards for the tabernacle of shittim wood standing up . . . and thou shalt make bars of shittim wood . . . and thou shalt hang it upon four pillars of shittim wood . . . and thou shalt make for the hanging five pillars of shittim wood."

The Ark of the Covenant, which the Lord ordered Moses and the Hebrews to construct, was a sacred chest made of *Acacia* wood overlaid with gold, the lid of which constituted the "mercy seat," or place of propitiation, over which two cherubim extended their wings. This is described in Exodus 25:10, when the Lord said to Moses: "And they shall make an ark of shittim wood: two cubits and a half shall be the length thereof and a cubit and a half the breadth thereof, and a cubit and a half the height thereof." This was placed in the tabernacle, which was also built of shittim wood; so were most of the furnishings as mentioned above. Citations of shittim wood occur in large numbers in the Old Testament. Apparently it was a favored building material.

Incense and spices were in wide use during Biblical times. They appealed to the senses and the spirit and are often mentioned in both testaments. Some of these aromatic materials were derived from trees. The aloes of the Old Testament supposedly refer to *Santalum album* or sandalwood. In Psalms 45:8 we read, "All thy garments smell of myrrh, and aloes, and cassia," and in Song 4:14, ". . . myrrh and aloes, with all chief spices." Aloe was probably mixed with myrrh when wrapped among the burying garments in embalming.

The incense or frankincense of the Bible was derived from a species of *Boswellia,* a tree related to the gumbo limbo of the Florida keys and West Indies. Among the many, many references to frankincense in the Old and New Testaments we can cite Jeremiah 6:20, "To what purpose cometh there to me incense from Sheba, and the sweet cane from a far country?" Perhaps the most famous reference is in part of the Christmas story from Matthew 2:11, "And when they were come into the house, they saw the young child with Mary his mother, and fell down, and worshipped him: and when they had opened their treasures, they presented unto him gifts; gold, and frankincense, and myrrh."

At least two species of *Cinnamomum* entered into the spice cabinets of Bible cooks and into the boudoirs of maidens: *C. cassia* and *C. zeylanicum.* In Exodus 30:23-24 we read, "Take thou also unto thee principal spices . . . and of cassia five hundred shekels." The cinnamon of the Bible is directly translatable from the Hebrew "kinamôn." Thus, in Proverbs 7:17, "I have perfumed my bed with myrrh, aloes, and cinnamon." That often mentioned scent, myrrh, is derived from *Commiophora myrrh.* References to the use of myrrh are legion and it must have been a valuable article of commerce in ancient times. Myrrh is also a symbol of sensuousness, for it is mentioned in this way in the Song of Solomon, e.g., 1:13: "A bundle of myrrh is my well-beloved unto me. . . ." Many other examples of aromatic tree products occur throughout the Books.

There are a number of fruit trees in the Holy Land, and the ancients made wide use of those available. There is no doubt that the fruit of the date palm *(Phoenix dactylifera)* was exceedingly important—important as a comestible and as a symbol of fertility. The palm tree of the Bible almost surely refers to the date palm. At one time it was as common in Palestine as it is now in Egypt. In Psalms

92:12-14 it is stated: "The righteous shall flourish like a palm tree . . ." and in Jeremiah 10:5, "They are upright as the palm tree . . ." The Hebrew word for the date palm is "tamar." This palm became the Jews' symbol of grace and elegance and was often bestowed by them upon women, as, for instance, to the sister of Absalom. In Genesis 38:6 we find that, ". . . Judah took a wife for Er his firstborn, whose name was Tamar." In II Samuel 13:1 is the reference to Absalom's sister: ". . . Absalom . . . had a fair sister, whose name was Tamar."

Other fruit-bearing trees mentioned in the Bible are: the almond *(Amygdalus communis);* the "husks" in Jesus' parable of the prodigal son were no doubt the pods of the carob tree *(Ceratonia siliqua);* the fig *(Ficus carica)* is mentioned abundantly in both testaments; the sycamore of Amos is also a fig *(Ficus sycamorus);* the fruit of the olive *(Olea europea)* was the source of anointing oil, cooking oil, oil for lamps and medicinal oils; the fruit or nut of the pistachio *(Pistacia vera);* the apple of the Bible was probably a plum or near relative *(Prunus armeniaca); punica granatum,* the pomegranate, was known to the ancient Israelites; and the grape *(Vitis vinifera),* although not a tree, should be included here if only for its overwhelming importance.

Trees have always been used for the shade which their leafy branches have provided. Man, through the ages, has sought relief from the scorching rays of the sun under the shelter of trees. "The shady trees cover him with their shadow; the willows *(Salix* spp.) of the brook compass him about," is found in Job 40:22. Hosea 4:13 also gives reference to the shade provided by trees: "They sacrifice upon the tops of the mountains, and burn incense upon the hills, under oaks *(Quercus* spp.) and poplars *(Populus alba)* and elms *(Pistacia terebinthus* var. *palaestina),* because the shadow thereof is good."

One of the oldest ways in which the tree has served man is as a source of fuel for warmth and cooking. Man might not have survived without this protection of his life, and its importance is even mentioned in Proverbs 26:20: "Where no wood is, there the fire goeth out."

One of the questions very often asked concerning the woods of the Bible is, "What kind of wood was the cross made of?" Although there is no definite answer to this given in the Bible, the legend of the flowering dogwood has often been told. This legend, although very beautiful, is entirely fallacious. As the legend goes, at the time of the crucifixion, the dogwood tree was the size of the oak and other forest trees. This tree was so sturdy that it was chosen as the timber for the cross. It is said that, "To be thus used for such a cruel purpose, distressed the tree so greatly, that Jesus who was nailed upon it, sensed this, and in His gentle pity for all sorrow and suffering, said to it: 'Because of your regret and pity for my suffering, never again shall the dogwood tree grow large enough to be used as a cross. Henceforth it shall be slender and bent and twisted, and its blossoms shall be in the form of a cross—two long and two short petals. And in the center of the outer edge of each petal there will be nail prints, brown with rust and stained with red, and in the center of the flower will be a crown of thorns and all who see it will remember.' " The flowering dogwood *(Cornus florida)* to which this quotation refers, occurs in eastern North America where it is native. It was completely unknown in Biblical days. The "petals" in the story above are not petals but colored bracts, while the actual flowers of the tree compose the central "crown of thorns." Other, similar legends revolve about the wood used for the cross. Early Christian legendry states that the aspen *(Populus)* was so used. At the time of the crucifixion, aspen trees everywhere shuddered when the nails were driven into the wood and the holy blood gushed forth upon the cross. This may be an allusion to the European trembling aspen, *Populus tremula.*

Another often-told legend concerns a tree which, while not mentioned in the Bible, is often associated with it. The redbud has long been called the "Judas tree," because of the legend which tells how Judas Iscariot, after betraying Jesus, hung himself on a Near East cousin of the redbud, *Cercis siliquastrum.* It is said that the white flowers of this tree blushed red with shame and have remained so ever since. Just how it was that tradition selected this tree of all the Palestinian trees as the one on which Judas committed suicide, is not clear. In any event, it has been known as the Judas tree for much over 200 years. The poplar *(Populus)* is another of the trees on which ancient legend says that Judas hanged himself.

REFERENCES

Moldenke, H. N., and A. L. Moldenke. 1952. Plants of the Bible. Chronica Botanica Co. Waltham, Mass.

state trees

RESEARCH SHOWS THAT TREE SPECIES now growing in North America existed long before the country was inhabited by man: maples as long as 60 million years; and poplars, oaks, pines, elms and possibly other trees, grew here during the Ice Age. Greenland is named because of its trees, to differentiate it from Iceland, which is almost without trees.

The commercial forest lands of the United States consist of about 488 million acres. Old-growth saw timber covers 50 million acres; second-growth timber, 133 million. There are 120 million acres in the cordwood areas, 102 million acres are of fair-to-satisfactory restocking areas, and 83 million acres are poor-to-nonrestocking areas.

There are about 180 different species of trees in the United States that may be ranked as commercially important, although only relatively few species of wood are ordinarily readily available except in the larger cities. Forest regions and principal types of forests are shown on the accompanying map, Fig. 1.

The individual states of the United States have long recognized the importance of trees, and each state has selected a particular tree with which to identify itself. This has been done by acts of the state legislatures, garden clubs, or by vote of the people. Or, in some cases, because it is the most prominent tree, or the most valuable tree, growing in that state. New York State took the lead in 1889 in selecting the sugar maple as its official tree, and was followed by the other states.

At the end of the chapter the states are listed alphabetically with the common name of the tree. The botanical name and individual description of the wood may be found by referring to each of the individual woods described in this book.

93

EASTERN LEGEND

■ Spruce-fir (with admixture of hardwoods)
▨ Birch-beech-maple-hemlock forest
▤ White, red, and jack pine
▦ Oak-hickory
▨ Oak-chestnut-yellow poplar
▨ Oak-pine
▨ River-bottom hardwoods and cypress
▨ Longleaf-loblolly-slash pine

NEW ENGLAND
MIDDLE ATLANTIC
LAKE
CENTRAL
SOUTH

WESTERN LEGEND

■ Spruce-fir
▨ Pacific Douglas fir
▨ Sugar pine-ponderosa pine
▨ Redwood
▨ Western larch-western white pine
▨ Lodgepole pine

▨ Ponderosa pine
▨ Pinyon-juniper
▨ Chaparral

NORTH ROCKY MOUNTAIN
SOUTH ROCKY MOUNTAIN
PACIFIC COAST

Fig. 1. Forests of the United States (except Alaska and Hawaii)

Maine — Eastern white pine
New Hampshire — Paper birch
Massachusetts — American elm
Rhode Island — Red maple
Connecticut — White oak
New Jersey — Northern red oak
Delaware — American holly
Maryland — White oak
West Virginia — Sugar maple

Vermont — Sugar maple
New York — Sugar maple
Pennsylvania — Eastern hemlock
Virginia — Dogwood
North Carolina — None
South Carolina — Cabbage palmetto

Florida — Cabbage palmetto (cabbage palm)

District of Columbia
None (although American sycamore and black cherry are mentioned on some lists)

Michigan — Apple
Ohio — Buckeye
Kentucky — Tuliptree
Tennessee — Tuliptree
Georgia — Live oak
Alabama — Longleaf pine
Mississippi — Southern magnolia

Wisconsin — Sugar maple
Illinois — Bur oak
Indiana — Tuliptree
Missouri — Dogwood
Arkansas — Shortleaf pine
Louisiana — Southern magnolia

Minnesota — Red pine
Iowa — None
Oklahoma — Eastern redbud
Texas — Pecan

North Dakota — American elm
South Dakota — Black Hills spruce
Nebraska — American elm
Kansas — Cottonwood

Montana — Ponderosa pine
Wyoming — Balsam poplar
Colorado — Blue spruce
New Mexico — Pinyon pine

Idaho — Western white pine
Utah — Blue spruce
Arizona — Blue paloverde

Washington — Western hemlock
Oregon — Douglas fir
Nevada — Singleleaf pinyon pine
California — California redwood

Alaska — Not yet officially designated. It will probably be either the Alaska red cedar or the Sitka spruce

Hawaii — Not yet officially designated. (It will probably be either the monkey pod or the ohia)

Most states have designated an official state tree as shown on the map. A few states have not taken formal action

STATE	COMMON NAME
Alabama	Longleaf pine
Alaska	Not yet officially designated. It will probably be either the Alaska red cedar or the Sitka spruce
Arizona	Blue paloverde
Arkansas	Shortleaf pine
California	California redwood
Colorado	Blue spruce
Connecticut	White oak
Delaware	American holly
District of Columbia	None (although American sycamore and black cherry are mentioned on some lists)
Florida	Cabbage palmetto (cabbage palm)
Georgia	Live oak
Hawaii	Not yet officially designated. (It will probably be either the monkey pod or the ohia)
Idaho	Western white pine
Illinois	Bur oak
Indiana	Tuliptree (yellow poplar)
Iowa	None (although black walnut is sometimes called the state tree)
Kansas	Cottonwood
Kentucky	Tuliptree (yellow poplar)
Louisiana	Southern magnolia
Maine	Eastern white pine
Maryland	White oak
Massachusetts	American elm
Michigan	Apple
Minnesota	Red pine (also called Norway pine)
Mississippi	Southern magnolia
Missouri	Dogwood
Montana	Ponderosa pine
Nebraska	American elm

STATE	COMMON NAME
Nevada	Singleleaf pinyon pine (aspen also is sometimes referred to as the state tree)
New Hampshire	Paper birch
New Jersey	Northern red oak
New Mexico	Pinyon pine
New York	Sugar maple
North Carolina	None (although yellow poplar is sometimes mentioned)
North Dakota	American elm
Ohio	Buckeye
Oklahoma	Eastern redbud
Oregon	Douglas fir
Pennsylvania	Eastern hemlock
Rhode Island	Red maple
South Carolina	Cabbage palmetto
South Dakota	Black Hills spruce
Tennessee	Tuliptree (yellow poplar)
Texas	Pecan
Utah	Blue spruce
Vermont	Sugar maple
Virginia	Dogwood
Washington	Western hemlock
West Virginia	Sugar maple
Wisconsin	Sugar maple
Wyoming	Balsam poplar (sometimes referred to by the general name "cottonwood")

drugs from trees

TREES ARE OFTEN THOUGHT OF PRIMARILY as producers of timbers and of edible fruit. Less commonly known is that some of our important medicinal constituents are tree products. Although many drugs previously acquired from natural sources are now prepared synthetically, others are still in wide use.

As with all drugs, drugs derived from trees have been replaced with more potent preparations. On the other hand, new drugs secured from trees become evident from time to time. Pharmaceutical companies are still eager to support botanical expeditions with the hope that some previously unknown drug product may result from new collections. Drug companies, during the year in which this book is being printed, are expected to spend over five million dollars for research on medicinal plants and trees. This is more than double the amount spent on plant research a couple of years previously. Most United States drug houses employ botanical hunters who ship many of their newly found specimens to the Department of Agriculture's Plant Introduction Gardens in Glendale, Md., where some must undergo quarantine.

Aboriginal tribes are still found employing tree products as drugs of which we have had no previous knowledge. Drugs of this nature were employed from the earliest times. It is known, for example, that an extract from the juniper tree was used as a cancer "curative" by the ancient Greeks and Romans.

A few of the more common medicinal products obtained from trees are described below. It is not possible here to list and describe all the known trees that produce drugs.

ACACIA *(Acacia senegal)* The gum of *Acacia senegal* is the gum arabic of present-day commerce and is that referred to as Sudan gum, Somali gum, etc. It is a characteristic tree throughout the drier parts of the Sudan and southern Sahara. It is said that the gum is yielded only when the tree is unhealthy, and efforts to improve its condition are followed by a reduction in yield. Gum arabic is an exudation from the tree, used as a base for many mucilages and as an emulsifying agent in pharmacy, and in tannic acid which is used in the treatment of burns.

ALLSPICE *(Pimenta officinalis)* A fragrant tree sometimes 40 ft. high, the allspice is native to Jamaica, Cuba, southern Mexico and parts of Central America. The berries, while still green, are gathered and dried for export. Although used chiefly in cookery, allspice is employed as a carminitive and stimulant in drug preparations.

ARECA *(Areca catechu)* This is a tall palm tree, from 30 to 50 ft., indigenous to the Malay Archipelago. The seed, or betel "nut" of commercial and native use, is chewed by the natives to produce the garish red mouth and black teeth considered in good fashion. It is rarely used in human medicine, but frequently employed by veterinarians as a vermifuge because of its active principal, the alkaloid arecoline.

BALM-OF-GILEAD *(Populus candicans* and other species) The dried winter buds of this species possess a natural resinous substance which imparts a tendency to prevent rancidity in ointments. Applied externally, the resin is useful in healing wounds. Internally it is a stimulating expectorant in the treatment of bronchitis.

BALSAM OF PERU *(Myroxylon balsamum* var. *pereirae)* The range of this variety extends from southern Mexico southward through Central America, mostly on the Pacific side. Its principal value is in its vanilla-scented resin which is known as balsam of Peru. The drug was introduced into Europe by the Spaniards in the sixteenth century. Its source has been the Balsam Coast, originally a part of Guatemala, now of Salvador, and the misleading name derives from the fact that in colonial days the product was frequently sent to Callao, Peru, for transshipment to Spain. To obtain the balsam, the trees are beaten until the bark falls off. The resulting gummy exudation is collected on rags, which are then boiled to remove the gum, packed in bladders and taken to market. It is used in medicine as a stimulant dressing for indolent ulcers, tuberculosis of the bone and skin, and as a dressing for wounds.

The South American trees also yield oleoresin, sometimes called "balsamum tolutanum" or balsam tolu. It is considered inferior to the Salvador product. Its main use is in the preparation of syrup tolu —a feeble stimulant-expectorant of pleasant taste and as a vehicle for cough mixture.

BENJAMIN TREE *(Styrax benzoin)* This tall tree, native of Sumatra and Java, is covered with whitish, downy bark. Once a year the bark is wounded in the vicinity of the lower branches to permit exudation of sap, which hardens on exposure to air and produces gum benzoin, a white, fragrant gum used in medicine as a stimulating expectorant. Tincture of benzoin compound, universally used and known, is made with this product and is employed in steam inhalators for the relief of bronchitis and laryngitis. In the East Indies, the gum is burned by the Hindus as a perfume in their places of worship.

BOLDO *(Boldea boldus)* The leaves of this strongly aromatic tree, native to the dry sunny hillsides of Chile, are used as a seasoning for foods and as an antispasmatic and hepatic stimulant. The bark is a source of tannin.

CACAO *(Theobroma cacao)* This is a small, handsome evergreen tree, indigenous to Mexico, West Indies and South America. The pods (fruits) of this tree produce numerous large seeds which, when roasted and ground, give us our cocoa or chocolate of commerce. Cacoa butter is used in many food substitutes, and medicinally as a base for emollients and suppositories. At one time, it was practically the major treatment for sunburn.

CAMPHOR TREE *(Cinnamomum camphora)* This evergreen tree sometimes attains a great size and is native to Formosa, Japan and some parts of China. It grows so slowly that 50 years or more usually elapses before the drug, camphor, is removed from the bark by the process of sublimation. Camphor was used for many years by "old wives" as a charm, as a cure for many illnesses, and hung in bags around the neck to ward off plagues. It is used in medicine mainly as a local remedy and counterirritant, and as an ingredient in many ointments for relieving muscle pains. A derivative is also used hypodermically as an emergency stimulant in some cases of heart failure.

CANELLA BARK or WHITE CINNAMON *(Canella winterana)* The white cinnamon is native to the Florida Keys and West Indies. Its yellowish inner bark is cinnamon-scented and is employed as an aromatic stimulant and tonic.

CASCARA *(Rhamnus purshiana)* This small tree grows in northwestern United States and British Columbia. Because of the large demand for the wood, the trees in Oregon and Washington have been depleted, but they are more readily available in Canada. The wood, which is yellow, orange-brown or orange, is easy to work, takes a good finish, but has little or no commercial value because of the small size of the timber. The inside of freshly cut bark is bright yellow, turning to brown when exposed to the sun, and has a bitter taste. The bark is the source of the drug known as cascara sagrada, used in medicine as a laxative and cathartic. An average tree will yield about 10 lbs. of dried bark. The bark is stripped from the tree during the dry season, hung on wires to dry in the shade, and shipped in 100-lb. bales or bags to dealers. The bark must age for a year or more before being used medicinally. Cascara is also known under a number of different names, as brittle wood, buckthorn, yellow wood, polecat tree, bitter bark and wild coffee.

CASSIA *(Cassia fistula)* Cassia is a large tree which may reach 45 ft. in height. It is native to India and possesses a hard, heavy wood. The trunk is covered with a smooth, ash-colored bark. It is now distributed throughout the world tropics under the name of "golden shower" and is used as an ornamental shade tree. The crushed fruit of this tree is officially known as cassia pulp and is employed as an aromatic flavoring and mild laxative.

CASTANEA *(Castanea dentata)* The American chestnut is a large, spreading deciduous tree often attaining 100 ft. in height, but now almost extinct, due to a pernicious fungus-caused blight. Attempts are currently in progress to obtain disease-resistant varieties. The leaves were used in medicine as a treatment for whooping cough; however, modern pharmacology attributes to them no other properties than that of a mild astringent.

CHALMOOGRA *(Hydnocarpus kurzii* or *Taraktogenos kurzii)* For centuries leprosy has been one of the most dreaded diseases of mankind and it was long thought to be incurable. It was known, however, that the natives of Burma and other parts of southeast Asia used the seeds and oil obtained from the chalmoogra tree in the treatment of skin diseases. Experiments carried on at the University of Hawaii utilized this oil in the development of a successful treatment for leprosy.

CINCHONA *(Cinchona succiruba)* The Peruvian bark tree is native to the high mountains of Peru and Ecuador. It is also widely cultivated throughout the tropics in Java, Sumatra and elsewhere. The bark from this tree has been used since the seventeenth century in the treatment of malaria. Official drugs obtained from the bark of this tree are numerous: mainly, quinine, quinidine, cinchonine, cinchonidine. Quinidine is much depended upon in treating some forms of heart failure. Modern synthetic drugs such as chloroquine and primaquine have proven superior to quinine in the treatment of malaria.

CINNAMON *(Cinnamomum loureiri* or *Cinnamomum zeylanicum)* The cinnamon tree is native to China and Japan but now cultivated in India and other tropical lands. Several species are used in the production of the cinnamon of commerce. Cinnamon is among the most delightful of aromatics, efficient as a flavoring in candies and in cooking. It is warm and cordial to the stomach, flavorful in medicine and efficient as a carminitive.

CLOVE TREE *(Eugenia caryophyllata)* It is a small evergreen tree, indigenous to the Moluccas and perhaps the southern Philippine Islands. Throughout the year it is covered with a succession of beautiful, rosy flowers. The dried flower buds give us our commercial cloves, an aromatic spice much prized by chefs. An aromatic oil expressed from these cloves is used in many forms of pharmaceutical preparations, most familiar of which is the oil of cloves used to control toothaches.

COCA *(Erythroxylon coca)* This shrub or small tree is native to the eastern slopes of the Andes from Colombia to Bolivia but is grown throughout tropical South America and in Java and surrounding islands. The leaves of this and other species are the source of cocaine and its component alkaloids. Natives chew the leaves for their stimulating effects. During the reign of the Incas, athletic prowess was attributed in part to the strength and sustaining power derived from masticating dried coca leaves. The drug, cocaine, acts internally as a circulatory and respiratory stimulant. Externally it is

The leaves and flowers of the cinchona tree

used mainly as a local anaesthetic to deaden pain quickly. It takes over 100 lbs. of the leaves of this tree to make a pound of cocaine.

CURARE *(Strychnos toxifera* and others) This tree produces one of the most violent poisons known. The Indians of northern South America have long used curare as an arrow poison. In preparing curare, portions of the bark and roots are boiled down, the impurities skimmed off and the residue filtered. Catalytic agents are added and the whole mass is boiled to a syrup. This is exposed to the sun and dried to a paste, which is kept in tightly covered gourds or bamboo tubes. The paste, if introduced into the circulation in minute quantities, paralyzes the motor nerves almost instantly and soon causes death by cardiac failure. The lethal effects are due to certain alkaloids. One of these, curarine, has now been made available to medicine for use in shock therapy and is an ideal muscle relaxant.

EASTERN WHITE PINE *(Pinus strobus)* The bark of this tree, which grows throughout the whole eastern portion of the United States and Canada, is used as an ingredient in cough syrups and in the treatment of bronchial afflictions.

EUCALYPTUS *(Eucalyptus globulus* and other species) The genus *Eucalyptus* comprises large evergreen trees, sometimes 300 to 350 ft. in height. *E. globulus* grows in Tasmania where it is called blue gum. Medically, oil of eucalyptus, which is distilled from the leaves, is an active germicide and is used locally in infections of the upper respiratory tract. It is also used as an astringent.

GUAIACUM *(Guaiacum officinale)* Guaiacum or gum guaiac is a hard resin that exudes naturally from the stems of lignum vitae trees. It is obtained commercially from incisions in the bark or from the cut ends of logs. Gum guaiac is used as a stimulant and laxative.

JAMAICA DOGWOOD *(Piscidia piscipula)* These medium-sized trees occur in countries bounded by the Gulf of Mexico and the Caribbean Sea. The bark is used medicinally as an anodyne and hypnotic. Natives use the bark to stupefy fish, hence the name fishfuddle tree.

KOLA *(Cola nitida* and *C. acuminata)* These large trees are native to Guinea and western tropical Africa. They are also cultivated in the West Indies and South America for their seeds which when dried are used commercially in some medicines as a stimulant. The nuts contain much caffeine and when chewed confer considerable power to sustain fatigue. They form a staple in the diet of natives (cf. coca). It is also used as an ingredient in some of the carbonated drinks commonly used, like Coca Cola.

104

Eucalyptus forest in Australia

MANNA or EUROPEAN FLOWERING ASH *(Fraxinus ornus)* A native of southern Europe, this ash is widely cultivated in Italy and Sicily, where it grows to 20 or 25 ft. in height. Incisions are made in the lower portions of the tree to permit the flow of a sugary substance which dries naturally on the trees in small globules. Manna is a gentle demulcent laxative usually prescribed with other laxative agents.

NUTMEG *(Myristica fragrans)* This is a small tree, somewhat resembling an orange, native to the Mollucas. Grown from seed, it flowers and fruits after the ninth year. The dried kernel of the nut, commonly known as nutmeg, is a valuable flavoring and cooking agent. Mace, another food flavoring, is obtained from the fleshy covering of the seed (the aril). Nutmeg owes its medicinal properties purely to the volatile oil. It has stimulant and carminitive properties, but in large doses nutmegs are highly toxic and produce convulsions.

NUX VOMICA *(Strychnos nux-vomica)* Nux vomica or the strychnine tree grows in India, parts of China and Ceylon and provides from its seeds, strychnine, a deadly poison. This powerful drug is used as a heart stimulant and tonic, either alone or in conjunction with other drugs.

QUASSIA *(Quassia amara)* This bitter-tasting species has a natural range extending from northern South America through the West Indies, Central America and southern Mexico. The wood has been an item of commerce from Surinam since about the middle of the eighteenth century, being called in Surinam quassia or bitterwood. It was introduced into the London Pharmacopoeia in 1788, but in the 1809 edition was superseded by Jamaica bitterwood *(Aeschrion),* which was obtainable in larger sizes. The bitter principle of both kinds of wood (quassin) is readily soluble in cold water and for many years there was a demand for cups, called bitter cups, turned from the wood. The drug is employed as a tonic and vermifuge, and formerly as a febrifuge; it is used as an insecticide and as an ingredient of certain proprietary medicines.

QUERCUS *(Quercus alba)* A large, handsome tree, native to North America, it is one of the more than 50 species of oaks in the United States. The dried inner bark is used externally in medicine because of its astringent properties. Tannic acid is probably the active ingredient.

RAUWOLFIA *(Rauwolfia serpentina* and other species) Extracts from the roots of these shrubs have been employed in India for the treatment of nervous disorders for many centuries. Records show

Sassafras tree

that roots and leaves of *R. serpentina* were employed in Ayruvedic medicine as antidotes against bites of reptiles and the stings of insects and as a remedy for diarrhoea. It has only been in recent years, however, that the dried and powdered root of *R. serpentina* was introduced into clinical medicine here for the treatment of hypertension and nervous troubles, including insanity. Various drugs (serpentine, rauwolfinine, reserpinine, reserpine) derived from the powdered root constitute a general class of tranquilizers so commonly used today.

SASSAFRAS *(Sassafras albidum)* A delightful tree of eastern North America, all parts of which are aromatic. The bark of the roots is the source of the commercial oil of sassafras. Small roots in asparagus-like bunches are a common article of local commerce and are used in making sassafras tea, a beverage of reputed medicinal virtues, particularly as a "spring tonic." Root bark is also active as a diuretic.

SENNA *(Cassia acutifolia* and other species) This ancient drug is obtained from the dried leaflets, and also the pods, of several species of *Cassia* which are indigenous to the arid regions of Egypt and Arabia. Wild plants are still used as a source of the drug in Egypt. Medicinally, senna acts as a purgative.

STAR ANISE *(Illicium verum)* Although not the true anise *(Pimpinella anisum),* the star anise is also employed as a flavoring and is active medicinally as a carminitive. The Chinese prepare a medicinal tea from the fruits and regard it as good for colic and constipation. Interestingly enough, all other species of *Illicium* except *I. verum* are poisonous.

WILD BLACK CHERRY *(Prunus virginiana* and *P. serotina)* This tree from North America furnishes a bark which upon infusion yields hydrocyanic acid and is employed in the treatment of bronchitis. "Cherry stalks" act as a mild stomachic and bitter tonic.

REFERENCES

Burkill, I. H. 1935. A dictionary of the economic products of the Malay Peninsula. Crown Agents for the Colonies. London.
Hill, A. F. 1952. Economic botany. McGraw-Hill. New York.
Penick, S. B., and Co. 1952. Price list and manual. New York.
Record, S. J., and R. W. Hess. 1943. Timbers of the New World. Yale Univ. Press. New Haven.

trees
that provide
edible products

TREES ARE ONE OF OUR MOST IMPORTANT SOURCES of foods and beverages. In Europe, in America, in the tropics and in temperate regions, our edible fruits to a great extent are borne on trees. Some of our most common beverages—coffee, tea and cocoa—are tree products. Many of our favorite carbonated beverages are prepared from the powdered seeds of the cola tree. It is safe to say that a great portion of the world population lives in large part from the products of the coconut palm. The large terminal buds of certain palm trees are even employed in salads. A few of these edible products from trees appear below.

BEVERAGES

COFFEE (*Coffea arabica* and other species) From the commercial standpoint, coffee is the most important beverage plant, even though more people use tea. Its native home is Abyssinia, but over 500 years ago it was taken to Arabia. For two centuries, Arabia supplied most of the world's coffee. The coffee plant was slowly introduced elsewhere—to Ceylon and Java by 1700, to the West Indies in 1720 and to Brazil in 1770. Actually, coffee has been used as a beverage only for about 250 years.

The coffee plant is a shrub or small tree. Its white, starlike flowers and smooth evergreen leaves make it very attractive. The red-ripe fruits are sometimes known as "cherries," and each produces two greenish-gray seeds, the "beans." Coffee is a distinctly tropical crop and grows best in a hot, moist climate up to an altitude of 6,000 ft.

Today Brazil is uppermost as a producer of coffee and its production accounts for over 50 per cent of the world supply. Colombia, Venezuela, Costa Rica, Guatemala, Salvador and Haiti rank next to

109

Brazil. Indonesia and the British African possessions also are large producers of coffee. One of the most important by-products of coffee is caffeine, 0.75 to 1.5 per cent being available in the roasted beans. It is this alkaloid which is responsible for the stimulating effect of the beverage.

TEA *(Camellia sinensis)* A relative of the shrub which produces our ornamental camellia, the tea plant is native to Assam in India and China. Although in cultivation the tea plant is pruned to a height of 3 to 4 ft., in nature the tea plant becomes a small tree. Tea has been known in Europe since the sixteenth century, but did not become important until a hundred years later. Great Britain is the world's chief consumer of tea today.

That portion of the plant supplying the popular beverage is, of course, the leaves. Constant pruning stimulates new growth, and leaves are gathered from this young foliage. Tea leaves are hand picked, although scissors may be used. The grade of tea depends upon the age of the leaves, the youngest leaves being the choicest. The flavor and quality vary with the soil, climate, age of leaf, time of picking, and the method of preparation.

CACAO *(Theobroma cacao)* A native to the lowlands of tropical America, the cacao or cocoa tree thrives only in the shade of taller trees. However, about 53 per cent is received from the west coast of Africa. It is small with many spreading branches, seldom over 25 ft. tall. The flowers and fruits are borne in a peculiar manner on short stalks growing directly from the main branches. The pods are gathered when ripe and allowed to rot, thus releasing the seeds, or "beans." After being dried in the sun to remove the pulpy covering, the seeds are roasted in revolving ovens, the "shells" are broken and

110

winnowed, and the remainder of the material is ground into an oily paste. This mass is the bitter chocolate which is the starting point for further processing.

Chocolate was the main beverage of the Aztecs and other native American peoples. The drink was unknown in Europe before the first quarter of the sixteenth century. Chocolate is the most nutritious of all beverages, and its use as a flavoring has steadily increased since its introduction to northern peoples.

MATÉ *(Ilex paraguariensis)* Although few of us may realize it, maté or yerba maté is a beverage next in importance to coffee, tea and cocoa. *Ilex paraguariensis* is closely related to our Christmas holly, *Ilex opaca,* and this small tree grows wild in the mountains of southern Brazil, Paraguay and Argentina. In these countries, maté was strictly a native drink; however, it was adopted by the European colonists and is now a universal beverage.

Twigs bearing leaves are toasted over fires; the crispy leaves are then beaten from the twigs and dried in an ovenlike structure. Threshing and sifting follow. Maté is then prepared in a gourd by pouring boiling water over the leaves, after which sugar and lemon are added, much as in making tea. The drink is sipped through a straw with a perforated end. The latter acts as a strainer.

Maté is greenish in color with a pleasant odor and somewhat bitter taste. Its restorative and stimulating properties are probably due to the 0.5 per cent theine, a volatile oil, in the leaves. Although maté is the most popular beverage for millions of South Americans, it has not become popular in the United States.

FRUITS

COCONUT *(Cocos nucifera)* One of the most important plants in the daily lives of millions of the native peoples of the South Pacific and other tropical areas is the coconut palm. Originally a native of the Malay Archipelago, the coconut has been carried around the world so that it is now found throughout the tropics and subtropics, usually near the sea.

The fruit of this tree is certainly marvelous, for besides producing food and drink, its husk provides a useful fiber, its hard shell is used for fuel and vessels, and the "meat" is expressed for cooking oil and for soap and is employed as a confection. The other parts of the tree have equally numerous uses.

APPLE *(Malus pumila)* In temperate regions, the apple occupies the foremost position among fruits in importance and extent of cultivation. Although it is a native of eastern Europe and western Asia, the apple is cultivated throughout the temperate regions of the world.

111

For over 3,000 years the apple has been cultivated, hybridized and selected so that today there are more than 6,500 horticultural varieties.

The apple is a low, round-crowned tree which seldom becomes more than 40 ft. high. The wood is hard and dense and is mostly used for saw and other tool handles. Occasionally small quantities of apple-wood veneer are available, but its use has been discouraged because of the frequently defective material and small sizes.

PEAR *(Pyrus communis)* Like the apple, the pear is native to Eurasia and was known to the ancients. The pear is a close relative of the apple, and the fruits of each are similar. The trees are also alike, but the pear is more upright in aspect. Pears are less hardy and have a more restricted range than the apple. Pears are most extensively grown in Europe, France being the principal producer. The United States grows only 23 per cent of the world crop. Over 5,000 kinds of pears are recognized. Pear wood is highly prized in veneer form for cabinetmaking and for inlaying. The wood is light cream-colored, hard and with small pores and fine texture.

CHERRY *(Prunus* spp.) Cherries are trees with a birchlike bark, white or pinkish flowers, and small long-stalked fruits with a smooth round stone or pit. Cultivated cherries are all native to Eurasia. The sweet cherry, *Prunus avium,* is a tall, long-lived tree with a yellow or greenish fruit. It has a restricted range in the United States and is grown near large bodies of water in New York, the lake states and on the Pacific coast. The sour cherry, *Prunus cerasus,* is a smaller tree with heavy wood and red fruits. Unlike the sweet cherry, the fruits of the sour cherry are mainly used for canning and for freezing. Over 300 varieties are grown. The wood of the cherry is extensively used in furniture manufacture, and the reader is directed to its description under the alphabetic listing, Part 2.

APRICOT *(Prunus armeniaca)* The apricot still grows wild over wide areas of its native home in Asia. An ancient fruit, it was under cultivation in China in 2000 B.C.! It was introduced into Europe in the first century A.D. The apricot is a small tree 20 to 30 ft. tall with pink flowers that precede the appearance of the leaves in the spring. Susceptible to frost, the apricot is grown only in warm temperate regions, chiefly in China, Japan and northern Africa. Most of the crop in the United States is grown in California.

PLUM *(Prunus* spp.) The commercial plums of the United States come from three main sources: European plums *(Prunus domestica* and others), American species *(Prunus americana* and others) and

112

Citrus lemon tree growing in the tropics

Japanese species *(Prunus salicina* and others). Plums are usually shrubs or small trees which bear white flowers and large, smooth, blue-colored, clustered fruits. The fruits are used fresh or are employed in cooking, canning and preserving. A fine brandy is also manufactured from plums.

PEACH *(Prunus persica)* Next to the apple, the peach is the most important fruit in the United States. The peach is a native of China and has been under cultivation there for thousands of years. It

113

reached Mediterranean Europe in early times and the ancient Romans were familiar with at least six varieties. Today the peach is grown in southern Europe, the United States, South Africa, Japan and Australia. Between 2,000 and 3,000 varieties are grown; however, only a few ever are marketed.

The peach is a low tree, somewhat short-lived and quite susceptible to frost injury. The lovely pink flowers are produced prior to the leaves in the spring. The globular fruits have a velvety covering and a pitted stone. Peaches are eaten fresh and are the most popular canned fruit. A smooth-skinned peach, the nectarine *(Prunus persica* var. *nectarina),* is a common and delicious table fruit.

FIG *(Ficus carica)* In southern Arabia, the fig has been cultivated since time immemorial. It is one of the most frequently mentioned fruits in the Bible and must have been very important in those times. Today figs are grown in nearly all subtropical areas. The fig is a shrub or small tree with characteristically lobed leaves. What is eaten as the fruit is, in reality, the fleshy terminal portion of the stalk, which bears the tiny flowers. The gritty "seeds" inside are really the one-seeded fruits. Several different types of figs occur: common figs, caprifigs, Smyrna figs and San Pedro figs. Figs grown in the United States come mainly from Texas and California; imported figs are obtained chiefly from Turkey, Greece and Italy.

OLIVE *(Olea europea)* The olive is one of the oldest of fruits and was grown even in prehistoric eras. We know that the Egyptians of 1700 B.C. were familiar with the olive, and it is frequently mentioned in the Bible and in ancient Greek and Roman literature. It is now cultivated throughout the Mediterranean area and in California, where it was introduced for ornamental purposes in 1769.

The tree is a small evergreen sometimes becoming 40 ft. high. The fruit is one-seeded and purplish-black when ripe. Olives grow to a great age with proper care, and old trees are often grotesquely distorted. Spain, Italy, Portugal, Tunisia, Turkey and Greece are the main olive-producing countries.

NUTS. Technically speaking, a nut is a kind of fruit; however, many of the nuts of commerce are really seeds (borne within fruits). Below is a listing of some of the more important nuts of commerce borne by trees: Brazil nut *(Bertholletia excelsa),* cashew nut *(Anacardium occidentale),* coconut *(Cocos nucifera),* hazelnut or filbert *(Corylus* spp.), hickory nut *(Carya* spp.), Macadamia nuts *(Macadamia ternifolia),* pecan *(Carya illinoensis),* pine nuts *(Pinus edulis, P. monophylla* and others). Walnuts include the black walnut *(Juglans nigra),* butternut *(Juglans cinerea)* and English walnut *(Juglans regia*—a

Drawing of the trunks of large pagoda fig trees. Note the figures of men and camels

115

native of Iran). There are also the almond *(Prunus amygdalus)*, beechnuts *(Fagus grandifolia)*, pistachio nuts *(Pistacia vera)* and chestnuts *(Castanea dentata* from America and *C. sativa* from Europe).

A great number of tree-borne fruits, especially of the tropics, have been omitted. Perhaps a short list will serve to illustrate the abundance of fruits of the tropics, some of which are little known in the north: sweet orange *(Citrus sinensis)*, sour orange *(Citrus aurantium)*, mandarin orange *(Citrus reticulata)*, grapefruit *(Citrus paradisi)*, lemon *(Citrus limon)*, lime *(Citrus aurantifolia)*, kumquat *(Fortunella japonica)*, citron *(Citrus medica)*, custard apples (Annona spp., chiefly *Annona cherimolia* and *A. squamosa)*, date *(Phoenix dactylifera)*, avocado *(Persea americana)*, durian *(Durio zibethinus)*, guava *(Psidium guajava)*, litchi *(Litchi chinensis)*, loquat *(Eriobotrya japonica)*, mango *(Mangifera indica)*, mangosteen *(Garcinia mangostana)*, pomegranate *(Punica granatum)*, sapodilla *(Achras zapota)*, tamarind *(Tamarindus indica)*, ad infinitum.

Indeed, the edible fruits of temperate zones are few compared with those of the tropics. Some of these fruits would suit northern tastes. However, many are perishable and do not stand the frequently long voyages involved in bringing them to northern markets.

hands off!
poisonous

EVEN A BRIEF DISCUSSION on the general subject of trees calls for a mention of trees that are poisonous, for they are more numerous than the average woodworker realizes. There is a great variation in regard to the part of the tree which is toxic: leaves, fruits, wood, bark and so forth. Furthermore, what may be harmful if taken internally may be innocuous to the skin. People vary also in their reaction to toxins; some individuals may be particularly allergic to a given poison, while other people are scarcely affected. What may be a virulent substance to humans may be harmless to animals. "Many hypotheses have been advanced to explain the significance of toxic substances produced in plants, as, that they are developed to protect the plants against herbivorous animals, are waste products, are stages in the processes of metabolism. Of these suggestions the first appears least acceptable and the last most plausible." (W. C. Muenscher. 1944. Poisonous plants of the United States.)

Poisonous trees and other plants may be classified in many ways: 1) by the toxin produced, 2) by the action of the toxin, 3) by the natural groups to which the plants belong, 4) by the portion of the body affected. To cover all these facets requires a book in itself. Below, some of the more interesting poisonous trees and other woody plants will be described. It should be noted, that many toxin-producing plants are employed in medicine and rightly come under that topic.

ARCWOOD (*Tabebuia guayacan*) Arcwood is a heavy tropical timber derived from a tree having beautiful yellow flowers. The timber is considered one of the best available for durable construction. However, one of the drawbacks to its use is the yellow dust which arises in milling operations. This dust produces reddish stains on the sweat-moistened parts of laborers' clothing and gives rise to a mild dermatitis. Breathing of this dust may cause a severe irritation of the upper respiratory passages. Consequently, dust filters should be worn when milling this wood.

BUCKEYE *(Aesculus* spp.) Many know the buckeye as the horse chestnut. Species occur in eastern North America and in California and Nevada. All species possess several harmful glucosides borne in leaves, young shoots, nuts (seeds) and bark. Ingesting of any of these parts of the tree may cause inflammation of the mucous membranes, vomiting, depression, lack of coordination, paralysis and weakness. Remember! the horse chestnut seed is not the edible chestnut *(Castanea* spp.) of commerce.

CAROLINA ALLSPICE *(Calycanthus fertilis)* A small shrub of the Allegheny Mountains, the Carolina allspice is a widely grown ornamental. The seeds, however, contain the alkaloid calycanthine which has an effect similiar to strychnine.

CASTOR BEAN *(Ricinus communis)* Although only an herb in temperate regions, the castor plant becomes a small tree in the tropics. It is probably native to tropical Africa. The poisonous principle is due to ricin, a severe irritant and blood poison. All parts of the plant are deadly, but especially the seeds (beans). The same property which enables the oil to act as a cathartic (irritant) will in large doses cause severe nausea, vomiting, gastric pain, diarrhoea, thirst and great diminution of vision. General weakness occurs and collapse results immediately, followed by convulsions and death. No wonder children dislike castor oil!

CHERRIES AND PLUMS *(Prunus* spp.) All these are trees or shrubs. The observant ones of us have probably noticed the bitter almond odor of cherry bark and leaves. This odor is due to the presence of hydrocyanic acid (prussic acid) which is produced as one of the decomposition products formed by the action of enzymes on the glucoside, amygdalin. Results of eating large quantities of cherry leaves or bark causes convulsions, heavy breathing, relaxation of muscles and rapid death. Poisoning by hydrocyanic acid is so quick that it is difficult to administer an antidote once symptoms are noted. Caution! Cherry fruits are edible, but the leaves and bark are formidable.

CHINABERRY TREE *(Melia azedarach)* Sometimes called pride of India, the Chinaberry is adventive from Asia. It is extensively planted as an ornamental in the southern United States. Its hard wood is reputedly more moth repellent than eastern red cedar. The wall of the fruit contains a toxic substance of narcotic nature which attacks the entire central nervous system. Children and various animals have died from eating fruits. Death is preceded by complete paralysis, irregular respiration and suffocation.

ENGLISH IVY *(Hedera helix)* This common woody climber is extensively employed as an ornamental. However, a poisonous glucoside, hederin, is present in all parts of the plant. Children have been stricken by eating the berries; some individuals develop a severe dermatitis by merely touching the foliage.

JAPANESE LACQUER TREE *(Rhus verniciflua)* This species is very similar to poison sumac, but it is native to Japan and China. It is the source of the Japanese black lacquer used on wooden articles which sometimes appear on the American market. A number of cases of poisoning have been traced to contact with lacquered articles. Results are the same as in poison ivy and poison sumac. The toxic principle, urushiol, was isolated from *Rhus verniciflua* in Japan before it was found in the native species of *Rhus*.

MAIDENHAIR TREE *(Ginkgo biloba)* Introduced from eastern Asia, the maidenhair tree is now frequently planted as an ornamental. Its fleshy-coated seeds produce butyric acid which may cause severe dermatitis resulting from handling crushed seeds.

MANCHINEEL TREE *(Hippomane mancinella)* A small tree with smooth, pale brown bark, manchineel is characterized by a milky juice in all parts. It is fairly common in Caribbean countries and frequently grows by the seaside. The milky sap, which may be ejected from turgid bark on lacerating, is a powerful irritant. Although not all people are susceptible, contact with the juice may cause blistering of the skin. Smoke from burning wood has produced severe inflammation of the eyes. Records show that the early Spanish explorers in South America, believing the fruit to be crab apples, ate them, in some cases with fatal results.

MOUNTAIN LAUREL *(Kalmia latifolia)* This glossy, tough-leaved shrub is fairly common in the mountains of eastern North America and in other acidic soil locations. The toxic material is called andromedotoxin and also occurs in other members of this family (Ericaceae, heath family). Poisoning follows the eating of leaves and causes increased salivation and tearing, vomiting with convulsions and eventually paralysis of the limbs. The lovely pink and white flowers of late spring belie the poisonous nature of this favorite shrub.

119

OLEANDER *(Nerium oleander)* Although a shrub, it reaches tree-like proportions in the tropics and is commonly found as a house plant in temperate regions. The poisonous principles nerioside and oleandroside are similar in properties to the poisonous principles of digitalis, the narcotic. Since ancient times it has been known that the leaves of this species are highly noxious, both dried and fresh. Some people also acquire a contact dermatitis from the leaves. This handsome ornamental can produce vomiting, dizziness, decreased pulse rate, irregular heart action, unconsciousness, respiratory paralysis and finally, death.

OSAGE ORANGE *(Maclura pomifera)* A tree native from Arkansas to Texas, it is widely planted in fence rows, particularly in the Midwest. Its milky juice produces a contact dermatitis in certain individuals.

POISON IVY *(Rhus toxicodendron)* Poison ivy may be a weak, almost herbaceous plant, or in favorable areas, a vigorous robust woody vine or shrub. The effects of ivy poisoning are too common to state; it is sufficient to say, contact with any part of the plant, winter or summer, causes a severe dermatitis in susceptible individuals. The poisonous principle is believed to be due to urushiol, a yellowish, slightly volatile oil produced in the resinous juice of the resin ducts of leaves, flowers, fruits, and bark of stems and roots.

POISON SUMAC *(Rhus vernix)* These erect woody shrubs grow in clumps or as small trees in wet, swampy areas. The drooping flower and fruit clusters distinguish poison sumac from the harmless sumacs. The poisonous effects are the same here as in poison ivy.

POISON WOOD *(Metopium toxiferum)* A member of the poison ivy family, this noxious tree is the bane of the wood collector in south Florida and the West Indies where it is ubiquitous in the woods. Lovely to look at, but deadly to touch, is a suitable motto. The mottled orange-brown bark, the glossy dark green leaves and hanging orange fruits actually make this tree an interesting ornamental. The poisonous effects are much like those associated with ivy poisoning, and in this case also it is the resinous juice which carries the toxic principle.

POSSUM WOOD *(Hura crepitans)* The possum wood tree belongs to the same family as the manchineel *(Euphorbiaceae)* and also possesses a milky latex. This latex acts as a vesicant and may cause severe skin irritation, accompanied by blistering.

GIANT NETTLE TREE *(Laportea gigas)* One of the most potent

120

of the poisonous trees, the giant nettle grows in Queensland and New South Wales, Australia. The leaves of this tree are covered with hairs, tipped by tiny poison-filled sacs, which break off at the mildest touch. The result of touching one of these is practically instantaneous. One experiences a stabbing pain, practically unbearable. In a few minutes an entire arm and the whole side of the body from toe to head may be affected. Sometimes this is followed by temporary paralysis and numbness, and the affected skin may remain very sensitive for months. Animals are equally affected and sometimes must be shot to relieve them of their misery.

TREE OF HEAVEN *(Ailanthus altissima)* A native of eastern Asia, the tree of heaven is also the tree that grew in Brooklyn. Several instances of dermatitis have been reported from contact with its leaves.

WEST INDIAN BOXWOOD *(Gossypiospermum praecox)* The West Indian boxwood is a small to medium-sized tree of the Dominican Republic, Cuba, the Maracaibo Lake region of Venezuela and parts of eastern Colombia. Certain individuals are severely affected during milling operations involving timber from this tree. The face swells enormously, and highly susceptible people often require hospitalization.

Actually, the total number of poisonous trees and other plants with which the craftsman or woodworker may come in contact are few. Some of the more noxious trees and shrubs have been mentioned above. It is well to reiterate here, that all humans do not display the same susceptibility to all poisonous plants. If you know, or have heard, that a tree is poisonous in some way, use care, wear gloves, do not contact the tree unnecessarily; above all, do not eat any of its parts! Avoid breathing the smoke of burning poisonous trees and use a dust filter when milling woods which are suspected of yielding harmful effects.

REFERENCES

Muenscher, W. C. 1944. Poisonous plants of the United States. Macmillan. New York.

Record, S. J., and R. W. Hess. 1943. Timbers of the New World. Yale Univ. Press. New Haven.

121

interesting and
unusual woods

MOST PLANTS AND ANIMALS ATTAIN A FORM which is considered typical for their kind. They attract little attention and therefore are not of especial interest in this regard. We do know, however, that certain kinds of animals are distinctive for one reason or another and these usually draw a great deal of attention. The kangaroo with its ponderous tail, bipedal form of locomotion and abdominal pouch (marsupium) in which the normally premature young are carried is a good example of an unusual animal. The elephant and its trunk, the ostrich, a flightless bird, aquatic mammals such as whales and seals, flying mammals such as bats—these are all of extraordinary interest because of some unique anatomical structure or mode of life.

Certain woody plants and trees are the kangaroos and bats of the vegetable kingdom and are of importance for the same reasons these animals are important: they differ in some outstanding respect from their relatives. Some of the more exciting of these unusual woody plants will be described and illustrated below. Some will be trees; others, woody vines; still others, shrubs. In some cases the shape of the trunk is noteworthy; in other instances the wood itself is unusual. It is apparent that not all peculiar woody plants can be included in the space of a short chapter. Our purpose is merely to introduce the reader to the kinds of peculiar woody plants in which the peculiarity is normal to the species.

In some trees a portion of the root system is aerial and extends above the surface of the ground. The red mangrove *(Rhizophora mangle)* is a common tropical tree which inhabits the margins of muddy salt flats. The trunk, strangely enough, is borne aloft on a network of stiltlike aerial roots (Fig. 1). Forests of red mangrove

122

Fig. 1. Interior of mangrove swamp on Plantation Key, Florida, showing the tangled mass of aerial roots. This forest is periodically innundated

form impenetrable masses along certain seacoasts because of these interwoven stilt roots.

Aerial roots are frequently formed by the baldcypress *(Taxodium distichum)* of the southeastern United States. In these trees the aerial roots are referred to as "knees" because of their resemblance to human knees. The baldcypress commonly grows in swamps; the knees, which are in reality branches of the underground root system, project above the surface of the water. Craftsmen often fashion these knees into novelties, lamp bases being a favorite (Fig. 2).

One of the most curious trees is the papaya *(Carica papaya)* of tropical lands. A close examination of the structure of the main stem often prompts the question, "When is a tree not a tree?" In the papaya we have a treelike plant which may attain a height of 30 ft. or more. It has an unbranched trunk bearing a crown of long-stalked leaves. If we cut the trunk apart and examine the structure

123

Fig. 2. Aerial roots formed by the baldcypress

microscopically, we find that the only "woody" material present is confined to strands which are embedded in a matrix of an almost pulpy, pith-like material. The main supportive material in the stem is a network of thick-walled fibers in the bark! Many a wood collector has found, to his dismay, that on being dried, the trunk of the papaya reverts to a soupy mass. After complete drying, the only solid material remaining is the meshwork of bark fibers. The papaya is really an arborescent herb!

Most of us are familiar with members of the lily family. We know that these are, in general, low-growing herbaceous plants. However, some of the tropical members are anything but low-growing and herbaceous. *Cordyline australis* is a tree lily which exhibits a slender woody trunk surmounted by a crown of strap-shaped, lilylike leaves. At this point it might be well to mention that many plant families, which in the temperate zone are only represented by herbs, have tropical members which are treelike and have decidedly woody stems. The lobelias become arborescent and woody in the tropics; members of the sunflower family (Compositae) reach tree proportions in the

Fig. 3.　Cross section of fronds of arborescent fern

Andes; the forget-me-not family (Boraginaceae) in the tropics is represented by commercially important timber trees (e.g., *Cordia* spp.). In a sense, these tree representatives of plant families commonly considered as herbaceous are noteworthy.

Along this same line, most of us are acquainted with ferns merely as lowly, though attractive, plants of the woods and fields. The breath of the tropics must invigorate certain of the ferns, for there they reach majestic proportions (for ferns, that is). They "get up on their hind legs" as it were. The normally underground horizontal stem becomes vertical and increases in diameter to support a massive crown of leaves. The fronds on some tropical, arborescent ferns may exceed 10 ft. in length (Fig. 3). These tree ferns are a far cry from the potted Boston fern which stood in Grandmother's window.

Tropical vines often assume bizarre forms both externally and internally. Certain species of *Bauhinia* (legume family) are called *escalera de mono* or monkey ladder, an allusion to the sinuate nature of the vine which supposedly enables monkeys to use them as ladders (Fig. 4). A cross section of the stem of a native passion flower

125

Fig. 4. Tropical vine *(escalera de mono* or monkey ladder)

(Passiflora multiflora) reveals wood which is almost unbelievably complex in outline. Instead of a cylindrical woody body, we are confronted with a highly convoluted and dissected mass (Fig. 5). Many vines exhibit curiously lobed and parted xylem masses; these may occur even when the stem is cylindrical externally!

Certain species of mylady *(Aspidosperma* spp.) from the Guianas have trunks which are actually deeply lobed in cross section (Fig. 6). Flanges taken from these trunks are fashioned into paddles by the natives of British Guiana. This practice has given rise to the common name of paddlewood for this tree. Similar lobing also occurs in other tree species of different families.

The baobab tree *(Adansonia digitata)* of Africa is the elephant of the plant kingdom. It is elephantine from its thickly folded bark to its greatly distorted massive trunk. Perhaps the most curious feature of this tree is the sharply tapered trunk, which in the extreme

126

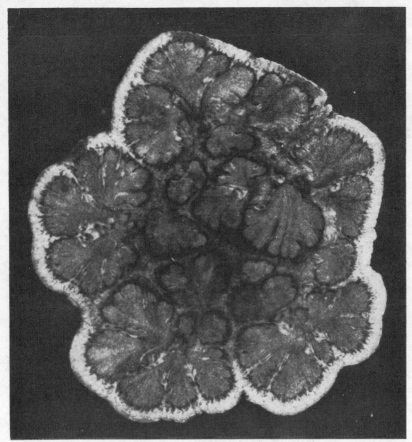

Fig. 5. Cross section of the anomalous stem of the many-flowered passion flower *(Passiflora multiflora)*. Notice the numerous convoluted masses in the stem—each a portion of the wood axis. The actual size is approximately that of a silver dollar

is almost pear-shaped. Occasionally these trees will have several main stems and this heightens the outlandish appearance. Imagine, if you will, three pear-shaped trunks of immense girth, united at the base, each with thickly folded bark, tapered abruptly at the apex and bearing a ridiculous crown of short, stubby branches which are leafless during part of the year.

Many tropical timber trees, although of normal structure, bear

Fig. 6. Cross section of trunk of *Aspidosperma*

Fig. 7. Winged fruit of *Centrolobium*

128

Fig. 8. Fruit from the cannon-ball tree

Fig. 9. The tropical *Aspidosperma* has flattened fruits of leg-of-mutton shape

129

Fig. 10. A banyan tree near the beach on Tahuata Island in the Marquesas

fruits which are truly unsurpassed in form. The winged fruit of *Centrolobium* (a legume) is far different from the pod of the pea which belongs to the same family (Fig. 7). The candle tree *(Parmentiera cerifera)* bears quantities of smooth yellow hanging fruits which greatly resemble long wax candles. Supposedly these "candles" provide excellent feed for cattle. The cannon-ball tree *(Couroupita guianensis,* (Fig. 8), of the Brazil nut family, is noted for its huge, hard cannon-ball-like fruits. Other members of this family also have large woody fruits which may open with a lid much as a teapot. The sausagelike, drooping fruits of *Kigelia pinnata* have no doubt given rise to the common name of sausage tree for this species. The underside of a tree bearing fruit reminds one of standing in the cooler of a delicatessen amid the hanging salami and Bologna sausages. The tree is a fairly common ornamental in the tropics and subtropics and is cultivated in Florida. *Aspidosperma,* a tropical relative of the milkweed, bears flattened fruits of leg-of-mutton shape. The most interesting feature here is the thin, wafer-like seeds which are stacked like pancakes within. The wind can no doubt blow these seeds for many miles (Fig. 9).

Another peculiar tree is the banyan *(Ficus bengalensis),* growing principally in India and Burma Fig. 10). It is considered sacred by the Hindus and little of the wood is available commercially; however, it is not particularly suitable for general use. This tree is very large and throws down numerous aerial roots from the branches. These root in the ground and grow into separate trunks. A banyan tree has been recorded with a spread around the branches of 2,000 ft.

These few examples have been drawn from a vast number of tree curiosa and only serve to illustrate that trees are not all "run-of-the-mill." A little study will uncover many more such oddities for the interested woodworker. As mentioned previously, tree peculiarities can often be put to practical use in the construction of craft objects.

the collection
of woods

HOW TO COLLECT WOODS

ONE OF THE MOST FASCINATING AND INTRIGUING of all occupations is the collection of woods. As in other fields of pursuit, there is a correct, scientific way in which to collect woods, and incorrect, careless methods. For a sample of wood to be scientifically valuable, it must be correlated with a specimen of the leaves, twigs and flowers (herbarium specimen) gathered from the same tree from which the wood was extracted. The manner in which woods with herbarium vouchers are collected is discussed in this chapter.

Let us imagine that we, as wood enthusiasts, have undertaken to collect wood samples in the tropics, say in the Republic of Panama. In the tropics we find the greatest diversity of woody plants, and we know our collecting should yield commendable results. However, without the proper equipment and know-how, no expedition can be successful. What then, shall we take?

Remember, the material will depend in large part on the duration of the trip, facilities available in the field such as lodging, transportation and food, the terrain, climate, and so forth. Panama is a tropical area, generally of high rainfall, heat and relative humidity. The western portion, at least on the Pacific side, is fairly well inhabited. Food and lodging of a sort are available, and we can obtain a vehicle with which we can travel the Inter-American Highway. Here is an actual, though greatly abridged, list of equipment taken by members of Yale's Samuel James Record Memorial Collection on a wood-collecting expedition to Panama:

String tags, 1,000
Compass
Paper bags, 100
First aid supplies
Leather-palmed gloves
Film, color and black-and-white
Light meter
Machetes
Presses, botanical
Driers, botanical
Ventilators, botanical
Twine, butcher's
Pliers with cutter
Rope, ¾" hemp
Files, mill bastard
Field notebooks
Binoculars

Botanical literature (manuals, etc.)
Saw, hand
Saw, chain
Axes, felling
Camera, 35mm. single-lens reflex
Camera, 120, double-lens reflex
Pencils, graphite
Pencils, indelible
Diameter tape
Flashlights and batteries
Pruning shears
Stove, gasoline
Lamp, gasoline
Altimeter
Preserving fluids and jars
Shotgun with ammunition

You will notice that camping equipment, drugs, food, fuel and other necessaries have been omitted. Even so, the list is quite extensive. A trip to a more remote area would require many more pieces of gear.

The wood sample should be obtained from the main stem or trunk of the tree. Because the latest formed wood is anatomically most mature, the collector should attempt to include some in his sample. To extract the sample, the tree may be felled or a piece of wood may be split from the trunk as illustrated in Fig. 1.

PATH OF AX
TO SPLIT SECTION
FROM TREE
①

Fig. 1.   How to split wood samples from the trunk of a tree

The latter method is by far the easier, but requires more skill although less brawn than the former. A sample split out in this way will be acceptable, and if the cuts are deep enough, both heartwood and sapwod will be represented. A note of caution must be raised here: samples should not be cut from buttresses. The latter frequently have an entirely different wood structure than the remainder of the trunk. Wood from small trees and shrubs may be best obtained by the use of a saw. In this case it is common to select a small segment of the trunk of a small tree or a few sections from the main stems of a shrub.

After wood samples have been taken, voucher specimens should be gathered from the same plant. Voucher specimens comprise leafy twigs bearing flowers and fruits if possible. When collecting in remote or poorly known areas, it is almost imperative that flowers be collected. Identification is largely based on floral structure and it is frequently impossible to determine a species from a botanically poorly known region without flowers. It is, therefore, the practice of many collectors, when in remote areas, to gather specimens only from plants which are in flower or at least have fruits.

One should select representative material in abundance to aid in identification. Voucher material may be collected by climbing the tree, felling it, or by shooting down branches with a shotgun. The latter method is frequently easiest, though with certain extremely tall trees, it is not too successful.

We now have our wood sample and corresponding herbarium material. Both kinds of samples are numbered identically; the wood with an indelible pencil or numbers impressed with steel dies, the herbarium vouchers with a numbered string tag. Notes regarding the collection are entered into our field book under a number corresponding to that on the samples. Such data as the height and diameter of the tree, characteristics of the bark, whether buttresses are present, flower color, flower aroma, peculiarities of the leaves and fruits, habitat of the tree, exposure, soil, geographic locality, altitude, date of collection, and other information are among those recorded in the field book.

In moist tropical lands it is essential that we care for our specimens immediately to prevent deterioration by fungi. Woods season best when stored in an airy, shaded location. Large pieces should be split to facilitate drying.

Herbarium specimens require more care. These must be pressed flat and dried, no mean task in the tropics. To perform these operations a botanical press and a heat source must be utilized. A botanical press is a simple affair consisting of two lattices of wooden strips fastened at joints with copper rivets (Fig. 2). Ash or hickory is best for this use as presses so made will stand a great deal of abuse.

Plants to be dried are placed carefully into a folded half sheet of newsprint. This is then placed between two blotters (driers) which are, in turn, placed between two pieces of corrugated cardboards (ventilators) as shown in the illustration. The sandwich is built up within the press; ventilator, drier, plant in newsprint, drier, ventilator and so on. After a convenient-sized sandwich has been made, the

134

Fig. 2.   Simply made press for herbarium specimens

press is closed, and pressure is applied by straps as illustrated. In the field, the press is supported over some heat source—gasoline or kerosene stove, auto engine, cooking fire—so that the corrugations act as flues for the hot air. Specimens are examined periodically, the dried ones removed, others rearranged for better drying and the press restrapped and set over the heat source again. Dried specimens should be so stored as to prevent their again becoming moist. Polyethylene bags containing a desiccant are useful for this purpose. Specimens may be shipped, suitably wrapped, in these containers.

Herbarium vouchers may be sent for identification to several botanical institutes in this country.[1] It is customary that those who identify material are privileged to keep the specimens in return for the identifications. The herbarium voucher, thus retained by a botanical institution and bearing the collector's name and number (the same as is on the wood sample), provides a means whereby the identification can be verified in the future. It is an indispensable record and makes a wood sample scientifically valuable. The identification of woods may be open to serious question when not substantiated with a herbarium voucher stored in a botanical institution.

COLLECTIONS OF WOODS
Collections of woods may be divided into two categories: institutional collections and private collections. Presently there are over 65 insti-

---

[1] Identifications may be requested from The New York Botanical Gardens, Bronx Park, New York, N.Y.; The U.S. National Herbarium, Smithsonian Institution, Washington, D.C.; Chicago Natural History Museum, Chicago, Ill.; Harvard University Herbarium, Cambridge, Mass.; Samuel James Record Memorial Collection, Yale School of Forestry, New Haven, Conn., and other institutions. Wood samples may be identified by writing the Director, Forest Products Laboratory, Madison, Wis. It is always best to write first and ask the curators if they would be willing to accept material for identification.

tutional wood collections in the world, the largest containing over 52,000 samples and maintaining its own herbarium of voucher specimens. Some of the more important of these collections are located as follows: Forest Research Institute, Bogor, Indonesia (32,000 specimens); Harvard University Herbarium, Cambridge, Massachusetts (25,000 specimens); Chicago Natural History Museum, Chicago (18,000 specimens); Forest Products Research Institute, College, Laguna, Philippines (10,526 specimens); Forest Research Institute, P.O. New Forest, Dehra Dun, India (14,337 specimens); Forest Research Institute, Kepong, Malaya (7,000 specimens); Museums of Economic Botany, Royal Botanic Gardens, Kew, England (between 16,000 and 20,000 specimens); V. L. Komarov Botanical Institute of The Academy of Sciences of the U.S.S.R., Leningrad, U.S.S.R. (8,000 specimens); Forest Products Laboratory, Madison, Wisconsin (17,330 specimens); The Samuel James Record Memorial Collection, School of Forestry, Yale University, New Haven, Connecticut (52,500 specimens); Centre Technique Forestier Tropical, Nogent-sur-Marne, France (10,117 specimens); The Imperial Forestry Institute Wood Collection, Department of Forestry, University of Oxford, Oxford, England (18,700 specimens); Forest Products Research Laboratory, Princes Risborough, England (23,000 specimens); Division of Forest Products, C.S.I.R.O., South Melbourne, Australia (17,000 specimens); and Harry Philip Brown Wood Collection, College of Forestry, State University of New York, Syracuse, New York (25,000 specimens).

Most of these collections perform several functions, the major one of which is to act as a repository of specimens. Research in wood structure, plant anatomy and taxonomy are carried on in many wood collections and associated laboratories. Wood samples are made available to reputable scientists for their own studies. Exchanges are carried out whereby duplicates from one collection are transferred to another. In short, the wood collection is like a library with wood samples for books—always available for research and study.

Many private collections of woods are maintained throughout the world. One example is the Constantine Wood-O-Rama (Fig. 3). Private collections are kept for various reasons, the uppermost, I suppose, being the love of the collector for woods. Some collectors pride themselves in keeping botanically accurate records on collections and identifications; others are interested in the woods from the craftsman's point of view, and still others hold both motives. Frequently the amateur collector of woods is instrumental in providing needed samples for study to scientists. At other times they help to

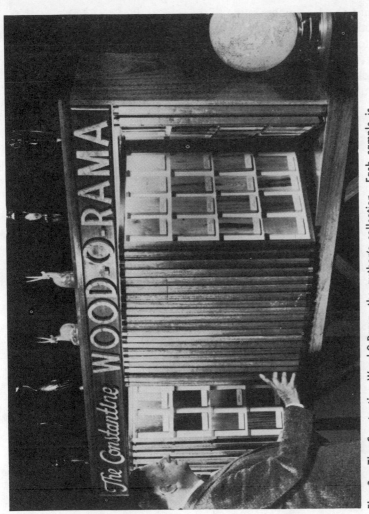

Fig. 3. The Constantine Wood-O-Rama, the author's collection. Each sample is mounted so that it may be individually handled to note the weight and study, the end grain and both the finished and the unfinished surface. This collection is open to the public in the Constantine Building, New York

acquaint the lay public with the beauty of wood and the need for protecting forest resources. A large number of these nonprofessional collectors have banded together to form the International Wood Collectors Society, "A non-profit organization of scientists, botanists, dendrologists, technologists, wood collectors, hobbyists and craftsmen for mutual reciprocation and assistance."

REFERENCE

Stern, W. L. 1957. Guide to institutional wood collections. Tropical Woods 106:1-29.

modern craftsmen use a wide variety of woods

IF YOU WERE ASKED TO NAME the most popular furniture woods, you would have no hesitation in saying mahogany, walnut, maple and oak, but beyond that, you might begin to wonder which woods to list next. To what extent is white pine now used in furniture? How about cherry? Does anyone use teak for furniture these days? "Of course teak is used," you'd quickly answer, because you would recollect the advertisements you had recently seen for modern Scandinavian furniture made of teak—and beech, too.

By the time you were through considering all aspects of this subject, you would probably have quite a list of furniture woods. And if you stopped to compare it with the woods associated with the great periods of furniture design, you would begin to suspect that probably more different woods and veneers are being used for furniture in the twentieth century than at any time in the past.

If a cabinetmaker wanted to reproduce a chest of drawers or a gateleg table of the Jacobean period, there would be no question about the wood to use; it would be oak. We associate oak with the Jacobean and Cromwellian styles, and nowadays would not think of using anything else in a reproduction, although oak was not, by any means, the only wood used. Much common furniture built in that period of English history was made of less expensive woods such as deal, chestnut and beech.

With the development of the William and Mary style, walnut became popular. In early Colonial days in America, native woods were largely used—pine, oak, maple, birch, walnut, cherry and others. After the middle of the eighteenth century, a good deal of mahogany was imported for the more expensive types of furniture.

Mahogany, of course, was the principal wood in Chippendale and

139

Fig. 1. Credenza or cabinet made by Anthony M. Bosco, Everett, Mass. The panels and doors are laminated from sheets of ⅛" European birch plywood. The face veneers are crotch mahogany; the borders, tulipwood veneer

Fig. 2. Pembroke table made principally of African mahogany and striped satinwood veneers, by Dard Hunter, Jr., Chillicothe, Ohio. The top of the table is veneered on pine; the remainder on black walnut

Fig. 3. Small inlaid picture by Norman L. Maile of London. He used only walnut, ebony and sycamore for the picture itself. The base is solid oak 100 years old, veneered on back and sides with walnut and on the front with harewood

141

Fig. 4.   Another astonishing example of virtuosity in the use of veneers. Olan J. Cooper of Chico, Calif., who made it, calls it an "animated theater." The cabinet is constructed of mahogany, oak, walnut, pine and gumwood, and 80 different wood veneers are embodied in the inlays and inlaid pictures

Fig. 5.   Maple and spruce are the woods used for the principal parts in a pair of violins made by 71-year-old Leonard V. Porter of Kansas City, Mo.

Fig. 6.   Cherry wood was used by H. Lloyd LeCompte, Jr., Towson, Md., for a Chippendale cupboard

Fig. 7.   This interesting clock case was made of Honduras mahogany by Arthur L. Armstrong, Missoula, Mont.

Fig. 8.   Captain Victor Goudey, U.S. Air Force, of Middletown, Pa., built this mahogany clock case shown. He used cherry wood for the columns and finial

Fig. 9.   Rotating bar with carved front panel designed and made almost entirely with hand tools by Mrs. Alicia R. Delvers, in Kobe, Japan. Sakura (cherry wood) and sakura plywood were used for the cabinet. Two pieces of katsura, or Japanese Judas tree, were glued to form the panel for the dragon carving

Fig. 10. Secretary of American cherry by Trimble Sharber, Nashville, Tenn.

Fig. 11. Myrtlewood, seen so often in beautiful turned bowls, tobacco humidors and the like, is used with bold originality in this credenza by Chris H. Groneman, College Station, Texas. The drawer fronts are faced with myrtle veneer and are built of plywood bent in wooden forms. All other exposed surfaces are ¾" or thicker solid myrtle wood

Fig. 12. Howard Everngam, New York City, made this harpsichord. The case is solid walnut, but the lid is plywood to resist warping. The inside supporting members are maple and the sounding board is spruce. The keyboard is covered with thin boxwood and the sharps are solid ebony

Fig. 13.   Inlaid jewel box by Theodore Cichy, Philadelphia, Pa.

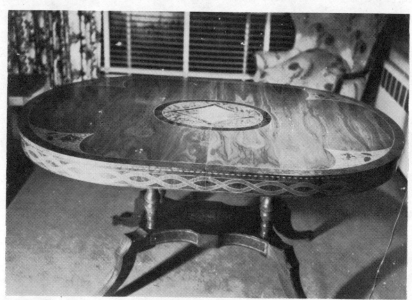

Fig. 14.   Dining-room table. The top is leaf-figure walnut with border of red-wood burl. Corner inlays: a rose with lacewood background. Center inlay: butt and burl walnut with rosewood border. Table base: walnut columns, mahogany legs. By Peter Passalacqua, Malverne, N.Y.

146

Fig. 15. Hutch cupboard of white pine made by Edward Schreier, Waupaca, Wis.

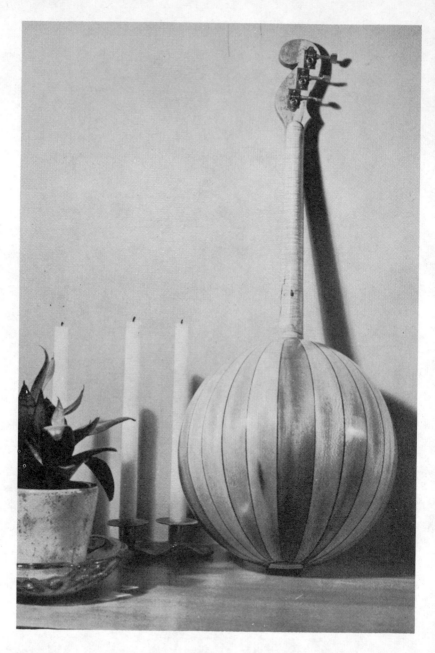

Fig. 16. Alto domra, a three-stringed musical instrument. Woods: bird's-eye maple, fiddleback maple, soft maple, sycamore, black ebony, white pine, spruce. Veneers: black-dyed maple, black walnut, holly, zebrawood, snakewood, vermilion (also pearl for inlay). Nicholas Cichonovich, Detroit, Mich.

Fig. 17. An unusual example of a great number of different kinds of woods in the ¼" thickness is shown in this oriental cocktail table by Simon Ramia, Detroit, Mich. He inlaid 30,202 separate pieces of wood in a mosaic design

Fig. 18. This table is a cross section of an American walnut tree mounted on four turned legs. The sapwood has been left on to form a border around the table top. C. C. Whittaker, Pittsburgh, Pa.

149

Hepplewhite furniture. Much satinwood and other fine veneers were used in veneering Hepplewhite pieces. Sheraton-style furniture also was mainly made of mahogany; many surfaces were veneered with mahogany and other veneers, and inlays often embellished the cabinetwork. Furniture of the Louis XIV, XV and XVI periods made use of oak and walnut, linden (basswood) *Tilia* spp., pear and other so-called "fruit woods."

Duncan Phyfe, the New York cabinetmaker who set the highest standards of American cabinetmaking, was especially particular about the woods he used. He gained a reputation for purchasing only the finest available mahogany and figured mahogany veneers. Choice mahogany logs were highly prized—and correspondingly expensive.

Thomas Constantine, one of the author's ancestors, was a cabinetmaker who must have known Duncan Phyfe quite well because they were neighbors for some time. Thomas Constantine was so interested in the importation of mahogany that in 1812 he became one of the founders of Constantine & Company, which for many years dealt principally in the distribution of mahogany.

In a somewhat later period rosewood became the favorite wood for the more expensive types of hand-carved Victorian pieces. The strength, hardness and density of that rich, dark-colored wood made it possible for furniture makers to let their imaginations run wild in designing curved and ornately carved members.

All the cabinet woods of the classical furniture periods, as well as an extraordinary variety of veneers, are now available to every woodworker—even those in localities far distant from any of the principal woodworking centers. And these woods and veneers are being used with taste and skill by both professionals and amateurs. This was well demonstrated in connection with the 1958 Constantine Woodworking Awards, presented to amateur craftsmen, in a contest which drew entries from all over the United States, as well as Canada, England, Scotland, Germany, Japan and Africa. The most spectacular use of rare and beautifully grained woods was found, of course, among the entries in which the use of veneers was featured (Figs. 1-4, 11, 13, 14 and 17).

It will be seen from these examples and also Figs. 5-10, 12, 15, 16 and 18 that craftsmen are using a great variety of woods and veneers—and doing it with great skill and ingenuity. They are displaying boldness and originality. They are striking out in new directions. Even if they follow traditional designs and build reproductions of period furniture, they still show a creative spirit. They must, indeed, gain much of their inspiration from the beauty and infinite variety of the woods and veneers with which they work.

150

wood quiz

THERE IS NO BETTER OR MORE PLEASANT WAY to review one's knowledge of a subject than by the question-and-answer method. This chapter has therefore been written in the form of a quiz. Since many will read right through these pages for general information rather than to test their grasp of various details about woods, the answer will be given directly after each question. Another reason for adopting this style of treatment is that some facts are presented in this chapter which have not been mentioned elsewhere in the book. However, those who wish to use the quiz for review purposes—to check on what they already know about woods—may do so readily by using a card to cover the answer in each instance until they have considered the question and endeavored to recall the required reply.

Ques. 1 What American tree produces a sap from which a well-known syrup and candy are obtained?
Ans. Sugar maple.

Ques. 2 What wood is the favorite for butchers' blocks?
Ans. American sycamore, because of its toughness.

Ques. 3 What is the species of tree referred to in the book *A Tree Grows in Brooklyn?*
Ans. Ailanthus.

Ques. 4 What wood gives a sticky feeling to the touch which remains noticeable even after a great many years of exposure to weather?
Ans. Pyinkado, known as the ironwood of Burma.

Ques. 5 What native wood is considered one of the best for arrows?
Ans. Port Orford white cedar.

Ques. 6 What wood is the most satisfactory—and is used in large quantities—for storage-battery separators?
Ans. Port Orford white cedar.

Ques. 7 What is the wood most preferred in the manufacture of artificial limbs?
Ans. Black willow and Ohio buckeye.

Ques. 8 What woods are often used in the manufacture of wood excelsior?
Ans. Balm-of-Gilead poplar and black willow.

Ques. 9 What wood is the most desirable for manufacturing containers for liquids?
Ans. White oak, because the pores are filled with tyloses which do not permit liquids to penetrate.

Ques. 10 What native wood is used in the manufacture of fly rods?
Ans. Lancewood or the downy serviceberry.

Ques. 11 What tree has a red sap which exudes like blood from wounds on a body?
Ans. Banak.

Ques. 12 What wood when freshly cut has an odor resembling that of Fuller's earth?
Ans. Alstonia.

Ques. 13 What tree has gum, white in color and resembling wax, which is used for candles and which burns freely?
Ans. Canarium.

Ques. 14 How was the town of Flagstaff, Arizona, named, and what tree was involved?
Ans. On July 4, 1876, lumberjacks stripped the tallest ponderosa pine of all its branches to fly the American Flag.

Ques. 15 What is the only American wood whose name has been reviewed by the U. S. Supreme Court?
Ans. Ponderosa pine.

Ques. 16 What wood growing in Malaya has its principal value in the latex used in the manufacture of chewing gum?
Ans. Jĕlutong.

Ques. 17 What tree has aerial roots?
Ans. Bald cypress.

Ques. 18 Which tropical American wood is it that, when the leaves are bruised, has a strong odor like that of garlic?
Ans. Salmwood.

Ques. 19 What is probably the largest hardwood tree in the world?
Ans. The mountain ash from Tasmania. Some trees have been reported in excess of 326 ft. in height.

Ques. 20 What wood is used for the making of manicure sticks?
Ans. Sour orange.

Ques. 21 What wood has been called rarer than diamonds?
Ans. Pink ivory.

Ques. 22 What wood is used in the manufacture of the famous Hawaiian ukuleles?
Ans. Koa.

Ques. 23 What is the hardest, heaviest and closest-grained wood known?
Ans. Lignum vitae from Central America.

Ques. 24 What wood is often referred to and sold under the name of white mahogany?
Ans. Prima vera.

Ques. 25 What type of pine furnishes a figure similar to that seen in bird's-eye maple and is sometimes referred to as bird's-eye pine?
Ans. Lodgepole pine.

Ques. 26 What wood is generally used in the manufacture of toothpicks?
Ans. Paper birch.

Ques. 27 What tree did the Indians believe to be a manifestation of the Great Spirit?
Ans. Pecan.

Ques. 28 What spruce was first discovered on Pike's Peak?
Ans. Blue spruce (in 1862).

Ques. 29 What American tree in the southwest was one of the foremost reasons for the shedding of blood between the early white settlers and the Indians?
Ans. Single-leaf pinyon, as the Indians strongly objected to the destruction of this tree.

Ques. 30 What trees did the Indians consider to be immortal?
Ans. Redwood trees because of their long life.

Ques. 31 What trees have leaves so rough and tough that the natives use them for sandpapering?
Ans. Teak.

Ques. 32 What pink-colored wood has the same figure as bird's-eye maple?
Ans. Medang tabak from Borneo.

Ques. 33 What wood is known as the "ebony of America"?
Ans. Persimmon.

Ques. 34 What is the principal wood used in the manufacture of high-grade heads for golf clubs?
Ans. Persimmon.

Ques. 35 What wood is known as Australian mahogany?
Ans. Rose mahogany from Malaya.

Ques. 36 What is the wood known in England as Borneo teak?
Ans. Ipil.

Ques. 37 What wood is known as Persian lilac?
Ans. Chinaberry, from Texas.

Ques. 38 What wood could be used as a substitute for balsa because of its texture and characteristics?
Ans. Erima, from New Guinea.

Ques. 39 What wood is used in Japan for cutting into thin veneers to line small articles, and for business cards?
Ans. Empress tree.

Ques. 40 What wood is generally known abroad as "red wood"?
Ans. Danzig or Scotch pine.

Ques. 41 What is the hardest and heaviest wood produced in Japan?
Ans. Japanese oak.

Ques. 42 What American wood is particularly suitable for food containers?
Ans. American beech, because it does not impart taste or odor.

Ques. 43 What wood is used for violin bows?
Ans. Beefwood is sometimes used for the manufacture of the cheaper violin bows, but the more expensive bows are made of Pernambuco wood or brazilwood (Caesalpinia echinata). Growing in eastern Brazil, this wood is a rich bright red color and mainly used as a dyewood, but the best pieces are selected for turning and for making violin bows. Many violinists will use no other kind for their bows because of the peculiarly strong, resilient spring which is found only in this wood. When planed, it has a bright, metallic, lustrous surface and shows fine snakelike ripple.

Ques. 44 What wood resembles American black walnut but is much lighter in color?
Ans. Butternut.

Ques. 45 What wood is principally used in printing for the backing blocks on which engravings and electrotype plates are mounted?
Ans. Black cherry.

Ques. 46 What woods are particularly adaptable for bending?
Ans. American beech and white ash.

Ques. 47 Nearly 80 per cent of what wood is used in the manufacture of wooden tool handles?
Ans. Hickory.

Ques. 48 What is the most desirable wood for making excelsior?
Ans. Quaking aspen.

Ques. 49 What wood is used in making matches?
Ans. Quaking aspen.

Ques. 50 How many different kinds of forest trees are there in the U.S.?
Ans. The number usually given is 1,182.

Ques. 51 What state has the largest number of different kinds of trees?
Ans. Florida—314 species of native and naturalized trees. Texas, Georgia and California follow in that order.

Ques. 52 What state has the least number of different kinds of trees?
Ans. North Dakota is almost treeless except for the cottonwoods and willows that grow along the streams. That is no aspersion, however, against the beautiful, happy state of North Dakota as a grass region. And it does, in fact, have an official tree—the American elm.

Ques. 53 What is the biggest living tree in the world?
Ans. It is nearly 115 ft. in circumference, 270 ft. in height and in volume it contains 600,120 board feet of lumber.

Ques. 54 What is the world's tallest known standing tree?
Ans. Founders Tree, a redwood in the Humboldt State Redwood Park near Dyerville in California. It was 364 ft. tall in 1947.

Ques. 55 How large do pine cones grow?
Ans. The sugar pine of the Pacific Coast produces the longest, some exceeding 20″ in length. The Mugho pine of Europe produces cones from less than 1″ to 2″ long.

Ques. 56 How many Christmas trees are produced in the U.S. each year?
Ans. About 21 million trees of which 87 per cent are produced in private forest lands. About a million are harvested in the national forests. About 100,000 acres of woodland, most of them owned by farmers, are devoted solely to growing Christmas trees.

Ques. 57 How much wood is used for fuel?
Ans. It is estimated that 63,000,-000 cords of wood are used annually for fuel—about one eighth of all the wood used in the U.S.

Ques. 58 How many crossties are required for a mile of railway track?
Ans. About 3,000 crossties are used in a mile of track.

Ques. 59 How many crossties are there in railway track throughout the U.S.?
Ans. More than one billion.

Ques. 60 How many wooden fence posts do American farmers use?
Ans. About 500 million a year.

Ques. 61 What is the hardest American wood in terms of density?
Ans. Black ironwood, of a little known species found in southern Florida. Has a specific gravity of 1.04. It is so heavy it sinks in water.

154

Ques. 62 What is the softest American wood in terms of density?

Ans. Corkbark. Found in parts of Arizona and New Mexico. Gravity 0.28.

Ques. 63 How much pulpwood does a newspaper use?

Ans. The N.Y. Times, Sunday edition, has a consumption of 800 cords of pulpwood—a product of 800 acres.

Ques. 64 What wood was the *Constitution* ("Old Ironsides") made of?

Ans. Live oak.

Ques. 65 What wood was used by the South Carolinians to build the stockade on Sullivan Island where the British fleet was defeated in 1776?

Ans. The trunks of the cabbage palmetto.

Ques. 66 What southern tree of the U.S. has no heartwood until it is 18 years of age or over?

Ans. Longleaf pine.

Ques. 67 What American wood in the early 1700's was proclaimed by Great Britain as belonging to the British Crown for the masts of the Royal Navy?

Ans. Shortleaf pine.

Ques. 68 How did the eastern cottonwood receive its name?

Ans. From the cottony fluff that is on the seeds.

Ques. 69 The buds of what tree were preserved by the ancient Chinese to use for seasoning their rice?

Ans. Magnolia.

Ques. 70 What tree did Andrew Jackson plant on the grounds of the White House in memory of his wife, Rachel?

Ans. Southern magnolia.

Ques. 71 What product other than wood does the blue gum tree of New South Wales produce?

Ans. Oil of eucalyptus, obtained from the distillation of the oil in the leaves of this tree and other species of eucalyptus.

Ques. 72 What two woods in the Far East are known as particularly good for fire-resistant qualities?

Ans. Burma teak and blue gum.

Ques. 73 What wood grows in Queensland and is used largely for the manufacture of electrical equipment because of its high insulating value?

Ans. Queensland walnut.

Ques. 74 What English tree at times has been sold as a substitute for lacewood?

Ans. London plane tree.

Ques. 75 How was partridge wood, which comes from Venezuela, named?

Ans. Because the figure it produces has a resemblance to the markings on a partridge wing.

Ques. 76 What is the wood in which the sapwood is of much greater value than the heartwood?

Ans. American persimmon.

Ques. 77 What tree provides us with the product to control toothaches?

Ans. The clove tree, with the oil of cloves.

Ques. 78 What tree provides us with a base for many mucilages?

Ans. The acacia or the shittim wood of the Bible.

Ques. 79 What tree provides us with the tincture of benzoin?

Ans. The benjamin tree of Java.

Ques. 80 What tree provides us with the base used for suppositories?
Ans. *The cacao tree of Mexico and South America.*

Ques. 81 Where is the largest known collection of woods?
Ans. *At Yale University in New Haven, Conn. There are over 52,000 scientifically labeled specimens of wood and shrubs.*

Ques. 82 How many products have been listed in which wood enters into in some degree?
Ans. *More than 10,000 products, and wood enters to some degree into the manufacturing processes or delivery of practically all other products.*

Ques. 83 What tropical tree starts to deteriorate after seven years of age if it is not cut?
Ans. *Balsa wood.*

Ques. 84 What wood was probably named because its appearance resembles raw beef?
Ans. *Beefwood from British and Dutch Guianas.*

Ques. 85 What is the whitest known wood and what is the blackest?
Ans. *American holly and Gaboon ebony.*

Ques. 86 What has long been the favorite wood for making the top grade pipes?
Ans. *Briar root. Over 10,000 tons a year are consumed.*

Ques. 87 What is the wood from which practically all lead pencils are made?
Ans. *Red cedar.*

Ques. 88 What wood has long been considered one of the best for the planking of boats?
Ans. *The Atlantic white cedar, because of its light weight and firmness of texture.*

Ques. 89 What American trees are becoming extinct because of the large loss due to the blight that is killing them?
Ans. *American elm, which is attacked by the Dutch elm disease.*

Ques. 90 What trees are called "the oldest and biggest of living things?"
Ans. *The giant sequoias of California.*

Ques. 91 From what wood is English harewood produced?
Ans. *The English sycamore tree.*

Ques. 92 What wood provides us with decorations at Christmastime?
Ans. *The American holly with its berries and leaves.*

Ques. 93 What tree provided the early American settlers with a substitute for coffee?
Ans. *The Kentucky coffeetree.*

Ques. 94 How many woods are referred to in the Bible?
Ans. *About twenty-one.*

Ques. 95 What wood from Cuba and other places is noted for its large use in the making of bows for archers?
Ans. *Lemonwood.*

Ques. 96 What wood is known as African walnut?
Ans. *Lovoa.*

Ques. 97 How many species of oaks are growing in the U.S.?
Ans. *Over 50 different species.*

Ques. 98 What American wood is used for dyewood and the making of bows?
Ans. *Osage orange.*

Ques. 99 How many different species of trees are there classified under the name of palm throughout the world?
Ans. *Nearly 1,200.*

Ques. 100 What tree was originally believed capable of renewing the youth of the human race?
Ans. Sassafras.

Ques. 101 How was Brazilian rosewood named?
Ans. Because of the odor of roses from the freshly cut trees.

Ques. 102 What wood when burning will produce restful slumber and also kill canary birds?
Ans. Ceylon satinwood.

Ques. 103 What tree, while not producing the berry, has a name similar to one of our most tasteful berries?
Ans. The strawberry tree.

Ques. 104 What African wood is often used as an alternative for the European beech?
Ans. Abura from Nigeria.

Ques. 105 What South American wood resembles greenheart and can also be used as a substitute for teak?
Ans. Acapu.

Ques. 106 What west African wood resembles Burma teak and has been used as a substitute for teak?
Ans. Afrormosia from west Africa.

Ques. 107 What tree has been called the "bark cloth tree"?
Ans. Antiaris from West Africa because the natives formerly used the inner bark for making a white cloth.

Ques. 108 What wood is called Nigerian satinwood?
Ans. Ayous from the west coast of Africa.

Ques. 109 Which tree provides us with cacao butter?
Ans. The cacao tree.

Ques. 110 Which tree supplies us with cascara?
Ans. The cascara tree.

Ques. 111 What tree supplies us with quinine, used for malaria?
Ans. The chinchona tree from Peru.

Ques. 112 From what tree do we obtain cocaine?
Ans. The coca trees of Colombia and Bolivia.

Ques. 113 What tree is responsible for Coca Cola and other cola drinks?
Ans. The kola tree of western Africa.

Ques. 114 What tree provides us with strychnine?
Ans. The nux vomica from India.

Ques. 115 What tree provides us with many of our tranquilizers?
Ans. The rauwolfia from India.

Ques. 116 What tree provides the oil that permits the successful treatment of leprosy?
Ans. The chalmoogra.

Ques. 117 How long has coffee been used as a beverage?
Ans. Only about 250 years.

Ques. 118 What tree provides us with our chocolate?
Ans. The cacao.

Ques. 119 How long has the apple tree been cultivated and how many species are there?
Ans. For over 3,000 years and with 6,500 horticultural varieties.

Ques. 120 What European wood in figure resembles bird's-eye maple?
Ans. Alpine burl or European white birch.

Ques. 121 For what purpose is apple wood particularly utilized?
Ans. For the heads of golf clubs.

Ques. 122 When is a tree not a tree?
Ans. When it is a papaya tree.

Ques. 123 What wood has been favored many times in the construction of church altars?
Ans. American butternut.

Ques. 124 What wood, when cut on the quarter, very much resembles sapele?
Ans. Danta from the Gold Coast.

Ques. 125 What tree does the wood come from which has the most offensive odor—one that can best be described as similar to rotten cabbage?
Ans. Essia from the west coast of Africa.

Ques. 126 How many seeds are there to the pound, from the fruit of the holly tree?
Ans. Over 30,000.

Ques. 127 What wood from Borneo has the same figure as our native bird's-eye maple?
Ans. Jongkong.

Ques. 128 How did the American smoketree receive its name?
Ans. Probably because the small yellow and purplish flowers that appear in clusters, when they turn to a rosy haze, have the look of a puff of smoke or a thin film spreading over the foliage.

Ques. 129 How did snakewood receive its name?
Ans. Probably because of the markings in the wood similar to that seen on the backs of many snakes.

Ques. 130 What commercial value has American sourwood?
Ans. Outside of landscaping, only for certain extracts from the sap of the tree. These are used in medicine for the treatment of fevers.

Ques. 131 How was the strawberry tree named?
Ans. Because of the fruits produced, which are orange-red to a bright scarlet color, round in shape and rough on the outside, with small, tiny grains.

Ques. 132 What wood has a peculiar scent similar to that of old shoe leather?
Ans. Teak.

Ques. 133 Which tree has the largest leaf of any tree?
Ans. Indian teak, which has a leaf 10" to 20" in length and 7" to 14" in width, of oblong shape.

Ques. 134 How is the weight of teak logs reduced so that they will not sink in water?
Ans. Before felling, the trees are first girdled completely round into the heartwood, in which condition the trees die and in about three years become lighter than water. Then they are cut down.

Ques. 135 What tree has its cortical tissue ground up to form a filler for certain floor coverings?
Ans. Cork oak tree.

Ques. 136 What tree is stripped of its bark every ten years and continues to grow and thrive for 150 years or more?
Ans. Cork tree.

Ques. 137 How many pounds of rubber does each rubber tree yield in a year?
Ans. An average 4 to 5 lbs.

Ques. 138 Who was the first one to report the existence of rubber in South America?
Ans. Christopher Columbus on his second visit.

PART 2
WOODS FROM ABURA TO ZEBRANO

full-color chart for wood identification

THIS NATURAL COLOR REPRODUCTION of the well-known Constantine Identification Panel portrays the color of each wood as well as the individual characteristic markings. All types of crotches, swirls, burls and stripe and mottle figures are shown, although it is impossible to include all of these figures for each kind of wood.

To identify any wood on this panel, locate the number on the corresponding square of the black and white reproduction and check it against the following list.

No.		No.	
1	Amboyna burl (Amboyna)	52	Maple, burl (U. S. A.)
1A	Ash, quartered (England)	57	Oak, quartered (England)
1B	Applewood (U. S. A.)	57A	Oak, burl (England)
2	Aspen, crotch (U. S. A.)	58	Olivewood (Italy)
4	Aspen, mottle (U. S. A.)	59	Oriental wood, stripe (Australia)
4D	Mahogany, mottle (Africa)	61	Padouk, stripe (India)
7	Avodire, mottle (Africa)	64	Pearwood (European)
7A	Avodire, crotch (Africa)	66	Piqua, figured (Africa)
7B	Balustra (South America)	67	Purpleheart, figured (Dutch Guiana)
9	Benin, stripe (Africa)	68	Prima vera, stripe (Central America)
10	Blackwood (Australia)	71	Rosewood, leaf figure (Brazil)
12	Boxwood (West Indies)	72	Rosewood, stripe (East Indies)
14	Bubinga, stripe and mottle (Africa)	73	Rosewood, crotch (East Indies)
15	Butternut (U. S. A.)	77	Satinwood, mottle and bee's-wing
16	Carpathian elm burl (France)		(Ceylon)
17	Cedar crotch (Dutch Guiana)	78A	Satinwood, crotch (West Indies)
18	Cherry, figured (Africa)	79	Snakewood (Surinam)
19	Cherry, plain (U. S. A.)	81	Sycamore (England)
23	Ebony, Macassar (India)	83	Tamo, peanut figure (Japan)
26A	Goncalo alves, stripe (Brazil)	85	Teak, figured (India)
28	Harewood (England)	86	Thuya, burl (Africa)
29	Holly (U. S. A.)	87	Tulipwood (Brazil)
30	Kingwood (Brazil)	91	Walnut, quartered stripe (U. S. A.)
32	Koa wood (Hawaii)	94	Walnut, butt (U. S. A.)
34	Lacewood (Australia)	95	Walnut, crotch (U. S. A.)
35	Laurel wood (India)	96	Walnut, burl (U. S. A.)
37	Madrone burl (U. S. A.)	97	Walnut Circassian, leaf figure
41	Mahogany, crotch (Africa)		(Russia)
45	Mahogany, crotch (Cuba)	98	Walnut, stripe (French)
49	Maple, curly or fiddleback (U.S.A.)	100	Yuba, mottle (Australia)
50	Maple, bird's eye (U. S. A.)	101	Zebra wood, stripe (Africa)

A large mahogany tree in the Central American jungle

description of
individual woods

FOR UNIFORMITY AND CONVENIENCE OF REFERENCE, information on
the different woods has been given as indicated in the following list.
Except for a few woods, the derivation or origin of the scientific
name has been mentioned—the first time, so far as is known, that this
has ever been done in a work of this kind.

1. Preferred common name
2. Scientific name—in italics
3. Derivation
4. Other common names
5. Brief description of tree, size, peculiarities, etc.
6. Range of species—native range and, in some instances,
   areas of cultivation outside of native habitat
7. Color of wood
8. Physical properties of wood, as specific gravity
9. Seasoning behavior
10. Strength properties
11. Dimensional stability (shrinkage)
12. Workability
13. Utilization
14. Other information

As you will note, not only the preferred and scientific name has been
given, but whatever other common names are in sufficient usage in
various parts of the world to warrant their being mentioned. The
preferred common, scientific and other common names have all been
listed alphabetically in the INDEX OF WOODS at the back of this book
—some 1,200 or more names in all. When referring to any particular
wood, you can quickly locate its description by turning to the page
number given.

165

ABURA *Mitragyna ciliata* (Mitra —headdress; gyna—pertaining to the female organ of the flower; ciliata—bearing hairs)

This tree is also known as BAHIA and SUBAHA.

It is a relatively small tree, growing in Nigeria. The wood is of a pinkish-brown or light yellow color and is without figure. In Europe, where it is particularly used in furniture, it is often substituted for European beech.

This wood shows a tendency to split, but in seasoning it dries very rapidly without any difficulty. It is a very stable wood when seasoned, but will buckle if bent. Since it is a popular wood, a good deal of the timber is exported from Africa in the form of boards and planks. The width in lumber averages about 8 in.; and the length, 8 ft.

ACAPU *Vouacapoua americana* (Vouacapoua—probably derived from a native name "wacapou," "wakapo" or "acapu"; americana—of America)

The weight per cubic foot is 63 lbs. and the tree is native to South America.

This valuable timber strongly resembles the dark-colored greenheart. It has light and dark lines similar to partridge wood and also could be used as a substitute for teak, although it is harder and more difficult to work than teak.

Acapu stands up well and a fine finish may be obtained on the surface.

AFRORMOSIA *Afrormosia elata* (Afr—pertaining to Africa; ormosia—pertaining to the legume genus *Ormosia;* elata—elevated)

This tree is also known under various names as KOKRODUA, REDBARK, DEVIL'S TREE and BONSAMDUA.

It is a medium-sized tree, growing in west Africa, and the weight is 45 lbs. per cubic foot. It is sometimes found in the forest along the banks of rivers, but generally it grows on stony and rocky ground. The tree at times has a crooked stem. The bark is blotched with red and orange, which is why it has acquired the common name of red-bark. The figure runs from a straight grain to some mottle.

After it has been cut for some time, it resembles Burma teak, changing from a yellow color to a warm brown with exposure to air and light.

Afrormosia is considered an attractive wood and it works satisfactorily with all tools. It is sometimes used as a substitute for teak, the main difference being that this wood, after repeated scrubbings, remains a dark color. It is useful for decking.

AFZELIA *Afzelia africana* (Afzelia —after Adam Afzelius, 1750-1837, a Swedish botanist; africana—of Africa)

This wood is also known under the names of ALIGNA, APA, BILINGA,

COUNTERWOOD, MAHOGANY-BEAN TREE and UVALA.

The trees grow in Nigeria. Logs may be obtained as large as 4 to 5 ft. in diameter with lengths of 30 ft. or more, usually straight and cylindrical. The wood weighs 50 lbs. per cubic foot.

The color varies considerably from a golden-brown to a reddish-brown shade, the color darkening appreciably upon exposure. The grain is irregular and often interlocked; the texture is coarse but even. Afzelia is an exceptionally stable wood, being comparable to teak in this respect, and is often used as a substitute for teak. It also has a distinct resemblance to iroko. No particular trouble has been experienced in seasoning, and the timber can be kiln-dried satisfactorily from the green condition. The wood is very durable and is reported to be proof against termites and the teredo. The hardness of this wood is comparable to oak.

The wood works well and is used in general paneling and for doors and high-grade cabinetwork. During World War II, afzelia was accepted as a substitute for teak in the United Kingdom for use in shipbuilding and for switchboards, laboratory benches, etc. Comparatively little of this timber has been exported, but the amount is continually increasing.

AGALAI or AGLAY *Chukrasia velutina* (Chukrasia—origin of name unknown; velutina—velvety)

This wood is also known under the name of HULANHIK. It is a large tree, growing in Burma and the Cochin China province of Vietnam, and is hard and heavy, weighing around 45 lbs. per cubic foot. The sapwood is light brown in color and the heartwood is of different shades of reddish brown and brown, sometimes with a striped effect.

Agalai works well with tools and takes a high polish. It produces fine-quality timber, suitable for the better classes of furniture, cabinetwork, interior paneling of rooms, etc.

AGBA *Gossweilerodendron balsamiferum* (Gossweiler—after John Gossweiler; dendron—tree; balsam —a gummy substance; ferum—to bear)

This wood is known under the names of MODORON, TOLABRANCA; and, although somewhat misleading, it is also known, because of its appearance, as NIGERIAN CEDAR or PINK MAHOGANY.

The wood comes from Nigeria. It is a huge tree with a height of as much as 125 ft. and diameters up to 5 and 6 ft. This tall tree is often clear of branches up to over 100 ft. The girth is often very large, one known specimen measuring 21 ft. It is found in the rain forests, where it frequently forms local pockets. The trunk has the appearance of a round log set on end with no root swelling at all at the base. If the trunk is wounded or notched, thick gum or oleoresin exudes and hardens into large lumps. This is often sold in Africa and used as an illuminant and for other purposes.

The wood is unusual because of its light weight, only 32 lbs. per cubic foot when dried. It is of a pale cedar-brown appearance, resembling pale mahogany, with similar ribbon-grain characteristics when sawed on the quarter. There is little difference in color between the sapwood and heartwood. The latter is slightly darker, but the line of demarcation is somewhat indefinite.

This timber is easily dried and has little tendency to warp or split. However, while being kiln-dried, some gum exudation may be noted; therefore in the selection of the wood, it is advisable to obtain timber free of gum. Agba is resistant to decay and is about as strong as our Honduras mahogany.

It is an easy wood to work with most hand and machine tools, but sometimes there is a slight tendency for the saws to stick because of the gumminess of the wood. It is somewhat similar in working quality to Honduras mahogany but a bit milder to work with. It takes stain and polish well and an excellent finish can be obtained.

Agba is an excellent wood and undoubtedly one of the most useful timbers from west Africa.

AILANTHUS *Ailanthus altissima* (Ailanthus—native Mollucan name; alt—high; issima—a superlative)

This wood is also known as PARADISE TREE and STINKING CHUN, because of the very disagreeable, obnoxious odor, which is said to aggravate catarrhal infections. In China it is known as CHINESE SUMACH and also TREE OF HEAVEN, which is a translation of the local name Amboyna, though it has no relation to the wood known as Amboyna.

Ailanthus is native to China, but now may be found throughout most eastern parts of the United States. It weighs approximately 38 lbs. per cubic foot. It is not very well known or used. Because its color and graining resembles ash so closely, it could easily be mistaken for it. The great width of its annual rings is the main distinguishing

¼×

mark in comparison to ash. It is a very rapidly growing tree and if permitted, would soon crowd out the more desirable trees.

This is the wood referred to in the book and in the motion picture seen by many—*A Tree Grows in Brooklyn.*

ALBIZZIA *Albizzia ferruginea* (Albizzia—after Filippo del Albizzia, 18th century naturalist; ferruginea —rusty colored like iron)

This wood is found in east Africa and weighs about 45 to 50 lbs. per cubic foot. It has a reddish-brown,

Finland is one of the principal producers of alpine burl or European white birch. The upper view shows pulpwood in the Kemijoki River, Finland. That country has built up a wood-processing industry which provides nearly four fifths of its total exports. Lower left, aspen trees growing in New York State. Lower right, ailanthus trees warm color and generally shows a stripe when sawn on the quarter.

Although the wood is hard and heavy, it is not durable when used for outside construction, but for general purposes it is an all-around hardwood. In east Africa, and also on the west coast of Africa, it is used to a certain extent for canoes.

ALDER, EUROPEAN *Alnus glutinosa* (Alnus—a Roman plant name; glutinosa—like glue)

This tree originates in Europe and weighs between 26 and 41 lbs. per cubic foot. The wood is a light brown, tinged with red, and is soft, light and brittle. It is used in the manufacture of soles of shoes and in cheaper cabinetwork. It also has long been used in the manufacture of gun powder.

ALLACEDE *Wallaceodendron celebicum* (Wallace—after Wallace; dendron—tree; celebicum—of the Celebes Island)

This Philippine wood is of the same botanical classification as banuyo. It is a coarse-grained wood of light reddish-brown cast with a dark brown broken stripe and sometimes a mottled figure. A fair amount has been used in the veneer form for the manufacture of furniture and for general fixture work.

ALMIQUE *Manilkara jaimiqui* (Manilkara—derivation unknown; jaimiqui—from the native name)

This wood is also known under the names of ACANA and GONSELLA.

The wood comes from Cuba and has a deep, rich red color, with an oily appearance. It is principally used for inlay work and various

types of turning, and takes a lovely polish.

ALPINE BURL or EUROPEAN WHITE BIRCH *Betula alba* (Betula —ancient Latin name for birch; alba—white)

This wood is obtained from the forests of Finland, Sweden and Norway and sold in this country under the name of ALPINE BURL. However, in Europe it is commonly known as KARELIAN BURL and NORWAY BURL BIRCH, and sometimes the veneers are advertised and sold as FLAMY BIRCH.

In figure, this wood resembles bird's-eye maple, with swirls in a light tan surface covered with tiny V-shaped figures. At times this species contains a fiddleback figure.

ALSTONIA *Alstonia congensis* (Alstonia—after Charles Alston, 1683-1760, English botanist; congensis—of the Congo)

This is a rapidly growing tree, widely distributed throughout tropical Africa. It has such rapid growth that it is often found replacing trees from clearings in the forests. The growth rings are readily seen by a change in the color of the late wood. However, there is very lit-

170

Quarter-sliced striped amboyna or narra with mottle figure

tle difference in the color of the heartwood and sapwood. When the tree or lumber is freshly cut, a faint odor resembling that of Fuller's earth may be detected.

It can best be described as having a pale oatmeal color, off white, and it darkens very little upon exposure. What seems to be small brownish pin knots, widely separated, will be found upon examination to be latex ducts. This latex in the bark and wood remains in liquid form for a long time and may be seen oozing from the ends of boards when they are resawn, despite the fact that they were originally sawn many years before.

Alstonia is an easy wood to dry and does not present any problem when being worked with tools. In Africa this timber is subject to attacks by termites. It is generally used for household implements such as spoons, ladles, stools and also drums.

AMBOYNA *pterocarpus indicus* (Ptero—winged; carpus—fruit; indicus—of India or Indies)

The native Malayan name for this wood is ANGSANA. In some dictionaries KIABOOCA is given; this means twisted wood, and is applied to burls imported from Amboyna and Borneo. Amboyna wood was so named because it was originally shipped from the island of Amboyna.

Coming from Borneo, this tree

171

has a wide range of growth throughout the East Indies and a large variation in size, from small trees to 90 ft. high, with diameters of 2 to 3 ft. The wood has a weight of 39 lbs. per cubic foot.

The wood is brown, tinged with yellow or red, but changes with age to a dull brown leather color. It is marked with little twisted curls and knots in a manner more varied than bird's-eye maple. To the naked eye, it is difficult to distinguish between the burls of amboyna wood and thuya. The wood has a fairly coarse grain and is difficult to work with power or hand tools because of the extreme hardness and the quantities of gum in the pores. These characteristics tend to dull the edges of the tools.

Amboyna wood was used to a large extent in the manufacture of furniture during the Empire period, from 1804 to 1814. It has, however, become very scarce—almost a rarity—particularly in this country, and is available only in the veneer form.

Wood of the same botanical classification as amboyna, when received in this country in the log form, is known as narra. It is of a rose to deep red color, some of a golden yellow, having a distinct stripe when manufactured on the quarter. Some of the logs contain a ripple figure. It is a hard and heavy wood, not very strong or durable, but suitable for manufacture into veneers for furniture and high-grade interior work.

ANDAMAN MARBLEWOOD
Diospyros marmorata (Dios/pryos —fruit of the gods; marmorata— like marble or marbleized)

This is a medium-sized tree, averaging over 50 lbs. per cubic foot and its growth is restricted to the Andaman Islands, Ceylon and part of India.

The bark is yellow in color and the sapwood is pinkish-brown and clearly defined from the heartwood, which is dark gray with streaks of dark brown and black. A hard and heavy wood, it resembles in many ways Maccassar ebony, being used for the same purposes. When the seasoning process is not too hurried, the wood seasons well.

It is a difficult wood to work with hand tools because of its extreme hardness, and power saws require special spacing and shape of teeth for easy cutting. However, it is a fine wood for all turning purposes and useful for decorative furniture.

ANDIRA *Andira inermis*
This wood is also known as BITTERWOOD, BOIS PALMISTE, CABBAGE-BARK, MACAYA, MOCA, PARTRIDGE WOOD and PHEASANT WOOD.

This evergreen tree is considered one of Mexico's valuable woods. Occasionally it grows to 100 ft. in height. It has a ragged bark with a very disagreeable odor. The color of the wood is similar to old mahogany and the grain is like old English oak, being of coarse texture, fairly straight. It is heavy, hard, strong and durable and has a beautiful figure.

Andira is difficult to work with, but it can be finished smoothly. In the solid form, it is used for umbrella handles, billiard-cue butts, and canes; in the veneer form, it is particularly adaptable for the paneling of large rooms, churches and interiors.

172

ANDIROBA *Carapa guianensis* (Carapa—native name; guianensis—of Guiana)

This wood is also known as CARAPA, CEDRO or MACHO, CRAB-WOOD, DENERARA.

It originates in northern South America, is reddish-brown in color and, when quartered, has a nice stripe and parallel, irregular rays.

Andiroba is generally scarce but available at times in the veneer form. It is used in furniture and cabinetmaking.

ANTIARIS *Antiaris africana* (Antiaris—Javanese name of the gum-resin from the upas tree; africana—from Africa)

This large tree, 100 ft. or more in height, with a diameter of 3 ft. or more, emanates from the west coast of Africa and in Ghana is called the BARK CLOTH TREE. In Nigeria it is sometimes called the FALSE IROKO. It is closely related to the Upas tree, the botanical name of which is *Antiaris toxicaria*.

The wood is soft, 25 lbs. per cubic foot, and has been called the bark cloth tree because the inner bark was formerly used to make a white bark cloth in certain parts of west Africa. The tree is easily distinguished since its smooth bark is at times a pale, dirty white and at other times yellowish or almost pure white in color, with many numerous wartlike growths.

Antiaris will season without difficulty but requires extreme care after the tree is cut, otherwise a blue stain will develop. It is a good, all-round, lightweight utility wood and works well with both hand and power tools. In west Africa this wood has been used principally in the manufacture of canoes, but some logs are now being exported for the manufacture of veneers.

Unreliable rubber collectors in the past have used the pale-colored latex which the wood contains as an adulterant to rubber.

APPLE *Malus pumila* (Malus—classical Latin name for apple; pumila—small)

The apple tree from Europe has a weight of 48 lbs. per cubic foot. The heartwood is hard and reddish-brown while the sapwood is light red. If not handled carefully, this wood is apt to warp and split when drying. Apple wood is used for a variety of purposes, but is particularly utilized for the heads of golf clubs. It is the state tree of Michigan.

ARARIBA *Centrolobium* spp. (Centro/lobium—center lobe, a reference to the winged fruit)

In Brazil, where this wood originates, it is also known as AMARILLO, BRANCA, ROSA and VERMELHA. In the United States it is most generally marketed under the name of BALAUSTRE and occasionally as CANARYWOOD.

It is a fairly small tree with an average length of 8 ft. Diameters of the log run from 6 to 8 ins. It is shipped from the port of Rio de Janeiro. The background color of the wood is usually yellow with red and black streaks. The lumber is sometimes used in naval architecture, and in the veneer form it is employed for decorative purposes in cabinetwork.

ASH, BLACK *Fraxinus nigra* (Fraxinus—classical Latin name for ash; nigra—black)

Black ash is also marketed un-

Rotary-cut black ash

times, in Indiana, this was the favorite wood used in weaving all types of baskets. The tree generally grows in lowlands and swamps, which explains how it receives its different names. This wood is grayish-brown to light brown in color and often produces burls of high quality. Among items made from this ash are chair bottoms and barrel hoops.

der the name of BROWN ASH, HOOP ASH, SWAMP ASH and WATER ASH. Much of the northern black ash is converted into veneers of very attractive figure and marketed under the name of NORTHERN BROWN ASH.

The general growth of these trees runs along the Atlantic coast, from Canada down as far south as Virginia, and westward to Mississippi and Minnesota. In earlier

ASH, EUROPEAN *Fraxinus excelsior* (excelsior—elevated, high)

This is also known as ITALIAN OLIVE ASH.

The tree grows in England, Turkey, France and Hungary. The color of this wood is grayish-white, except that which grows in Hungary and this tends to be brownish-white to white.

The logs are usually rotary cut into veneers and produce very wavy, distinct, sometimes black,

174

One of the countries from which European ash comes is Turkey, which is developing its forestry program with the aid of experts from the Food and Agricultural Organization of the United Nations. At top, a log depot at Abant in Bolu Province, Turkey. Bottom, an apple tree in full bloom—in New Jersey streaks and dark graining. This ash, while available in the veneer form, in burls and half-round, is quite scarce and is fairly costly.

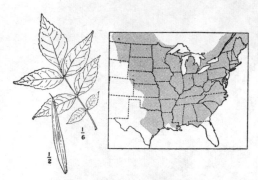

ASH, GREEN *Fraxinus pennsylvanica* (pennsylvanica—of Pennsylvania)

This tree is also known under the name of BLUE ASH and WATER ASH.

It is found throughout eastern Canada and most parts of the United States east of the Rocky Mountains. It is a good-looking tree and one of the ashes that is often planted for shade and ornamental purposes in landscaping. Green ash lumber is often marketed with the white ash and is used for the same purposes, as handles of all kinds, baseball bats and novelties.

ASH, OREGON *Fraxinus velutina* (velutina—velvety)

This is a fairly small tree with a height of from 50 to 70 ft. and diameters from 14 to 30 in. This ash is particularly interesting as it is the only species of ash found on the Pacific coast, where it extends all the way from British Columbia, in a narrow belt through the mountains, to southern California. It

grows best in rich, lowland soil and when found in higher elevations, the tree is greatly dwarfed and frequently crooked.

Oregon ash is one of the most valuable hardwoods throughout the West Coast area. While lighter in weight than the eastern ashes, other characteristics are quite similar and it is used for about the same purposes.

ASH, WHITE *Fraxinus americana* (americana—of America)

This is a heavy wood with an average weight of 42 lbs. per cubic foot. The heartwood is brown to dark brown, sometimes with a reddish tint. White ash is often confused with hickory but may be distinguished by the fact that the zone of large pores is much more dis-

176

A beautiful white ash tree

Quarter-sliced white ash, four-piece match

tinguishable in ash than in hickory.

This wood is strong and stiff, has good shock resistance and is noted for its excellent bending qualities. It is used almost exclusively for all types of sports and athletic equipment such as baseball bats and long oars. Almost universally it is also used for handles of shovels and spades, and the long handles of forks, hoes and rakes. In the lumber form it is particularly valuable for the bent parts of chairs. Occasionally, high-grade logs are cut into veneers which are very attractive in decorative work.

ASH, WHITE MOUNTAIN *Eucalyptus regnans* (Eu/calyptus—true cover; regnans—to rule, probably referring to the lordly size of this species—to 350 ft.)

This tree, from Tasmania, is also known as TASMANIAN OAK.

It is probably the largest hardwood in the world and amongst the tallest, as some trees have been reported in excess of 326 ft.

The *Eucalyptus* species, largely of Australian origin, produces a great variety of woods with wide range of texture, color and behavior, and the principal wood in this species is the White Mountain ash. It has a tan to golden-brown color, sometimes pinkish, and a blistered figure, fiddleback and with straight grain. It is very strong and durable and works well. Locally it is used for bridges, wood paving and other structural uses, but it is also suitable for use by cabinetmakers.

ASPEN, QUAKING *Populus tremuloides* (Populus—the classical Latin name; tremul/oides—resembling the European aspen, *P. tremula;* tremul—trembling)

This tree grows throughout the northeastern, northern and western parts of the United States as far north as Alaska. It is a short-lived tree as it decays early in life when approaching full growth. The bark is thin and whitish or gray-green in color. Quaking aspen is one of the lightweight hardwoods, aver-

178

the action of nails or screws. The wood seasons very easily by air drying or kiln drying. It is fairly easy to finish to a smooth surface with hand or power tools, takes stain very poorly, but can be painted.

Producers of cheese have always preferred this wood for use as containers because it is light in weight, of light color and free from any odor or taste.

Highly figured logs of aspen and also some crotches are occasionally cut into veneers, which are generally available to craftsmen. It has long been one of the perfect woods for the manufacture of high-grade excelsior. When sawed into lumber it is also used for paper pulp and matches.

Aspen crotch

aging around 26 lbs. per cubic foot.

This aspen shrinks very little and in bending properties it ranks with the best of hardwoods. It has a tendency, though, to split under

AVODIRÉ *Turraeanthus africana* (Turrae—after Anton Turra, 18th century Italian botanist; anthus— flower; africana—from Africa)

This wood is also known under such names as APAYA, APPAYIA and OLON.

It comes from the Ivory Coast, the Gold Coast and Liberia in west Africa. It originally came into this country with African mahogany logs, shipped from the west coast of Africa. Avodiré is a fairly light-weight wood weighing around 20 lbs. per cubic foot. In the past it has been offered for sale as African satinwood, African furniture wood and African white mahogany.

The wood possesses a golden yellow color with a firm, clean grain capable of producing a smooth, highly polished surface. It is very strong in relation to its light weight.

Avodiré is available both in lumber and veneer form. Large quantities of this wood have been used in the manufacture of store fix-

179

Avodire, rope figure, two-piece match

tures and furniture and in decorating the interior of fine offices and homes, and it is used quite extensively for various effects in marquetry.

AYAN *Distemonanthus benthamianus* (Di—two; stemon—stamen; anthus—flower; benthamianus—after Bentham, a 19th century English botanist)

This wood is also known under the names of BARRE, EYEN and MOVINGUI. Because of the color, the grain and the general beauty of the wood, it is also called NIGERIAN SATINWOOD.

This is a tall tree, often 90 ft. or more in height, moderately hard and heavy, about 45 lbs. per cubic foot, and grows in the forests of west Africa, through Ghana, the Ivory Coast, Nigeria and the French Camerouns.

Ayan has a bright yellow and orange color. It is said to be durable and termite-proof. It is a wood that is easy to season, providing the lumber is not exposed to the full force of the wind or direct sunlight until it has dried. This timber cuts smoothly, exhibiting a fine, lustrous appearance and works easily with both hand and power tools. It has been used for flooring, and the veneer is used in cabinetwork. The wood, however, has to be filled well when finishing in order to obtain a high polish.

AYOUS *Triplochiton scleroxylon* (Triplo—pertaining to threes; chiton—an outer covering; scler—hard; xylon—wood)

This wood is also known as AFRICAN WHITEWOOD, OBECHE, SAMBA, OKPO, WAWA and ABACHI.

It is a fairly large tree with an average diameter of 30 to 36 in. and a weight of 25 lbs. per cubic foot, emanating from the Gold and Ivory Coasts and the French Camerouns. It is creamy-white to light yellow in color, has a fine stripe when cut on the quarter, is fairly soft but firm, with a medium grain and even texture. In strength it is about equal to our American

Striped ayous, two-piece match

whitewood and it will not withstand heavy wear.

The logs deteriorate so quickly when cut that prompt transportation facilities are essential. Though light in weight, it is remarkably strong in relation to its weight.

At first glance one would get the impression of woolliness, but it works easily, and a smooth surface is quickly produced which takes a fine polish. A large amount of this wood is manufactured into veneers.

BALDCYPRESS *Taxodium distichum* (Taxodium—having the appearance of *Taxus*, the yew; dis-tichum—two-ranked, the leaves being in two rows)

This cypress goes under various names in the different states and a few of them are: BLACK CYPRESS, BUCK CYPRESS, COW CYPRESS, RED CYPRESS, SOUTHERN CYPRESS, SWAMP CYPRESS, WHITE CYPRESS and YELLOW CYPRESS.

The natural growth of cypress covers a large area along the Atlantic coast from Delaware to Florida and westward through all the Gulf states to Texas and through most of the mid-Atlantic states, northward to Indiana and Illinois. The appearance of the wood varies somewhat according to where the tree grows, but it is usually found in wet, low bottomlands and swamps.

The wood in the southern swamps is darker in color than that which grows farther north on drier land. Some of the baldcypress has light streaks through a dark background and this makes an attractive figure. The heartwood varies in color from a light yellowish-brown to a dark brown. The foli-

181

Faux satine (baldcypress) crotch, four-piece match

age is light green in color, something like celery in appearance, and in the far south the trees are usually found covered with drooping Spanish moss.

Baldcypress is a very durable wood and quite resistant to decay. It is medium hard, strong, with close, straight grain and is fairly heavy. When rubbed, the wood retains a greasy feeling. Cypress fingers are considered more valuable than all other American woods for durability in greenhouse construction, coffins and wooden drainboards.

Crotches cut from baldcypress trees are offered in the market, when available, under the name of faux satine.

BALSA *Ochroma lagopus* (Ochroma—paleness; lago/pus—rabbit foot)

This tree, from Central and South America, obtains a height

up to 70 ft. and is one of the lightest woods. Balsa wood was used by the natives of Central and South America for making boats and canoes, which is probably the original source of its name, the word balsa being the Spanish name for raft.

The wood is a whitish, pale yellow color, exceedingly porous and relatively very elastic and strong for its light weight. Under favorable circumstances, balsa trees are

Upper left, jungle of small bamboo shoots in India. Upper right, typical basswood tree, Pine Plains, N. Y. Lower left, blue paloverde. Lower right, butternut tree in spring with young leaves showing

183

ready for cutting when they are seven years old. Older trees often develop rot at the base and become worthless. The lighter colored wood is by far the best, weighing 5 to 10 lbs. per cubic foot, while the darker wood of old trees may weigh up to 25 lbs. per cubic foot.

Its lightness and good working properties favor its use as a packing material for highly finished surfaces. Because of its extreme lightness and relative strength, it is used extensively in the manufacture of model airplanes.

During the war of 1914 to 1918 this wood came into great prominence as it was in demand for many purposes, including the packing of armor plates for battleships. Impregnated with a hot paraffin solution, the wood was used extensively for life rafts because of its great buoyancy.

Today, in the United States, it is used for insulating material, refrigerator cars and in lifesaving appliances.

BAMBOO *Bambusa gramineae*
(Bambusa—typifies a tribe, Bambuseae, of the Poaceae; gramineae —grasslike)

Bamboo is often treelike with woody stems, growing from underground root stock, often crowded to dense clumps. It occasionally reaches 120 ft. in height. The slender stem is hollow and, as generally in grasses, has well-marked joints or nodes, at each of which the cavity is closed by a strong diaphragm. It grows throughout the tropical zone, extending into the subtropical and even into the temperate zone. Tropical Asia is richest in this species, the plant extending into Japan and to an elevation of 10,000 ft. or more in the Himalayas. There are very few bamboo plants in Africa. In South America they reach the snow line. Three species are natural to the United States, thriving best in the cotton states and the valleys of southern California.

Bamboo is considered one of the most rapid-growing of plants. In Ceylon, species have been observed to grow 16 in. a day. Importation of living bamboo and bamboo seeds has been forbidden in the United States since 1919 because of danger from pests.

In the United States, the use of bamboo includes furniture, landscape ornaments, fences, etc.

Clump bamboo stands up against hurricanes much better than most other plants and trees. In oriental countries, the bamboo has been called "one of nature's most valuable gifts to uncivilized man," for its use is almost endless. The soft shoots, just beginning to grow, are cut off and served like table asparagus. They are also salted and eaten with rice, prepared in the form of pickles. Joints of sufficient size form water buckets; smaller ones, bottles. In places in Borneo, bamboo is used for cooking utensils. It is used extensively as a timber wood, and houses are made entirely of the products. Complete sections of the stem form posts or columns; split up, it serves for floors or rafters; and interwoven in latticework, it is employed for the sides of rooms, admitting light and air. It is employed in shipping of all kinds. Some of the strongest plants are selected for masts of boats of moderate size, and the masts of larger vessels are sometimes formed by several joined bamboo stems. Bamboo is employed in the construction of all kinds of agricultural and

Upper left, paper birches often grow in clusters of two or three. Upper right, blackgum. Lower left, large American beech growing in Vermont. Lower right, baldcypress domestic implements and in the materials and implements required in fishery.

Bows are made by the union of two pieces bound with many bands. With the septa bored out and the lengths joined together, bamboo is employed to carry water to reservoirs or gardens. The outer cuticle of the oriental species is so hard that it forms a sharp and durable cutting edge, and it is so siliceous that it can be used as a whetstone. This outer cuticle, when cut into thin strips, is one of the most durable and beautiful materials for basket making. In China the interior portions of the stem are beaten into a pulp and used in the manufacture of the finer varieties of paper. Bamboo is exported to a considerable extent into Europe for the use of basket makers and for umbrellas and walking sticks.

BANAK *Virola koschnyi* (Virola —possibly referring to greenness; koschnyi—after Koschny)

This tree grows beside swamps and in forests along river valleys, all the way from Panama to British Honduras and Guatemala, often obtaining a height of 85 ft. and a diameter from 6 to 40 in. The bark of this tree is unusual inasmuch as it is red in color and contains red sap which flows like blood from a wound. The wood resembles somewhat the paler colored mahoganies, being pinkish brown when cut but darkening upon exposure. In British Honduras this is considered one of the more important woods.

Care is required in seasoning to prevent warping and splitting. It is a wood of medium hardness and from 35 to 40 lbs. per cubic foot

in weight, with generally a straight grain.

In strength it is comparable to the American whitewood. This wood is easy to work if tools are kept in sharp condition. The principal difficulty in marketing the wood is that a large quantity of the logs are damaged from stain and pin worms. The clean logs, however, are suitable for manufacture into veneers and the cheaper type of furniture.

BANANA

THE BANANA is a gigantic herbaceous plant belonging to the genus *musa*. This genus contains 30 species widely distributed throughout the tropics of the Old World and in some cases introduced into the New World. They are most successfully cultivated in a hot, damp, tropical climate. The unripe fruit is rich in starch which, in ripening, changes into sugar. The plants most generally used for fruits are derived from the species *musa paradisiaca* of which there are a number of varieties and forms existing in cultivation. No other class of tropical fruits is so widely known and only the coconut has greater economic value. The banana stands with the grape, apple, olive, orange and lemon among the leading fruits of the world. Since 1880 banana culture has expanded in the West Indies, Central America, Mexico and Colombia. The value of bananas shipped from these regions to the United States and Europe is over 50 million dollars yearly.

The plant is perennial, sending up from an underground root stock an apparent stem up to 10 ft. high, consisting of the closely enveloped

186

Path through banana grove in the Marquesas Islands in the Pacific leaf-sheaths. A true stem develops at the flowering period; it grows up through the hollow tube formed by the sheaths, emerges above and bears a large number of inconspicuous tubular flowers closely crowded in the axils of large, often brightly colored, protecting bracts. The fruits form dense clusters.

The best known species in east Africa are those which require cooking; they have greater importance as an article of food. There they will obtain nearly 2 ft. in length with the thickness of a man's arm. There is little or no value to the woody part of the stem, but the banana is being planted in many places for shade and decoration; the only other value lies in its fruit.

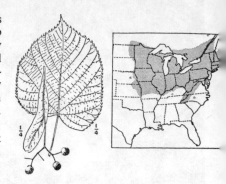

BASSWOOD, AMERICAN *Tilia americana* (Tilia—the classical Latin name; americana—of America)

This wood is also known under other names in various states, such as AMERICAN LINDEN, BEETREE, BLACK LIMETREE, LIME TREE, LINN, LINDEN, WHITEWOOD, WICKUP and YELLOW BASSWOOD.

It grows throughout the eastern half of the United States and more than half of the total quantity is found in the Great Lakes states. This is a lovely shaped tree and grows well in sandy soil near streams. The heartwood is creamy white to creamy brown and sometimes reddish.

Basswood is a lightweight hardwood, averaging 26 lbs. per cubic foot and it is fairly easy to air-dry

Rotary-cut basswood, two-piece match

188

or kiln-dry, staying in place well after seasoning.

The wood is weak, however, and there is a large shrinkage involved. The tree grows fast, has a heavy foliage, therefore is good for landscaping and a fine tree for shade.

The largest percentage of the basswood in this country is cut into lumber, the greatest portion of which is used for crates and boxes, the manufacturing of sash, doors and general millwork. Also, a considerable amount is manufactured into veneers for various specialized purposes and particularly as core material for the manufacture of panels.

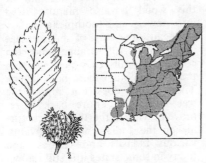

BEECH, AMERICAN *Fagus grandifolia* (Fagus—the classical Latin name, from the Greek word meaning to eat, in reference to the edible nuts; grandi/folia—large-leaved)

American beech grows in the United States from Maine to northern Florida and westward into Wisconsin and Texas. It is one of the heavier woods, having an average weight of 45 lbs. per cubic foot, and is readily distinguishable from other native species by its heavy weight and the conspicuous rays and tiny pores.

It is rated high in strength and shock resistance and, when steamed, is readily bent. However, considerable care must be taken during seasoning because the wood is subject to a very large shrinkage. If careful attention is not given during this period, checks and discolorations, in addition to warping, will be encountered.

Beech is used not only in the lumber form but also in veneering. It is particularly suitable for food containers since it does not impart taste or odor.

BEEFWOOD *Mimusops* sp. (Mimusops—monkey face)

This wood, growing in British and Dutch Guiana, is known locally under many different names, including BULLY TREE, BULLET WOOD, RED LANCEWOOD, HORSE-FLESH.

The wood from Dutch Guiana—Surinam—is of far better quality than that from British Guiana, which often contains considerable knots. This wood is generally exported in the form of square-hewn logs, from 8 to 18 in. square and in lengths from 12 to 30 ft.

The color of this wood is a dull plum red and somewhat resembles raw beef—which is probably the reason it was so named. Beefwood is very durable and stands exposure, but on the other hand is subject to attacks from worms and the teredo.

When planed, the wood produces a very smooth surface which glistens with minute shining specks of substance, contained in the pores. A very fine polish can be obtained. This wood has long been in demand for the best umbrella sticks because of its great strength. It is also used in making the cheaper quality of violin bows and in archery for the footings of arrows.

BILLIAN *Eusideroxylon zwageri*
(Eu/sider/oxylon—true ironwood;
zwageri—after Zwager)

Growing in Borneo and the Malaya Peninsula, this wood is commonly known as IRONWOOD in Borneo. It is one of the hardest woods emanating from those countries, weighing 70 lbs. per cubic foot. The color varies from light brown when first cut to almost a black upon exposure to light and air. Most of this timber is used in the construction of wooden buildings as the wood seems to be entirely impervious to white ants and teredos. Locally it is used for all types of heavy construction and is one of the best woods for telegraph and telephone poles, railway ties and piling.

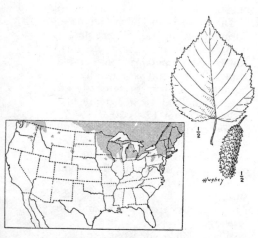

BIRCH, PAPER *Betula papyrifera*
(Betula—classical Latin name for birch; papyr/ifera—paper bearing, in reference to papery bark)

This species is also known as CANOE BIRCH and MOTHER TREE.

Paper birch grows in a greater number of localities than any other birch. It grows practically across the entire country of Canada from Alaska to Labrador and across the northern part of the United States from coast to coast, and is the state tree of New Hampshire.

When growing in the forest, it is the easiest birch to distinguish because of its smooth white bark. It reaches heights of from 55 to 75 ft. with diameters from 2 to 3 ft. The wood is white in color and there is little difference between the sapwood and heartwood. This birch is very easily worked and finishes smoothly.

One of its principal uses is in the form of candleholders for table decorations. It is the birch that you see in many forms in souvenir shops as baskets, toy canoes, or postal cards. A large amount of this wood is also manufactured into dowels and toothpicks.

Because the bark of this tree has inner layers of orange and tan color, it permits easy peeling from the tree to obtain these bark layers. The peeling does not injure the tree unless the entire bark is removed. This is the tree which furnished the Indians with wigwams, various utensils and canoes, and today in some states it is still known as canoe birch for this reason.

The tree is very ornamental, often growing in clusters of three. The reason it is also called mother tree is that it is frequently planted in memory of mothers. For example, around the Capitol grounds in Washington it was planted to honor the mothers of the Nation, and on the grounds of the White House to honor the mothers of our presidents. It is also planted in Arlington Cemetery and known as National Mother's Tree. While ornamental, it is not as long lived or as large as the other birches.

This is the tree that we remember from our school days from the Song

John Constantine Docherty, grandson of the author, standing alongside a freshly fallen log of Adirondack sweet birch of Hiawatha, written by Longfellow: "Give me your bark oh birch tree, I a light canoe will build me."

neers. The only loss involved was a small length from each end of the log, which had to be cut off because of the effect of the water.

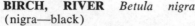

BIRCH, RIVER *Betula nigra* (nigra—black)

This is another species of birch, which is also known as WATER BIRCH, RED BIRCH and BLACK BIRCH. It is named river birch because it is always found along streams, brooks and swamp areas, growing across the southern part of our country from Florida to Texas and northward as far as New England.

This wood is more or less of similar texture and is used for the same purposes as other birches. The principal difference is that the bark on the branches of the younger trees is very smooth and has a lustrous, reddish-brown color as the tree grows older.

Birch logs can be stored with perfect safety for many years if they are kept immersed in fresh water. One large veneer firm recently learned of a large number of logs that had been buried in Lake Superior for 63 years on the site of an old sawmill. They had their men inspect the logs beneath water and then purchased the entire lot. They were fine, large logs of birch timber and when they were taken into the mill, produced some very fine ve-

BIRCH, SWEET *Betula lenta* (lenta—flexible or tough, referring to the twigs)

This birch is also known under the name of BLACK BIRCH and CHERRY BIRCH.

It grows mainly in the Adirondacks, in the eastern Appalachian area, although it can be found as far south as the northern Gulf states. The wood is brown in color, tinged with red, and the sapwood is thin and light brown or yellow. It has a heavy, very strong, hard, close grain, distinct but not prominent. Birch veneer is generally rotary cut and sliced and is used in all types of cabinetwork.

BIRCH, YELLOW *Betula alleghaniensis* (alleghaniensis—of the Allegheny Mountains)

This wood is also known as GRAY BIRCH, SILVER BIRCH, SWAMP BIRCH.

It grows in Canada, through the Great Lakes and in the New England states, down as far as North Carolina. Yellow birch is creamy or light brown in color, tinged with

Top, rotary-cut yellow birch. Bottom, flat-cut yellow birch. In the trade this is sold as "natural birch," which is not selected for color, and "selected white birch."

red with thin, nearly white sap-wood. The curly or wavy figure is often prominent, both in the rotary and sliced veneer. It is a heavy, very strong, hard, close-grained wood of even texture.

The wood works easily, takes a finish nicely and is available in both the lumber and veneer form. It is used in the manufacture of furniture, interior woodworking for doors and door fixtures, and is especially valuable for cupboards, school seating, etc., because of its durability and strength.

BITTERWOOD *Vatairea lundellii*
This wood is also known locally as BITTER ANGELIM and MOUN-TAIN COW-WOOD. The latter name was given because the purplish-brown bark, about ½″ thick, is often chewed on by mountain cows.

Bitterwood grows from southern Mexico to Brazil and is so named because of the extreme bitterness to the taste. The bitterness obtained from chewing a small splinter of the wood will remain with one for a long time.

At times these trees will grow as high as 125 ft. with diameters of 3 ft. The heartwood, which is yel-low when first manufactured, dark-ens to a warm golden-brown color. The wood is coarse, about 45 lbs. per cubic foot in weight, and has large pores. Its strength is some-what superior to Honduras ma-hogany, but it is a much more difficult wood to work with. Its principal use in Brazil is for general building and as an all-around util-ity wood.

BLACKBUTT *Eucalyptus pilularis*
(Eu/calyptus—true cover; pilu-laris—globular, pertaining to the spherical fruit)
This tree is found only in the forests of New South Wales, Vic-toria and Queensland, along the coast and in the tablelands directly behind the coast. It is a large tree, one of the tallest in the Eucalyptus family and is at times referred to as one of the best growing in Aus-tralia. The wood is very heavy, generally over 60 lbs. per cubic foot, and unusually hard. The bark is stringy and often is black on the lower part of the trunk, which is the reason why it is commonly called blackbutt. However, this condition changes and it is not a reliable identification for the wood. The heartwood is a pleasing pale light red color to pinkish brown, with small difference between the sapwood and heartwood. This wood is quite similar to tallow-wood.

In the countries in which it grows, because of its durability to the elements, it is often used on out-side construction. It is particularly desirable in the shipbuilding indus-try for planking. However, the silica generally found in the wood quickly dulls the edges of all cut-ting tools. Smaller sections of the tree are of special value for fence posts because of their long life.

BLACKGUM *Nyssa sylvatica* (Nyssa—the name of a water nymph, so called because the first described species, *N. aquatica,* grows in water; sylvatica—of the woods)

Although this wood is principally known as BLACK TUPELO, it also is known under the names of BOWL GUM, PEPPERIDGE, STINKWOOD, WILD PEARTREE and YELLOW GUMTREE.

These trees are found in practically all states east of the Mississippi and, like the water tupelo, grow wherever there is swampland and abundant water supplies as ponds or streams.

All four woods of the tupelo family are similar in appearance and texture and very difficult to distinguish from one another. They all have a tendency to warp; this is due to the interlocking grain of the wood, which also makes it difficult to split and nail.

Blackgum and water tupelo both take a good finish, but blackgum glues well, which the water tupelo does not. A better grade of lumber and a large quantity of veneers are obtained from the blackgum tree, and the logs, when manufactured into veneers, have an attractive figure.

The wood is used for paper pulp and general miscellaneous items of manufacture such as baskets, crates, cigar boxes, etc.

BLACKWOOD, AUSTRALIAN *Acacia melanoxylon* (Acacia—I sharpen, probably a reference to the spines borne by many species; melan/oxylon—black wood)

This wood grows in Tasmania and throughout Australia. The color varies from a rich reddish brown to almost black, with bands of golden brown. Blackwood has a close grain, very often curly, and an attractive mottled figure. Care has to be taken to see that it is properly seasoned.

This wood is easily worked and will produce a fine polish. A limited quantity is converted into veneer and used for furniture work, marquetry and in the paneling of interior rooms.

BLUE PALOVERDE *Cercidium floridum* (Cercidium—a weaver's comb; floridum—full of flowers)

This is a small tree, no more than 12 to 30 ft. tall and 15 in. or more in diameter. It is the state tree of Arizona and one of the three species of blue paloverde native to the United States and the most lovely in appearance.

The wood has little value. It can be detected when burning because of its very unpleasant odor. However, in contrast, it offers a food value from its pealike pods.

BOARWOOD *Symphonia globulifera* (Symphonia—grown together; globulifera– bearing globules or spheres)

In British Honduras it is called WAIKA CHEWSTICK and is known

195

in the West Indies as HOG GUM.

This is a large tree, growing in height from 60 to 120 ft. and as much as 3 ft. in diameter. It is widely distributed throughout Central America and the northern part of South America, extending from Guatemala and British Honduras down through Peru and Brazil, as well as Trinidad and the British West Indies.

Usually boarwood is found in the lowland forests and occasionally grows alongside of palms. It is a hard, medium heavy wood, about 40 to 45 lbs. per cubic foot. The bark contains a yellowish brown gum which darkens with exposure and sometimes has the resemblance of pitch.

The sapwood is almost pure white while the heartwood is yellow to a grayish brown or a pale olive brown, and several of these shades in the form of stripes may appear on a single piece of lumber. Considerable difficulty is experienced in seasoning, during which time it must not be exposed to the direct sun. Protection is necessary to the ends of the boards to prevent their drying out too rapidly.

This wood is comparable in strength to our American oak and while it is not as well known, except in the country it grows in, some of it is used as plywood on a small scale in Europe. Throughout Central America and the West Indies it is generally employed in the ordinary forms of carpentry and for boxes.

BOSSE *Guarea cedrata* (Guarea— from guara, a native name from Cuba; cedrata—pertaining to cedar)

This wood is also known as PIQUA, AFRICAN CEDAR, CEDAR MAHOGANY, CEDRON, OBOBO, OBO- BONE, KWI and SCENTED GUAREA.

This tree grows on the Gold and Ivory Coasts, is medium large in size, and at times logs up to diameters of 5 ft. are exported. The wood has a pleasing pink to light mahogany color, has a fine grain and comes in stripes and mottles. The amount of sapwood is small and whitish in color; the heartwood is pinkish-brown, darkening upon exposure, but not to the same extent as true mahoganies. The characteristic of this tree is that it is generally superior to the American mahogany. The grain is either straight or wavy and the mottle figure is fairly common, but the stripe is far less frequent than that found in sapele. The plain-cut stock shows a small zigzag figure. When freshly cut, a strong cedar-like scent results; occasionally the boards and veneers will be gummy, which has a dulling effect on saws. However, these gum spots may be easily sanded off before finishing.

The logs are a good size for widths and lengths, and the wood is stiff, tough and strong, comparing favorably with Honduras mahogany, but being considerably harder.

BOXWOOD, WEST INDIAN *Gossypiospermum praecox* (Gossypiospermum—having seeds like cotton, *Gossypium;* praecox—before or earlier to develop, precocious)

This tree, found in Venezuela, Colombia and the West Indies, obtains a height of 65 to 70 ft., generally without a single knot through its entire length. At the very top the tree branches out into a turf of foliage.

The color is yellowish-white, and this wood is of the same family as elm, with a leaf similar to the elm, two sides of which are unequal at

196

the base. As a rule it is a straight-grained wood, close, firm and smooth and of uniform fine texture. Occasionally logs will be found with irregularities. Chalky deposits will be found both in the heartwood and sapwood.

It is an extremely heavy and hard wood, easy to work, and is very satisfactory for turnery as well as carving. In this country it is used extensively for inlay work, in inlaid borders and many types of marquetry designs. Also it is used occasionally for handles of tools, brush backs, and for various mathematical instruments and backs of scientific and weather instruments. In some countries a great deal of it is used in the manufacture of small combs.

BRIAR *Erica arborea* (Erica—the heath; arborea—treelike)

Briar grows in small trees or shrubs and is a wood much sought after for the manufacture of the finest grades of pipes. It grows principally in countries around the Adriatic Sea, Turkey, Algeria and the island of Corsica. One hundred years ago the French town of St. Claude was the original manufacturing center for all briar pipes, but this industry has now spread to practically all countries.

The wood for the pipes is obtained from the roots of the tree when it is generally 25 years or more of age and usually from 9 to 14 ft. high. The roots lie from 6 to 12 in. beneath the surface of the ground, and any roots 4 in. or more in diameter are considered acceptable. Occasionally some roots are obtained as large as 8″. After being procured, they are roughly trimmed, piled in large heaps and watered frequently to prevent the roots from drying. They are constantly kept damp until they are ready to be cut into the blanks for the pipes. After this, they are boiled to improve the color and reduce danger of splitting. It is reported that over 10,000 tons a year are used.

From time to time the popularity of the wood has changed; sometimes the straight-grained wood is the most desired and at other times the burl or bird's-eye figure is preferred.

BUBINGA *Didelotia africana* (Didelotia—probably after Didelot; africana—of Africa)

This tree grows principally in Gaboon and the Camerouns and when rotary cut is known as KEVAZINGO. It is also known under the

Bubinga with stripe-and-mottle figure

197

name of ESSINGANG. While the botanical classification of Bubinga has been given by some, it should not be accepted definitely until it has been further verified. It is a wood which has obtained its name from the vernacular name of Bubingo. The French have referred to it in the trade as BOIS DE ROE D'AFRIQUE.

The average weight per cubic foot is 57 lbs. and the logs, when received in this country, are tremendous in size. Logs have been received which weigh as much as 10 tons. The color varies in different logs from a pale to a deep red, though the color is uniform in individual trees. It also comes in striped and mottled figures. Bubinga is valuable as a veneer for cabinetwork.

Striped bubinga

198

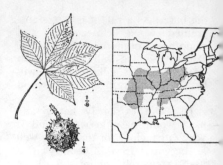

BUCKEYE *Aesculus glabra* (Aesculus—ancient Latin name of a European oak; glabra—smooth, hairless)

The twigs and flowers of this tree have a most disagreeable odor when they are crushed or broken, which is why it has also been given the name of STINKING BUCKEYE and FETID BUCKEYE.

This tree grows in the central states from Alabama to Pennsylvania. While originally it was brought from Germany, from the earliest days it has always been associated with Ohio, and is the official tree of that state.

Buckeye is a rather small to medium sized tree and in many ways resembles in appearance the horse chestnut. It is called buckeye because of the large seeds, which resemble the eye of a buck deer. Incidentally, these seeds are poisonous.

Buckeye is light in weight, soft in texture and nearly white in color except for streaks that sometimes occur from staining. It is a good-looking tree and generally bears leaves in the spring earlier than almost any other species.

Early settlers used an extract from the bark for medicine.

In lumber form the wood is easily distinguished by the appearance of ripple figures. It is used in the manufacture of paper pulp, various types of woodenware and for splints and artificial limbs. Some of the logs are also converted into veneers.

BULLET WOOD *Mimusops globosa* (Mimusops—monkey face; globosa—spherical, probably referring to the fruit)

This wood, coming from Brazil, the Guianas and Venezuela, is also known as BALATA, BEEFWOOD, RED LANCEWOOD and WILD BILLY.

It is reddish-brown with a purple cast, hard and heavy, and one of the strongest woods known. It is produced only in the lumber form and in limited quantities.

BUTTERNUT *Juglans cinerea* (Juglans—the classical Latin name of the walnut, meaning the nut of Jupiter; cinerea—ash-colored, pertaining to the bark)

The kernel of the nut is so delicious, rich and oily, the name

of OIL-NUT has sometimes been given to this tree.

The growth of this tree extends from Quebec down through the northeastern sections of the United States and westward to South Dakota and as far south as Arkansas, Mississippi and Alabama.

This wood is in many ways very similar in characteristics to American black walnut and has at times been called white walnut. Like walnut, the nuts are edible and highly prized. The sap obtained is sweet, and a syrup may be pro-

Flat-sliced butternut, two-piece match

199

duced, similar to syrup from the maple tree. Butternut wood is lighter in weight and not as strong and durable as black walnut. It is soft in texture but coarse-grained. The wood is easily worked with all types of tools, very sharp tools being desirable because of the softness of the wood. Lovely interior paneling has been done with butternut, and a small amount used in the manufacture of furniture. Also, many church altars have been made of this wood. It is also employed by wood carvers.

CAMPECHE *Sickingia tinctoria* (Sickingia—probably after Sicking; tinctoria—dyed)

This wood is known under a number of different names, as CARRETA, CORALITO, NADARA ROSITA, PALO ROSATO, PAU BRAZIL, QUINA ROJA and RED INDIA INK. It has long been associated with the red dye made from the bark, and small quantities have been brought into New York for use as a dyewood under the name of ARARIBÁ ROSA.

Campeche grows up to 60 ft. in height and with diameters from 15 to 18 in. The wood has a fine texture and straight grain, but has small commercial value. It works well, and locally in Brazil it is used for making fancy articles, bowls and spoons, and also for interior construction and general carpentry.

CAMPHORWOOD *Cinnamomum camphora* (Cinnamon—from the ancient Greek, *kinnamomon;* camphor—from the Arabic *kafur,* meaning resin)

This tree grows in Japan, China and Formosa and is a difficult wood to obtain. In China and Formosa,

capital punishment has been the penalty for cutting down camphor trees. This is known as the true camphorwood and the strong scent of camphor will last hundreds of years. The wood weighs about 41 lbs. per cubic foot and is light yellow to brown in color. There is little demand for it.

Oftentimes wood of the cinnamon tree (*Cinnamomum zeylanicum*) is sold in place of the true camphor. However, this wood shrinks, warps and swells. As long as it is in existence it has the strong scent of paregoric or balm of aniseed. The well-known seamen's trunks made in China and sold today in eastern markets as camphorwood are generally made of this inferior cinnamon tree, only a small portion being made of camphor wood to produce the scent of camphor.

There is another type of camphorwood from Borneo which does not have an odor like camphor. This wood also shrinks and can only be used after at least two years of air seasoning followed by kiln drying.

From Madagascar there is also a camphorwood (*Hernandia voyroni*) which has a strong and consistent odor of camphor but is greenish-brown in color, has a rough grain and is difficult to work with tools.

CAMPHORWOOD, EAST AFRI-CAN *Ocotea usambarensis* (Ocotea —a South American Indian plant name; usambarensis—of Usum-bura, capitol of Ruanda-Urundi, Belgian trust territory in Africa)

This large tree emanates from Kenya, in east Africa, at altitudes anywhere from 7,000 to 8,000 ft. and higher. It is one of the largest trees growing in Kenya.

When freshly cut, the wood is a pale, greenish color, but it darkens to a deep brown with exposure to air and light. It is light in weight, weighing around 35 lbs. per cubic foot, and has a distinct aromatic scent which probably is the reason for the name of camphor, though it differs entirely from the Asiatic camphorwood and no camphor is present in the tree. The leaves also contain an aromatic oil. This wood is closely related to the African stick wood and British Guiana greenheart.

This camphorwood needs to be dried fairly slowly to avoid any warping. With hand or machine tools the wood is easily worked, and locally it has been used in the manufacture of railway coaches and furniture, and small quantities have been exported to other markets. A fine example of the use of this wood can be seen in the Post Office at West Kensington, London, where all of the trim and cabinet-work has been done in this wood.

CANALETE *Cordia alliodora* (Cordia—after Valerius Cordus, 1515-1544; alliodora—smelling like an onion, *Allium*)

This tree, growing in Venezuela, is reddish-brown in color, works easily, is strong and is used locally for furniture, house construction and joinery. Occasional logs have

been brought into this country and manufactured into veneers.

CANARIUM *Canarium schwein-furthii* (Canarium—in reference to the Canary Islands; schweinfurthii —after Schweinfurth, a German botanist)

This is a large tree, often obtaining a height of 100 ft., which grows throughout the west coast of Africa. In France it is known under the name of AIELE, and sometimes it has been called WHITE MAHOGANY.

The wood is almost white in color, occasionally slightly pink, which later may turn to a pale brownish tint upon exposure and drying. When first cut, the bark is very aromatic, with a resinous odor, and contains a gum, nearly white in color, which, after solidifying, resembles wax used for candles and burns freely.

Canarium is of medium texture and weight and, when cut on the quarter, shows a prominent stripe. It has often been used in place of African mahogany for, after being stained, the appearance is so similar that it is very deceiving to almost anyone who does not have a thorough knowledge of these timbers. It also resembles obeche in appearance, texture and color except that it is somewhat harder and a little finer in texture.

It is a wood one does not care to work with, as a rule, because the edges of the tools are quickly dulled due to the amount of gum the wood contains. It should always be cut on the quarter because of its tendency to warp.

Canarium is used for shelving, interior fittings and general purposes.

CAPOMO *Brosimum alicastrum* (Brosimum—edible; alicastrum—wild wheat)

This wood, from Central America, is also known as BREADNUT, LAREDO, LERADO and OJOCHE.

It has a yellowish sapwood and a reddish heartwood. Capomo, which is hard, is generally manufactured into veneer on the quartered form, and shows a cross-ripple figure with considerable luster.

CARACOLI *Bucida spinosa* (Bucida—from ox, referring to the hornlike galls on the fruit caused by a mite; spinosa—spined, with spines)

This is a small tree, found in abundance along the coast of the West Indies and known under the names of BLACK OLIVE TREE, BULLET TREE, GREGORY WOOD, OLIVE-BARK TREE and PRIETO.

The heartwood is of an olive brown color. Caracoli has very little export value and it is fairly difficult to work with tools. Locally it is used for general carpentry and furniture work and because of its high durability, for pole posts and railroad ties. The bark of this tree is used in tanning.

CASCARILLA *Coutarea hexandra* (Coutarea—derivation unknown; hex/andra—ten stamens)

It also goes under the names of AMARGO, CAPARCHE, PAKERI and QUINA.

This tree, often with a height of over 100 ft. and a straight trunk, 18 to 36 in. in diameter, grows from Mexico to Argentina and throughout all of southern Brazil. The heartwood is a pinkish-brown color; it is hard, strong and heavy and has a uniform fine texture. This wood is easy to work with, takes a high polish and is highly esteemed locally for use in furniture.

⅙

CATALPA, SOUTHERN *Catalpa bignonioides* (Catalpa—the American Indian name; bignonioides—appearing like *Bignonia,* a vine of the same family)

This tree grows in the eastern half of the United States from Maine to the Gulf of Mexico and the tree is recognized by the long seed pods, which look like string beans and remain on the tree throughout the winter. These pods are from 9 to 12 in. in length and in some states, because of these, it is known under the name of bean tree. There is also a northern catalpa tree, very similar in charac-

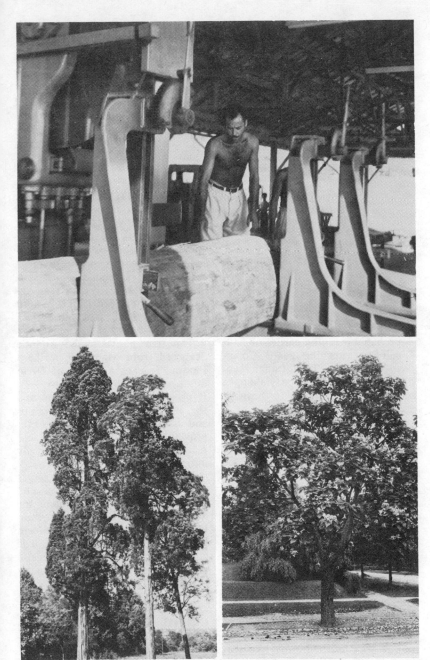

Top, sawing Spanish cedar at a sawmill in Santarem, Brazil.
Lower left, eastern red cedar. Lower right, catalpa tree

203

teristics to the southern species.

Catalpa wood is soft and weak and has a slightly aromatic odor. The supply of the lumber is limited. Locally it is used for fence posts, and it is also suitable for handles and picture frames because of its lasting qualities.

CATIVO *Prioria copaifera* (Prioria —probably meaning earlier or first; copaifera—after the genus *Copaifera;* copai—the Tupi Indian "copaiba," the copaiba tree yielding a medicinal resin; fera—to bear or yield)

In the trade this wood is also known as SPANISH WALNUT, TABASARA and TAITO.

It is the only broad-leaved tree in South America occurring in large groves. The tree grows to a height of 100 ft. with average diameters of 24 to 36 in., and larger specimens are not uncommon. The rather thick bark is smooth or with fine warts, and is a mottled gray-green on the surface but reddish-brown beneath.

In its unfinished condition, the wood is not very attractive in appearance, showing a number of narrow oily streaks and veins. With only a wax finish, however, a surface luster develops, with a rich striping of brown and many nicely variegated tones and shades such as one sees in English oak. When dry, the wood is odorless and without taste.

Its principal use in this country is for making veneers in limited quantity and it is recommended for making fine furniture. Cativo is worthy of attention from interior decorators for use in paneling rooms.

CEDAR, ATLANTIC WHITE *Chamaecyparis thyoides* (Chamaecyparis—from the Greek name of ground cypress, a dwarf shrubby Old World composite which resembles a dwarf cypress; thyoides —like *Thuja,* a related genus)

It is also known as FALSE-CYPRESS, JUNIPER, SOUTHERN WHITE CEDAR, SWAMP CEDAR and WHITE CEDAR.

This tree, native to the Atlantic Seaboard from Maine to northern Florida, reaches a height of 60 to 80 ft., with diameters up to 3 ft. It grows along small streams and the edge of fresh-water swamps and has a gray to light reddish-brown bark, smooth but in loose platelike scales which peel off easily into long strips.

Because of its durability, it serves well for fences, poles, shingles, etc. It is a wood in great demand for boat work and canoe construction because of its light weight, uniform texture and close grain. Also, it is a good wood for craftsmen to use and is excellent for making many novelties.

CEDAR, EASTERN RED *Juniperus virginiana* (Juniperus—ancient Latin name; virginiana—of Virginia)

Middle Tennessee has produced

more red cedar than any other part of the United States, but the bulk of production has been confined to a few counties which produce a higher class and more aromatic variety of wood than found elsewhere.

This widely distributed tree is called red cedar in most states. It grows slowly and thrives in almost any soil and situation, except deep swamps, and the trees often stand wide apart or solitary, yet in some states they grow in almost impenetrable thickets, particularly in Texas and the southern states. This cedar is red in color and the thin sapwood is nearly white. The grain is very fine and even except for occasional knots.

There is little trouble experienced with warping or shrinkage, and the heartwood is considered as durable as any other American wood. It has a delicate, agreeable fragrance. This odor is disagreeable to insects and for this reason chests and closets of cedar are highly appreciated as storage places for garments which are subject to the ravages of the moth and buffalo bugs.

Tests have proven that red cedar is 80 per cent as strong as white oak. The wood is easily worked. Although the most general use at the present time is for lead pencils, few people who sharpen one and smell the fragrant wood stop to wonder where it comes from.

Cedar was long used as one of the best woods for skiffs and other light boats and it was occasionally employed in shipbuilding for the upper parts of vessels. A little of it is still used for trim and finish, particularly for canoes, motorboats and yachts. Early chest makers selected clear lumber because it could be had and was considered to be better, but modern chest manufacturers cannot obtain sufficient clear stock and make the best of necessity by using boards filled with knots. The wood is finished with oils, the natural color remains, and the knots give chests a pleasing rustic effect.

An extract from the fruit and leaves is used in medicine, and oil of red cedar, distilled from the wood, is used in making perfume. To the taste, this cedar is sweet.

Aromatic eastern red cedar

CEDAR, PORT-ORFORD *Chamaecyparis lawsoniana* (Chamaecyparis—from the Greek name of ground-cypress, a dwarf shrubby member of the sunflower family which resembles a dwarf cypress; lawsoniana—after Peter Lawson and Sons, nurserymen of Edinburgh, who introduced this species into cultivation)

Locally this wood is called Lawson's Cypress and is also known as Oregon Cedar and Ginger Pine as the wood has a pungent gingerlike odor and, when freshly cut, a spicy, bitter taste.

This beautiful evergreen tree is found on the western slopes of the Pacific Coast from Coos Bay in Oregon southward to Humboldt County, in elevations up to 5,000 ft. The tree has a long clear trunk 80 to 100 ft. high before any branches appear, and it runs in diameter from 22 in. to 12 ft. and in height up to 200 ft.

Port-Orford cedar is a pale yellowish-white to yellowish-brown color. The wood is of fine even grain and light in weight. It is particularly durable.

This wood is one of the favorites for archers, being used for arrows, and it is also used in venetian blinds, boat construction and for furniture. It has long been the best wood for storage-battery separators.

CEDAR, SPANISH *Cedrela mexicana* (Cedrela—a cedar; mexicana —from Mexico)

This wood is also known as Brazilian Cedar, Cedro and Honduras Cedar.

It grows in every country south of the United States except Chile. The wood is light red in color, straight-grained and soft in texture; occasionally it is wavy and mottled. One of the principal uses of Spanish cedar is in the manufacture of cigar boxes. It is also used in boat building and pattern making, and for lead pencils and furniture.

CEDAR, WESTERN RED *Thuja plicata* (Thuja—from the Greek *thuia,* an aromatic wood highly prized in ancient times for choice, durable furniture and probably a

Western red cedar—a typical stand, bark and needles

GLEWOOD and STINKING CEDAR.

It grows all the way from southern Alaska to northern California and eastward to Montana and Idaho. It flourishes in moist soil and grows from sea level up to high altitudes in the Rocky Mountains. It is a slow-growing tree, large and long-limbed, reaching heights up to 200 ft. and diameters up to 14 and 16 ft.

Western red cedar is a dull red in color, but loses most of its reddishness upon exposure to the air. It has a distinctive odor although different in nature and degree from the characteristic pleasant odor of eastern red cedar. The wood is straight-grained, fairly coarse in texture, without any pitch, but it is easily worked with tools and takes a good finish.

The greater part of this species of cedar is used for shingles and miscellaneous millwork, boat building, etc.

———————

CEIBA *Ceiba pentandra* (Ceiba—a native name; pent/andra—five stamens)

This tree, originating in west Africa and Mexico, is also known under the names of KOPAK, ODOUM and SILK COTTON TREE.

The wood is a reddish-gray color,

juniper; plicata—folded, probably a reference to the scalelike leaves)

This tree is also known as CANOE CEDAR, GIANT ARBOR VITAE, IDAHO CEDAR, PACIFIC RED CEDAR, SHIN-

207

sometimes with yellowish or grayish streaks and is very absorbent, coarse-textured and soft when green but brittle when dry. In the lumber form it is used for tables, plates, trays and simple furniture.

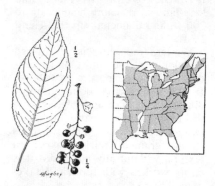

CHERRY, BLACK *Prunus serotina* (Prunus—Persian, or an old name for peach; serotina—late, probably referring to the late-maturing fruit)

This cherry is also known as CHOKE CHERRY, RUM CHERRY, WHISKEY CHERRY and WILD CHERRY.

It grows generally through the eastern part of the United States, the largest supplies being located in the Appalachian Mountains in New York, Pennsylvania and West Virginia. Black cherry is usually easily distinguished from other native species because of its distinctive color, the bark being dark with irregular scales which peel off easily, and with light to dark reddish-brown heartwood.

This wood is comparatively free from checking and warping; it stays in place well after seasoning, but has a moderately large amount of shrinkage during seasoning. It is a fairly heavy wood, averaging around 35 lbs. per cubic foot, moderately hard, stiff and strong.

The fruit of this tree is about the size of a pea and the purple, juicy colored pulp surrounding the seed has a bitter taste, but is edible and used principally to flavor jelly and beverages, especially in the making of rum cherry, cherry cider and a

Flat-cut cherry, cross figure

A stand of unusually large black cherry trees growing in North Carolina

Sliced American cherry, two-piece match

drink called cherry bounce. This is the reason why some of the common names mentioned above were given to this wood.

The wood is used for carving and works fairly well with all types of hand tools. Large amounts are used for backing blocks on which engravings and electrotype plates, used in printing, are mounted. In the cabinetmaking trade this wood has also been called New England mahogany. Choice logs are cut into veneers for furniture, cabinetmaking and musical instrument work.

CHESTNUT, AMERICAN *Castanea dentata* (Castanea—the classical Greek and Latin name; dentata —toothed, referring to the leaf margin)

This tree grows throughout the eastern part of our country and westward into Michigan and Illi-

nois. It is generally a broad tree with short trunk and large, overhanging branches. (Longfellow referred to this when he wrote: "Under the spreading Chestnut tree the village blacksmith stood.")

American chestnut is well known for the delicious nuts it produces. They have long been a delicacy, but are becoming harder to obtain each year. In addition to the nuts,

210

the bark from this tree has been a valuable product, being the principal supply of the tannin used in the leather industry. However, a fungus disease, known as chestnut blight, has almost entirely exterminated these trees, and no control for this disease has yet been found. Small insects eat the tree after it has been killed by the blight and then the lumber is sold as "wormy chestnut." Furniture, picture-frame moldings and other articles are made today from wormy chestnut.

CHINABERRY *Melia azedarach* (Melia—a classical Greek name for the ash tree; azedarach—from the Persian, meaning noble tree)

This tree, emanating from China and India, is also known as CHINA-TREE, CHINESE UMBRELLA TREE, INDIANA SOAP PLANT, SOAP BERRY and the TEXAS UMBRELLA TREE.

The chinaberry, so named because it originates in China, has long been used in that country as an ornamental tree. The wood, which is light reddish-tan with tints of yellow, while attractive in appearance, has little value as lumber, but it may be worked easily with tools and takes a good finish, making it suitable for use where obtainable.

COCOBOLO *Dalbergia* spp. (Dalbergia—after N. Dalberg, 1735-1820, a Swedish physician)

This wood comes from Nicaragua and western Costa Rica and has an average weight of 62 to 76 lbs. per cubic foot. The color of the heartwood varies greatly from light to deep red and the hues of the rainbow, and the grain runs fairly straight to interwoven.

Cocobolo is of high durability, but the wood is unsuited for gluing. If the smooth surface is rubbed with a cloth it will acquire a waxy finish without the use of any oil, wax, shellac or filler. Lengthy immersions in soapy water has little effect on the wood except for a slight darkening in color.

When working with cocobolo, care must be taken to protect oneself from the fine dust as it will produce a poisoning similar to ivy poisoning. It can become very painful. When affected, a person usually has to remain away from work for a week and then may never again be able to be in a room where there is any cocobolo dust.

This wood is used principally in the cutlery trade for knife and tool handles of all kinds. It is also used for scientific instruments, brush backs, steering wheels for boats, canes, chessmen, buttons, forks and spoons. Occasionally highly figured logs have been cut into veneers, but the supply is limited.

211

CORDIA *Cordia fragrantissima*
(Cordia—after Valerius Cordus, 1515-1544; fragrantissima — very aromatic)

This wood, native to Burma but growing occasionally in other parts of the East Indies, is also known under the name of KALAMET.

Cordia has a reddish-brown color, sometimes intermixed with darker streaks and beautiful mottled markings. When cut on the quarter, it produces a silver grain like our American sycamore. The wood seasons without difficulty and is of moderate weight and hardness.

Principally, this wood is of value because of its unusual fragrance. Like all odors in woods, however, it is strongest when first cut and as it dries out and becomes older the scent gradually disappears.

Only small quantities of cordia have been used so far in the lumber form. It can be worked with both hand and power tools.

CORK OAK TREE *Quercus suber*

This evergreen oak, growing in southern Europe and along the north African coast but principally cultivated in Spain and Portugal, provides the world with its supply of cork for forming bungs and bottle stoppers. Its lightness, combined with strength, is particularly suitable for life buoys, belts and jackets. On account of its lightness, softness and nonconducting properties, it is also used for hat linings and soles of shoes. Chips and cuttings are ground up and combined with linseed oil, gums, rubber and other materials to form floor coverings. Cork is also used in making artificial limbs.

The tree reaches a height of 30 ft. and the outer layer of bark, by annual additions from within, gradually becomes a thick, soft homogenous mass possessing the compressible and elastic properties upon which the economic value of cork depends. The first stripping of the cork takes place when the trees are from 15 to 20 years old. Subsequently, the bark is removed every 8 or 10 years during the months of July and August. The tree continues to live and thrive under the operation for 150 years and upwards, the quality of the cork improving with each period. The quality of the first stripping is very poor and is suitable only for a tanning substance or for forming rustic work in ferneries, conservatories, etc. The second stripping, still coarse, is suitable for making floats for nets and similar work.

There are other trees growing in different parts of the world which are known as cork wood but do not produce cork like *Quercus suber. Anona glabra,* a tree with a buttressed base which grows in southern Florida and the West Indies, is sometimes used locally, particularly the roots, as a substitute for cork in floats for fishing nets, stoppers of bottles and the like. It is also known as the ALLIGATOR APPLE, MONKEY APPLE, POND APPLE and BOBWOOD. *Ochroma lagopus,* the source of balsa wood, is sometimes called cork wood. *Pterocarpus officinalis,* growing in Jamaica, southern Mexico, throughout Central America and northern South America, is known in Venezuela as cork wood.

The wood *Leitneria floridana*—a small tree growing in the swamps of Florida, Georgia and Texas—has cork wood as its only common

The bark of cork trees being harvested in Spain

name. The wood is very light and brittle but has no commercial value because of its size and scarcity.

COTTONWOOD, EASTERN *Populus deltoides* (Populus—ancient Latin name; deltoides—triangular in reference to the leaf shape)

This tree is also known under several names as: ASPEN COTTONWOOD, CAROLINA POPLAR, RIVER POPLAR, WATER POPLAR, YELLOW COTTONWOOD.

The tree grows to a height of 100 ft. or more, with a diameter from 5 to 8 ft. It is at its best in moist soil, along the banks of rivers or edges of swamps. It has a wide distribution in this country and to the early pioneers in the midwestern plains the trees proved invaluable for shade and timber, and the leaves helped to feed the livestock. The bright green, broad leaves have a feathery appearance and flutter in the breeze like the quaking aspen. This is the state tree of Kansas.

The wood of this tree is very similar in texture and appearance to that of the other eight or ten species of this family. The tree was named from the cottony fluff that is attached to the seeds.

The color of the wood is creamy white, and the heartwood is white to light brown. It has a smooth, even texture and is slightly lustrous in appearance. Difficulty is experienced in seasoning cottonwood due to the large amount of warpage, but it is easily worked with tools and is a favorite wood for manufacturing boxes and packing crates because it takes the stencil ink so well. It is also used largely for rough carpentry work, excelsior, firewood, pulpwood and low-priced commercial veneers.

COURBARIL *Hymenaea courbaril* (Hymenaea—membrane; courbaril—the native name)

In the West Indies it is often referred to as STINKING TOE, in British Guiana it is known as LOCUST, and in South America under such names as ALGARROBO, GUAPINOL and JATOBA.

This tree grows in the West Indies and in South America, up to 100 ft. in height and 3 to 4 ft. in diameter. It is strong and hard, averaging around 60 lbs. per cubic foot. While the sapwood is often white in color, the heartwood is a reddish-brown to brown with pronounced darker stripes. The bark is fairly heavy and contains an

214

orange or yellowish gum which in fossilized form is sometimes dug up on sites which probably contained trees of this species. This gum is used in the manufacture of special types of varnishes and cements. Like our paper-bark birch, this bark may be stripped off in large sheets; it likewise is used in the construction of canoes.

Courbaril has a characteristic of woods in the family of Leguminosae; when the wood is planed it seems to glow from within. It turns well in the lathe but is difficult to work with tools. Generally, it is used for large construction work as in shipbuilding and general types of carpentry.

CRAB APPLE *Malus pumila*

It is known as CRAB, CRAB TREE and GARLAND TREE.

This tree is native to Southeastern Europe and Central Asia, usually growing wild individually, and it has become naturalized in the northeastern part of North America. It is a small tree, 20 to 30 ft. in height and 10 to 12 in. in diameter. The wood is hard, heavy, pinkish to grayish-brown in color, somewhat like the appearance of pearwood but with more color variation, and heavier and harder.

It is a fairly difficult wood to work with, has a dulling effect on tools, but is unusually fine for turning and for carving because of the even texture. It holds its place well when manufactured. Formerly it was one of the most popular woods for handles of handsaws and it is also used for the heads of wooden mallets.

The tart red fruit, called crab apples, are used for making preserves and jellies.

CRAMANTEE *Guarea excelsa*
(Guarea—from guara, a native West Indian name; excelsa—tall or elevated)

Growing in British Honduras, this wood is very similar to the scented Guarea of west Africa and the alligator wood of Jamaica even though separated by several thousand miles. It grows to a height of 100 ft. or more, with good-sized diameters, and weighs about 35 lbs. per cubic foot.

The heartwood is very similar in appearance to a pale-colored mahogany, but the grain is coarser in texture. The tree also bears white, scented flowers.

If seasoning is slow, no difficulties are encountered. The wood has good strength and other properties, comparable to its weight. Satisfactory logs are produced for sawing or for manufacturing into veneers. If the wood is turned, considerable sanding is necessary to insure a good surface, but it may be worked with tools as desired.

CUMBARÚ *Amburana cearensis*
(Amburana—a native name; cearensis—after a state, Ceara, in Brazil)

This wood, growing in Brazil, is also known under the names of AMBURANA, ROBLE and TREBOL.

The wood is light in weight, around 35 lbs. per cubic foot, light brown or a yellowish tinge in color, and of coarse texture. Great value is placed on the seeds of this tree; they have a very lovely scent and are used in perfuming toilet soaps and snuff. The resin of the bark contains a fragrant oil used in medicine, and the wood contains the same pleasant scent, which is

Top, a crabapple tree in full bloom. Bottom, chestnut tree in blossom

Top, cottonwood trees on the Navajo Reservation in Arizona.
Bottom, American elm

more noticeable when the wood is freshly cut.

This wood takes a very smooth finish and stays in place. Generally, the wood is used in northeastern Brazil for construction like crating and carpentry and it is often used in the manufacture of furniture in Argentina.

DAHOMA *Piptadenia africana* (Pipt—to fall; adenia—a gland or the genus *adenia* (?); africana—of Africa)

It is also known under the names of ATUI, BANZU, DAB'EMA, EKHIMI, MUSESE, MPEWERE, SINGA, TOM and TOUM.

This is a large tree of 110 ft. or more in height and grows throughout all of west Africa. It is a straight-grained wood, of fairly coarse and woolly texture. The heartwood ranges in color from grayish-brown to a warm golden-brown color. The texture is uniform, however, and the wood weighs around 38 lbs. per cubic foot.

Dahoma is a very difficult wood to kiln-dry because it tends to collapse and distort, and there is a large shrinkage. Until the wood has been dried, it has a very disagreeable odor; when freshly cut,

it has the unpleasant smell of ammonia and the sawdust is irritating to the eyes. Also, when the wood is dry, it may cause irritation and sneezing spells while one is working with it.

The strength value of this wood is good, resembling that of iroko; it has somewhat the appearance of iroko and has been used as a substitute when iroko was scarce. It is reported to be taking the place of that timber on the Gold Coast. The wood is very durable and resistant to termites.

Dahoma works well but has a dulling effect on tools. While small quantities have been exported, it has not met with too much favor due to the irritation caused when working with it and the offensive odor.

DANTA *Cistanthera papaverifera* (Cist—a box; anthera—anthers; papaver/ifera—poppy bearing)

This small tree from the Gold Coast and Nigeria is also known under the names of APRU, EPRO, KOTIBÉ, OLBORBORA, OTUTU, OVOUÉ and TSANYA.

The average diameter of the exported logs is from 18 to 30 in. and the weight per cubic foot is 46 lbs. The wood is reddish-brown in color, even textured and generally has a narrow stripe when cut on the quarter. When cut in this fashion it very much resembles sapele. The grain is typically interlocked and this produces the ribbon figure. Danta seasons fairly well but has a tendency to warp, and care must be taken to avoid over-rapid drying.

It is a wood that is used generally where extreme strength is required. In Europe it has a large use, similar to our American birch, for handles of tools. When the

218

surface is planed, it has somewhat of a greasy feel. This wood works well with most tools but has a tendency to pick up on quarter-sawn material. However, it turns excellently, takes a good finish and polishes well.

DINUANG *Octomelis sumatranus* (Octo/melis—light apple trees; sumatranus—of Sumatra)

This tree is also known under other names such as BILUAN, DANUANG, and DINONANG.

Dinuang grows in the moist lands and banks of rivers in the Philippines, Borneo and Sumatra where there are forests composed entirely of this species of tree. It is a large tree with a height at times of 70 ft. or more and diameters of 30 in. and up. However, it is a very lightweight wood, averaging 25 lbs. per cubic foot. While there is a large amount of sapwood, it is hardly different in appearance from the heartwood. The wood has little figure or grain, is reddish-brown in color, and the nearer the center of the tree, the darker the wood is.

There is no problem in seasoning this wood and it works easily with power or hand tools. At times this has been included in shipments of white lauan from the Philippines, but it is inferior in strength and texture. The wood has no special uses. In a general utility way it is suitable for the same purposes as other light hardwoods.

DOGWOOD, FLOWERING *Cornus florida* (Cornus—the Latin name of *Cornus mas,* the cornelian cherry dogwood of Europe, from the word horn, referring to the hardness of the wood; florida—flowering)

This tree is also known as ARROW WOOD, CORNEL, CORNELIAN and FALSE BOXWOOD.

The tree is small, between 30 and 40 ft. high, and 12 to 18 in. in diameter and is generally found at its best in the rich soils along the banks of streams in the eastern part of the United States from New York to Florida and westward to Michigan. Dogwood is the state tree of Missouri and Virginia and is also native to Texas.

Of the 20 or more species of dogwood in the United States, nine of which are trees and the rest flowering shrubs, the *Cornus florida* is the most beautiful of them all. It has a yellowish-brown color, a cubic weight per foot of 50 lbs., and when the tree flowers bloom, it is perhaps the most beautiful sight in the botanical world.

Early colonists prepared a medicine from the bark of this tree for the treatment of malaria. While this is not used today, some of the essence of dogwood is still used in parts of the south, in whiskey taken as a home remedy.

Dogwood is used for making shuttle blocks, golf-club heads, wood engravings and charcoal for gunpowder.

219

Top, dogwood blossoms. Bottom, flowering dogwood

DURIAN, WILD *Cullenia excelsa*
(Cullenia—probably after Cullen;
excelsa—high)

This wood, native to the island
of Ceylon, is also occasionally
found in southern India, where it
is known under the name of KATU-
BODA.

It is a medium weight wood,
averaging around 40 lbs. per cubic
foot, mostly straight-grained, and
an attractive pinkish-gray and reddish-brown in color. An interesting
feature about this tree is that it
bears annually large prickly fruits,
up to 6 in. in diameter, but these
are not edible.

After logging, this timber has to
be removed from the forest and
converted quickly, otherwise it
stains and then decay sets in. However, it dries without trouble and
is an easy wood to work with.

Little of this has been used outside of the country it grows in.
Small quantities of veneers have
been manufactured, but it is generally used for all-around purposes
in carpentry, partitions in buildings,
furniture backings, etc.

EBONY *Diospyros* spp. (Diospyros
—fruit of the gods)

The woods of this genus, belonging to the family of Ebenaceae,
are widely distributed throughout
the tropical and mild temperate
regions of the world and consist
of about 300 species of shrubs and
trees.

Ebony was amongst the articles
of merchandise brought to Tyre as
described in Ezekiel 27:15, and
Herodotus states that the Ethiopi-
ans every three years sent a tribute
of 200 logs of this wood to Persia.
It was employed by the kings of
India for sceptres and images, also
on account of its supposed antag-
onism to poison for drinking cups.

The best kinds are very heavy,
deep black, and consist of heartwood only. On account of its color,
durability, hardness and susceptibility of polish, ebony is much used
in cabinetwork, inlaying, turned
articles and piano keys of top-
grade instruments.

The most important varieties of
ebony originate in the East Indies
and in Ceylon, the best of the
species being the *Diospyros ebenum*

Macassar ebony, flat-cut

221

Quarter-sliced Macassar ebony, four-piece match

which grows in abundance in the flat country west of Trincomalee in Ceylon. This tree is easily distinguished by the smallness of its trunk, its jet-black charred-looking bark, beneath which the sapwood is perfectly white until the heartwood is reached. This wood is believed to excel all other varieties for the fineness and intensity of its dark color. However, a large percentage of the East Indian ebony is produced by the species of *Diospyros melanoxylon*, a large tree obtaining the height of 60 to 80 ft. and 8 to 10 ft. in circumference. These logs are streaked with yellow or yellowish-brown and are sometimes known as golden ebony or Macassar ebony. They are manufactured into veneers, sliced across the heart and on the quarter to produce fine, pronounced stripes.

The ebonies in Africa are available in the form of short logs or billets, with diameters of from 2 to 12 in. and lengths of 2 ft. and longer. The weight of ebony varies from 45 to 70 lbs. per cubic foot.

Of the American species of *Diospyros,* the largest and only one of commercial importance is the common persimmon, which is described under that name later on in this book.

Because of its extreme hardness and the dulling effect on tools, ebony is difficult to work though it finishes smoothly and produces a high polish.

Locally, some of the light-colored sapwood is used in the manufacture of tool handles. In the solid form ebony is used for turning and carving and in the veneer form for inlay work.

EKKI *Lophira alata* (Lophira—helmet tufted; alata—winged)

This wood is also known as AKOURA, AZOBE, BONGOSSI, HENDUI, KAKU and RED IRONWOOD.

It grows along the west coast of Africa and is a very heavy wood, weighing 65 lbs. per cubic foot. The tree is large and produces logs up to 55 in. in diameter.

222

Ekki has a deep, chocolate-brown color, sometimes turning to a dark red, and has a prominence of white defects in the pores. The wood is used when great strength is required, as in flooring, where the wood is subject to a good deal of wear. It is extremely difficult to season, however, because of the tendency to warp and split. Ekki is very resistant to decay and, as far as is known, is the most durable wood in west Africa, exceeding oak and teak as far as strength is concerned.

This timber is hard to work with hand tools, but can be worked by machine with less trouble. It holds its shape well when manufactured and a good finish can be obtained.

ELM, AMERICAN *Ulmus americana* (Ulmus—the classical Latin name; americana—from America)

This elm grows throughout the eastern United States, except in the Appalachian highlands and southern Florida.

It is a moderately hard and heavy wood, averaging 35 lbs. to the cubic foot and reaching a height of 100 ft. or more and a diameter of from 3 to 6 ft. It is the state tree of Massachusetts, Nebraska and North Dakota.

There are approximately 18 elm

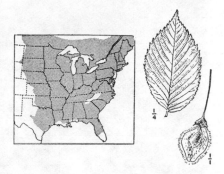

species known throughout the world, six of them native to the United States. Out of the six, the American elm is the handsomest and largest. It is not unusual for this tree to obtain an age of 200 years. It grows in rich, moist lands along streams and is one of the favorite trees supplying shade to lawns and streets. Unfortunately, the Dutch elm disease has wrought

Quarter-sliced American elm

223

Flat-sliced American brown elm

tremendous loss to our elm-shaded parkways and avenues.

The heartwood of this elm is brown to dark brown in color, sometimes containing shades of red. American elm, like the rock elm, has to be seasoned carefully to prevent warping.

Like all of the commercial elms, this wood has excellent bending qualities. However, there is a large shrinkage. A good part of the lumber is used principally for containers for furniture and dairy and poultry supplies. Because of its excellent bending qualities it is also used for barrels and kegs, and also for the bent parts of chairs. A smaller percentage of it is manufactured into veneers for plywood, used in the panel and cabinet trade, and sometimes it is sold under the name of prinz wood or apatalae. Some of this is used for furniture, quarter-sliced, and it is especially nice for decorative inlay work.

ELM, CARPATHIAN BURL *Ulmus procera* (procera—leader, chief or noble)

This elm is also known as ENGLISH ELM.

It grows in France, England and the Carpathian mountains, varies from an almost brick red to a light tan and has a beautiful medium to fine burl. However, defects of all kinds are found in almost every burl and a great deal of repair work is necessary before the burl can be used. This wood is used in fine cabinetry and decorative areas.

Importation of the logs has been banned in this country because of the elm disease. Only manufactured veneers are allowed to enter and these are quite rare and expensive.

ESSIA *Combretodendron africanum* (Combreto—from the genus *Combretum*; dendron—a tree; africanum—from Africa)

It is also known under various other names, as ABALE, BOSAKI, MINZU and WULO. This tree grows along the west coast of Africa from Sierra Leone to Ghana. In Ghana it is known as ESIA and OSA.

The tree is large in size, often reaching 130 ft. in height and about 30 in. in diameter. The wood is moderately heavy and hard, averaging around 35 lbs. per cubic foot, fairly straight-grained and coarse-textured. However, it is very attractive in appearance, the heartwood being pinkish-brown and mottled with reddish-brown shades. One can easily distinguish this wood as it is being logged in the forests or sawn in the mill as its most offensive odor can best be described as similar to that of rotten cabbage.

Care has to be taken in drying the wood and it is reported not to be very resistant to decay. The wood has a feeling of harshness to the touch. With careful attention, a good finish may be obtained.

Its principal use in Africa is in the manufacture of canoes, but in recent years small quantities have been exported to foreign markets.

FAUX ROSE *Dalbergia greveana* (Dalbergia—after N. Dalberg, 1735-1820, a Swedish physician; greveana—probably after a person)

This wood, from the island of Madagascar, is also known as FRENCH ROSEWOOD and MADAGASCAR ROSEWOOD.

Faux rose is pinkish-brown in color and has a striped figure when manufactured on the quarter. It is used in the manufacture of furniture and for decoration on musical instruments.

FIR, BALSAM *Abies balsamea* (Abies—the classical Latin name of the silver fir, *Abies alba*, of Europe; balsamea—ancient word for balsam tree, referring to the resin-

Carpathian elm burl, two-piece match

ous pockets or blisters in the bark).

This tree is also known under the name of CANADA BALSAM, EASTERN FIR and FIR-TREE. It grows throughout eastern Canada as far west as Alberta and through New England along the Appalachian Mountains as far south as Virginia. This could really be called the Christmas tree as it is one of the choicest—and the one most used—for Christmas trees throughout the country. The deep blue-green needles are shiny on the surface and light underneath, with blunt ends. They have a strong, lasting aromatic odor and large quantities are used for balsam pillows because of this pleasing scent and their softness. It is considered the best-shaped evergreen.

The resin obtained from this tree is an important factor in optical work, being used as a cement for the glass. Botanists also use it for mounting microscopic specimens.

Balsam fir is soft in texture, straight-grained, light in weight and cuts easily with tools. It is very useful in the manufacture of food containers since the wood is odorless and does not impart taste to the contents.

FIR, DOUGLAS *Pseudotsuga menziesii* (Pseudo/tsuga—false hemlock; menziesii—after Archibald Menzies, 1754-1842, Scotch physician and naturalist, who discovered it in 1791 at Nootka Sound on Vancouver Island)

This fir is also known under the names of DOUGLAS SPRUCE, FIR, YELLOW FIR, RED PINE, RED SPRUCE, RED FIR, OREGON PINE and others.

It grows only in the northwest from British Columbia and western Alberta throughout our northwest-

ern states, down as far as Arizona, New Mexico and a small portion of Texas. The tree grows to tremendous girth and height, one of the tallest being 415 ft., and a single record tree has produced over 70,000 board feet of high-grade lumber. This fir is one of the most important of our domestic commercial woods. It is estimated that over 490 billion feet remain growing, 75 per cent of this in the states of Oregon and Washington. Douglas fir has been made the official state tree of Oregon.

While the wood varies considerably, according to the particular part of the country it comes from, it is strong, medium hard and heavy. The wood is a yellowish and very light tan color. The bark is very thick, often 12", rich, reddish-brown and deeply fissured. This is a rapidly growing tree and its grain is attractive to many because of the large prominent growth rings seen when it is manufactured into rotary-cut veneers. This is the main wood for the manufacture of veneers used in plywood construction.

The wood is difficult to work with hand tools, but machines easily and glues well. It is a poor wood for painting and does not absorb preservatives.

226

Douglas fir

½

¼

FIR, GRAND *Abies grandis* (Abies
—the classical Latin name of the
European silver fir, *Abies alba;*
grandis—large)

It is also known under the name
of GIANT FIR, YELLOW FIR,
ROUGH-BARKED FIR and OREGON
WHITE FIR.

This tree is found exclusively
along the Pacific Coast, extending
from Vancouver well down into
California, and eastward into the
Rockies through Montana and
Idaho. It has been called a stately
tree because of its fine, straight
trunk, tapering to a narrow crown.
The tree needles are shiny, deep
yellow green on the top surface and
prominently white on the underside. The bark is of a brown color
with splashes of gray-white and is
deeply and closely furrowed.

As the wood is light in weight,
soft but firm and almost white in
color, with the absence of odor and
stain, the wood is highly desirable
for containers of all kinds, particularly food containers. The
main use, however, is for paper
pulp.

FUSTIC *Chlorophora tinctoria*
(Chloro/phora — greenish-yellow
yielding; tinctoria—useful as a dye)

The wood is called MORA in
Mexico and AMARILLO in Bolivia.

This tree grows in Central America and the West Indies, is a hard
and heavy wood weighing around
50 lbs. per cubic foot, and is

Stand of grand fir. Bark and needles

bright golden or greenish-yellow in color.

Fustic is a durable wood and does not warp. It saws and planes well and is used for mill rollers and occasionally in cabinetwork. One of the chief values of this wood is the yellow dye which it produces.

GABOON *Aucomea klaineana* (Aucomea—possibly after the native "okoumé"; klaineana—after Klaine, a collector in West Africa)

This tree is also known as ANGOUMA, GABOON WOOD, OKOUMÉ and ONGOUMI.

It is found only in the French Congo, Gaboon and Spanish Guiana. Gaboon grows to a large size and at times the diameter at the ground may run from 4 to 8 ft., but its growth is limited. It is light in weight, averaging 25 lbs. to the cubic foot, and closely resembles African mahogany, at times being given the name of mahogany.

This wood seasons easily with no tendency to damage, and in the solid form works well with both hand and machine tools. It takes a good finish and glues easily and this is why it is particularly desired for the manufacture of plywood.

GEDU NOHOR *Entandrophragma angolense* (Ent/andro/phragma—within the male membrane; angolense—from Angola)

This tree also goes under the names of ABENBEGNE, BUDONGO MAHOGANY, EDINAM, KALUNGI, TIAMA, TIMBI.

Botanically, it is a close relation to sapele with the exception that the color is darker in appearance and with a less pronounced stripe.

Like sapele, it is also a large tree and the average weight is 35 lbs. per cubic foot.

This wood seasons easily, but should never be used unless fully seasoned or it is liable to warp. It has good strength value for its weight, but is slightly inferior to African mahogany and sapele in this respect. It is easy to work with hand or machine tools and in all directions of the grain, taking an excellent polish if the grain is well filled.

It is used in veneering, general furniture and cabinetmaking work, and a considerable quantity is used in shipbuilding.

GONÇALO ALVES *Astronium fraxinifolium* (Astronium—star; fraxinifolium—with leaves like ash, *Fraxinus*)

This wood has been sold in this country under the name of BOSSONA, which was given to it by the late Albert Constantine, Sr.

Gonçalo alves is a wood with distinctive markings and belongs to the large group of over 400 species of trees and shrubs scattered throughout the world belonging to the sumach family.

This is a hard, heavy, close-grained wood which takes a glass-like finish, and craftsmen may obtain striking effects in using it for decorative purposes in combination with other woods. Another use of this is for the dampers in grand pianos.

GREENHEART *Ocotea rodiei* (Ocotea—a South American Indian plant name; rodiei—after

Rodie, a French physician)

Greenheart emanates from British Guiana and the West Indies and is a heavy, strong and hard wood, weighing approximately 65 lbs. per cubic foot. The color of this wood varies from light olive green to nearly black. As a rule, the logs are very straight of grain and unusually free of knots and defects. The sapwood is very thick, but it cannot be distinguished from the heartwood. The grain is fine, smooth and has a feel of coldness to the touch.

Greenheart is very strong and is a close second to teak in resisting the white ant. Occasionally worms may attack the sapwood, but they do not penetrate into the heartwood.

An interesting fact about this wood is that unusual care has to be taken when it is being sawn. Immediately after the saw has entered the log and air is admitted, the entire log may split apart with considerable noise. In one known instance, part of the log flew upwards, penetrating the roof of the sawmill. To prevent such accidents, it is customary to put a strong chain around the log immediately over the part that has passed the saw. These logs are usually long, from 20 to 60 ft., and are hewn square from 10 to 24 in.

Many people are susceptible to this wood. Those working with it must be very careful not to get any splinters, which will have a poisonous effect.

Most of this wood is used locally in the construction of docks, ships, flooring, piling, and for fishing rods. A fine sample of greenheart can be made into an exceedingly small top joint of a fishing rod which will bend to an unusual extent before breaking.

GUAMBO *Phoebe ambigens* (Phoebe—the Greek goddess of the moon, hence bright or radiant; ambi/gens—variable race)

This tree from Central America is very similar to the Brazilian imbuya. It is dark yellow-brown in color, lustrous, moderately heavy and so similar it may actually be the same wood. Also, the coarse texture and cross grain are very like imbuya.

GUANACASTE *Enterolobium cyclocarpum* (Entero/lobium—intestine lobe; cyclo/carpum—circle fruit, a reference to the twisted beanlike fruit)

This wood, emanating in Guatemala, British Honduras and Mexico, is also known as JENISERO, KELOBRA and PAROTA.

The color of the wood is brown with a greenish cast and sometimes streaked. It is of coarse texture and has a large figure with wavy lines. It is fairly scarce. Lumber is available, but generally it is manufactured into veneers on the quarter, producing some crotches and swirls. Guanacaste is used in furniture and cabinetmaking.

GUM, MURRAY RED *Eucalyptus camaldulensis* (Eu/calyptus—true cover; camaldulensis—probably after a place name, i.e. Camaldula)

This wood, from eastern Australia, is known also as LONG BEAK.

It is a heavy wood, about 52 lbs. per cubic foot, and renowned for its strength and resistance to fungus diseases. A great deal of it is used for wood paving.

GUM, SOUTHERN BLUE *Eucalyptus globulus* (globulus—globules)

Blue gum, growing in New South Wales, Tasmania and Victoria, has a life span of 300 years and at full maturity reaches a height up to 250 ft. with large diameters. It has been transplanted to other countries and one may see it as an ornamental tree in England, but it is very sensitive to cold weather and is apt to be killed in severe temperatures. The tree is named after the pale blue color of the bark, which is in no way reflected in the color of the wood. The heartwood is a lovely light pinkish color. It is a heavy wood, averaging between 48 and 52 lbs. per cubic foot.

Considerable care has to be taken in seasoning, otherwise a great amount of distortion and splitting will result in great waste. It is strong and unusually resistant to fire.

The usual run of these trees is not particularly attractive, but an occasional tree has a high fiddle-back figure which is prized for furniture and cabinetwork. The leaves of this tree, and also those of other species of the eucalyptus, contain a volatile oil which, after distillation, produces the oil of eucalyptus.

GUM, SPOTTED *Eucalyptus maculata* (maculata—spotted)

Spotted gum is one of the better-known trees growing along the coast of New South Wales and Queensland. The wood is a brown shade with tendencies to gray; the bark is whitish, smooth and mottled with various colored spots—perhaps the reason the tree is so named. It is coarse, somewhat like oak, and some of the lines have a particularly wavy figure which is sought after for use in paneling.

Though care is required in seasoning the wood properly, it works easily but has a tendency occasionally to dull the teeth of the saw. As it is figured and light in color, it is sometimes used as a substitute for satinwood, though it is not as good.

In Australia, spotted gum is probably employed in more varied types of work than any of the other eucalypt timbers. It is used in heavy construction, paneling of rooms and flooring, and is a favorite wood in the shipbuilding industry for framing, stem and sternposts and for planking beneath the water line. It is also often used for cabinet-making and the manufacture of furniture.

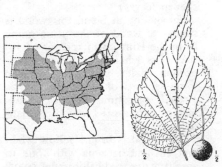

HACKBERRY *Celtis occidentalis* (Celtis—the classical Latin name of a species of lotus; occidentalis—western)

This tree is known under several different names, one of the most prominent being SUGARBERRY. It is also known as the BASTARD ELM, HACK TREE, HOOP ASH and NETTLETREE.

It grows from southern Canada

throughout the eastern part of the United States and is found in large quantities in the lower Mississippi Valley. For proper growth the tree requires large quantities of moisture and a rich soil. Outwardly, the tree is somewhat similar to that of elm in appearance, and it reaches a height of 25 to 45 ft.

The heartwood is light yellow; it is a fairly soft coarse-grained wood and works well with any type of tool. The lumber is generally sold along with ash and elm, and large quantities of it are used in the manufacture of farm implements. Hackberry takes a very fine finish and has an attractive appearance when finished in the natural color. Some of it is used in furniture and cabinetwork and for other general purposes similar to elm and ash.

HALDU *Adina cordifolia* (Adina —crowded; cordi/folia—heart-shaped leaves)

Emanating in Siam, this wood is similar to wood of the same name from the Himalayan regions of India. It is a heavy wood, averaging around 45 lbs. per cubic foot. In some sections of India the tree is girdled, some time previous to felling, to decrease its weight in handling.

The wood is bright yellow when first cut and darkens with time to an attractive reddish-brown color. It is straight-grained and in drying no difficulties are encountered, nor is there any trouble in working it with any type of tool.

Occasionally figured logs are found and these are used for cabinetwork and interior paneling.

HAREWOOD, ENGLISH *Acer pseudoplatanus* (Acer—the classical

Latin name for maple; pseudo/-platanus—false *Platanus,* the sycamore in U.S.A.)

This tree, sometimes referred to as SCOTCH PLANE, ENGLISH SYCAMORE or WEATHERED SYCAMORE, probably received the latter name because when the lumber seasons in the open it turns to a light brown color instead of remaining white.

This wood is not to be confused with the original harewood tree that grows in San Domingo and is known as Pino Matcho, which is yellowish and has a luster. The San Domingo wood is not used commercially and is practically extinct.

English harewood, or gray harewood as we now know it, is one of the products of the sycamores of western Europe and the British Isles. It is white in color, similar to our maple. When sold in this country in this form, it is known as English sycamore. In its natural form it is particularly desired for its lovely white color, and it is particularly adaptable for staining to any color desired. Outside of holly, this wood is the nearest to white that can be obtained.

When this wood is dyed a silver-gray color, it is sold under the common name of English gray harewood. It is interesting to note that while many people in this and other countries have attempted to secure the silver-gray color, only one firm located in London has been successful in obtaining the finest color and most permanent results. The logs are first cut into lumber or veneer and then placed in large vats where the dye is forced through the wood by hydraulic pressure. Generally it is used in the veneer form because of the high cost in lumber form.

The wood weighs approximately 37 to 42 lbs. per cubic foot and is

232

English gray harewood with fiddleback figure

a straight-grained timber which is easy to work, but difficulty is encountered when planing the highly figured logs. Particular care has to be given in the seasoning of the wood, not because of splitting or warping, but to prevent any staining or discoloration.

The wood is very much in demand for fine interiors and modernistic furniture, and the type of figure most desired is a strong fiddleback figure with straight grain.

for native hemlock; canadensis—of Canada)

Eastern hemlock ranges in size from 55 to 70 ft. though trees as high as 100 ft. have been recorded, with diameters of 2 to 4 ft.

The largest percentage of growth is in the northeastern states, but in the production of pulp, timber and tannin, Michigan now leads. It is also the state tree of Pennsylvania.

In Canada, eastern hemlock is the chief supply of material for their tanning industries. It supplies pulp for various types of paper and it is estimated that over 13 billion feet of eastern hemlock are still standing.

HEMLOCK, EASTERN *Tsuga canadensis* (Tsuga—Japanese name

HEMLOCK, WESTERN *Tsuga heterophylla* (hetero/phylla—various leaved)

It is also known as ALASKA PINE, HEMLOCK SPRUCE and PACIFIC HEMLOCK.

This is one of the important trees in the Northwest. It grows along the coastline from Alaska to central California and eastward

233

There are some 16 species and 20 varieties of hickory in North America, and the largest stands of true hickories are located in the lower Mississippi Valley region. True hickories include such trees as shagbark hickory, shellbark hickory, pignut hickory and mockernut hickory. Of these, the most important commercially is the shagbark *(Carya ovata)*. This species grows in the northeastern United

through Idaho and Montana at fairly low mountainous altitudes. Of the ten species of hemlock, this is the largest and reaches its greatest growth in the extreme northwestern portions of Oregon and Washington. It is the state tree of Washington. The most extensive growth is in Alaska, estimated as much as 63 billion board feet, and somewhere around twice this quantity in the United States.

Western hemlock differs from eastern hemlock inasmuch as the wood is of very fine texture, light in weight, straight in grain and about the same workability as pine. It has a thick bark, 1½ in., is dark reddish-brown and deeply marked. The needles are under an inch in length, flat, narrow, grooved and rounded on the end, like the eastern species. The small cones are twice the size of the eastern species.

Western hemlock is used for the making of quality paper, the largest output of the wood going into newsprint, and in the lumber form for all types of general manufacture. Practically all the commercial lumbering is confined to the states of Washington and Oregon.

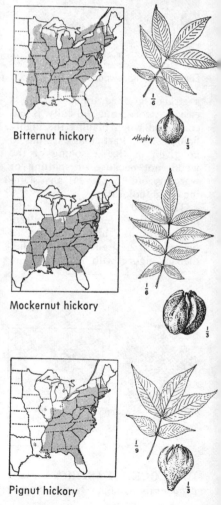

Bitternut hickory

Mockernut hickory

Pignut hickory

HICKORY *Carya ovata* (Carya—classical Greek for nut; ovata—egg-shaped, referring to the nut)

234

Upper left, eastern hemlock. Upper right, western hemlock.
Lower left, balsam fir. Lower right, hackberry tree

Shagbark hickory

Shellbark hickory

States to southwest Mexico. It is light cream in color, extremely tough and resilient though quite hard and unusually heavy. It is used in veneers, skis, molding and bent plywood which requires extreme strength.

The heartwood of the true hickory is brown to reddish-brown and the wood is very hard and heavy, averaging from 42 to 52 lbs. per cubic foot. Some woods are stronger than hickory and others are harder, but the combination of strength, toughness, hardness and stiffness possessed by hickory has not been found to the same degree in any commercial wood.

Hickory has a very large shrinkage and must be carefully dried to avoid checking, warping and other seasoning defects. Under magnification, the end grain shows numerous white lines paralleling the

growth ring. Nearly 80 per cent of the true hickory goes into tool handles, for which its qualities make it especially suitable. Other uses include agricultural implements, athletic goods and lawn furniture.

HINOKI *Chamaecyparis obtusa* (Chamaecyparis—from the Greek name for ground-cypress, a dwarf shrubby member of the sunflower family which resembles a dwarf cypress; obtusa—blunt)

This is one of the most highly prized woods in Japan and is one of the five royal trees which were reserved for imperial and religious uses in ancient times. The palaces of the Mikado as well as the temples are built of hinoki.

This wood is of a pale yellow straw color with wavy marks caused by intermittent darker streaks. It weighs approximately 22 to 25 lbs. per cubic foot, has a fragrant, agreeable scent and a lustrous sheen. Hinoki is used for the finest interior work and for buildings.

Hinoki also comes from Formosa, but this timber differs from the Japanese species, being of a bright yellow-brown, resembling somewhat the baldcypress of the United States, and is harder, heavier, and has a more marked grain than Japanese hinoki. Its strong, aromatic scent is not as pleasant as the Japanese wood.

HOLLY, AMERICAN *Ilex opaca* (Ilex—the classical Latin name of *Quercus ilex*, holly oak of Europe, which has holly-like leaves; opaca —dark, in reference to the dull green foliage)

About 175 species of holly are dispersed in various parts of the world, the largest number occurring

Easily recognizable trunk of shagbark hickory

½

½

in Guiana and Brazil. The largest trees are found in southern Arkansas and eastern Texas, while the holly growing in the New England states is always very small. Holly varies in size from small, straggly bushes to well-formed trees 50 or 60 ft. high and 2 to 3 ft. in diameter. It is the state tree of Delaware.

The wood of holly is white, light in weight and has almost a total absence of any figure, no matter which way the wood is worked. There is only a small quantity of holly cut into veneers and lumber each year. It has to be cut in the winter and manufactured before the hot weather, otherwise it discolors and then the pure white color is not obtained. It approaches ivory color more closely than any other American wood.

The principal value of holly is not in its wood but in the leaves and berries. The gathering of holly leaves and berries is an industry of much importance, and along the eastern coast of Maryland there are annually over 10,000 persons engaged in securing branches for manufacture into sprays and wreaths.

Our American holly, which is always thought of as a tree of decoration during the holidays, can be described as one that wears its decorations the year round. Its broad leaves, unlike our other native evergreens, with their needle-like leaves, always make an outstanding appearance.

The fruit of this tree is food for the wild turkey and other birds, as well as deer. The seeds are small, over 30,000 to a pound, and widely distributed through the forest by the birds. The seeds of holly are a long time in germinating and lie buried in the soil until the second year. Anyone who plants them without knowing this is apt to despair too soon. The trees are widely scattered and never found growing together.

The wood is employed for inlay work, is used on small musical instruments, as keys for pianos and organs, and brush-back manufacturers use it for their choicest brushes. Engravers also find it suitable for various classes of work. It is occasionally worked into small articles of furniture, but probably never is used on large pieces.

HOPHORNBEAM, EASTERN *Ostrya virginiana* (Ostrya—Latinized form of the Greek *ostrua*, a tree with very hard wood)

Growing in Indiana, this species was originally grown in Great Britain and continental Europe. It is also known as IRONWOOD in several states of this country and in Ontario.

It is yellowish-white in color, close-grained, hard, tough and strong, weighing about 51 lbs. per cubic foot. Engineers make use of this wood for cogs in machinery and agricultural implements.

HORNBEAM, EUROPEAN *Carpinus betulus* (Carpinus—classical Latin name; betulus—similar to

238

A fine example of the little-known American holly tree

birch, betula, in reference to the leaves)

It is also known as IRONWOOD.

This medium sized tree, from 40 to 65 ft. in height and with diameters averaging from 20 to 24 in., grows in Europe and Canada. The heartwood is white with an occasional yellow or greenish tinge. It is of fine, uniform texture, about the weight of oak and is considered one of the hardest woods growing in England. Because of the texture and hardness, it is considered superior to beech. At times in Europe it is stained black and used as a substitute for ebony in fancy articles and the backs of brushes.

Hornbeam is a very difficult wood to work, except when turned on the lathe, but when thoroughly dried it will take a fine finish. It is a favorite wood with manufacturers of wooden bench screws, tool handles and mallets, where great strength is required. Occasionally it is manufactured into veneers.

IDIGBO *Terminalia ivorensis* (Terminalia—border or terminus; ivorensis—from the Ivory Coast)

This is a large tree of 100 ft. or more in height and from 3 to 5 ft. in diameter, growing on the west coast of Africa—the Ivory Coast, Gold Coast and Nigeria. The heartwood is pale yellow with darker colored pores. It is of average weight, around 35 lbs. per cubic foot, and has a tendency to split badly in seasoning unless proper care is given. However, after seasoning it is a stable wood and easy to work with.

Logs have been cut into rotary veneer for the manufacture of plywood, and figured logs are sliced on the quarter to develop wood suitable for interior paneling.

IMBUYA *Phoebe porosa* (Phoebe—the Greek goddess of the moon, hence, bright; porosa—porous)

This wood is also known as BRAZILIAN WALNUT, CANELLA and IMBUIA.

This is a fairly fine-textured wood, growing in Brazil, and it weighs from 42 to 46 lbs. per cubic foot. The heartwood is yellowish or olive to chocolate brown, either plain or beautifully corrugated and figured.

When properly seasoned, the wood stays in place and is considered durable. Imbuya has a spicy, resinous scent and taste,

Imbuya, cross-fire figure, two-piece match

most of which is lost in drying. In sawing this timber, the fine dust which arises is particularly irritating to some and can cause sneezing spells.

In Sao Paulo in Brazil, imbuya is considered one of the most important woods and is used for high-grade flooring, furniture, interior trim and fixtures. It has a medium luster, is easy to work with and will take a high polish. However, the exports have not been too large as the local demand for the lumber has been about equal to the supply.

INDIAN SILVER GREY-WOOD
Terminalia bialata (Terminalia—border or terminus; bi/alata—two-winged, probably in reference to the fruit)

Originating in the Andaman Islands, this timber is sold in various wood markets of the world as DERDA, INDIA WALNUT, INDIAWOOD and IXORA.

An unusual feature of this tree is that it produces two different kinds of wood in color. One is of yellow straw color with variegated dark-colored streaks, which is generally marketed as white chuglam, and the other is considerably darker in color and is sold as Indian silver grey-wood. It is one of the largest trees growing in that area, 140 ft. or more in height, with a diameter of 3 ft.

The wood is medium heavy, averaging a little over 40 lbs. per cubic foot, has a medium texture, and is strong, although in working it there is a tendency to split. A large majority of the wood is manufactured into veneers, in which form this difficulty is not of importance. The wood takes a very high and lovely finish. It is employed in high-class cabinetmaking and decorative work.

IPÉ *Tabebuia avellanedae* (Tabebuia—after a native Brazilian plant name; avellanedae—drab)

This wood is often known as PAU D'ARCO.

Growing in the forests of Brazil, the tree presents a most beautiful appearance. It is one of the tallest trees of the Amazon region, reaching a height of 170 to 200 ft. The wood is plentiful throughout Brazil. The logs are available as long as 100 ft. and the weight per cubic foot is 70 lbs.

Ipé has a lustrous brown color, occasionally with a greenish tinge, resembling a dark greenheart but with a much closer and finer grain. Occasionally logs are highly figured with a small mottle and broken roe, and the veneers obtained from these logs are similar to a dark golden brown Ceylon satinwood. High-grade veneers are produced from these logs both in America and Europe.

IPIL *Intsia bijuga* (Intsia—a native name in Madagascar; bi/juga—two pairs, probably in reference to the leaflets)

In England it is known as BORNEO TEAK though it has none of the qualities of teak.

Ipil emanates in the Philippines. It is a heavy wood, averaging 61 lbs. per cubic foot, and hard—sometimes being considered one of the ironwoods. The color is a warm brown. With the passage of time and exposure, this color darkens to black.

IROKO *Chlorophora excelsa* (Chloro/phora—yellow-green bearing or yielding; excelsa—high or distinguished)

Iroko, originating on the west coast of Africa, is also known as

Striped iroko with mottle figure

AFRICAN or NIGERIAN TEAK (although in no way related to the teak family), MVULE, ODOUM, OROKO, IREME and FRAMERE.

The tree is large in size and it is not unusual to have logs up to 5 ft., but the average size is generally around 30 in. The color varies from a light brown to a rich golden brown. The wood is heavy, 40 lbs. to the cubic foot, not as strong as teak but often used as an alternative. The heartwood has unusual natural durability.

The wood is not difficult to work with and does not have the effect of dulling tools as quickly as when working with genuine teak, except when the logs have a defect known as "stone." When quartered, the wood looks somewhat like teak and is used for furniture and architectural panels.

IRONWOODS

OVER A PERIOD of many years, seldom a week or a month has passed in which some visitor to my office has not brought up, as one of the topics of conversation, the ironwood that grows in his particular state or country; also in letters there is often the mention of ironwood. This interest is confined not only to the United States but also is displayed by our overseas visitors and in correspondence from abroad.

From this personal experience we are led to believe that the common name of ironwood is not given by individuals to any single species of wood but is generally applied to whatever wood in any particular section of the country is considered the densest and the hardest—in the absence of any knowledge of what the wood actually is.

There are, in fact, over 80 distinct botanical species of wood which are listed in various parts of the world and referred to as ironwoods. In the alphabetic description of woods in this book, the following woods are referred to as ironwoods:

Billian
Hophornbeam, Eastern
Hornbeam, European
Ipil
Mesua
Pau d'Arco
Pau Ferro
Pyinkado
Quebracho

Other woods, referred to as ironwoods, have not been described in this text because of the lack of general interest. A few of them are: American hornbeam or blue beech referred to as ironwood in a few New England states; honey mesquite, known as ironwood in Texas; red ironwood in Queensland, also known as Cooktown ironwood; leguminous iron bark; and gangaw *(Mesuaferrea)*, which is native to India, Burma, Ceylon and the Andaman Islands, and also called locally Indian rose-chestnut and ironwood.

IVORY, PINK *Rhamnus zeyheri* (Rhamnus—the old Greek name; zeyheri—after Zeyheri)

This wood is often called rarer than diamonds and it is almost impossible to obtain. It is the royal wood of the Zulus and may be cut only by the chief of the tribe and his sons. When a chief's son is able to fell a tree and fashion a spear from the wood, he is considered to have reached manhood. Any other member of the tribe who cuts or possesses the wood is subject to death.

It is a medium sized tree, from 20 to 40 ft. high, with diameters from 7 to 12 in., growing very occasionally on rocky soils in Rhodesia, Transvaal and Natal.

The tree produces small black berries, in appearance resembling those on the buckthorn tree. The wood is extremely heavy and of very fine texture, though with little figure. The beauty of it lies in the lovely rich color.

This pink ivory works very easily, takes a fine polish, and is an excellent wood for special turnings. Very attractive pieces of jewelry can be fashioned by those few who have been fortunate enough to obtain a piece of this wood. Inasmuch as it is so scarce, it is more a museum piece than an article of commerce.

IVORYWOOD *Balfourodendron riedelianum* (Balfouro/dendron—Balfour's tree; riedelianum—after Riedel)

Ivorywood grows in Brazil and has a close, compact grain, displaying a smooth surface resembling ivory, which no doubt is the reason for its name. It weighs from 47 to 52 lbs. per cubic foot and is of a light yellow color with a greenish tinge. It is a rare wood, highly esteemed in Argentina, but commercially is not generally used.

JARRAH, CURLY *Eucalyptus marginata* (Eu/calyptus — true cover; marginata—enclosed with a border)

Curly jarrah grows in western Australia and is considered one of the most valuable native woods. It is found in greater profusion than practically any of the other important commercial trees. Diameters as large as 6 ft. are encountered, and heights of 120 ft. or more.

Fairly heavy—averaging around 50 lbs. per cubic foot—the wood is hard and often has a wavy grain. It is of a rich red color which darkens with exposure, resembling old American mahogany. A great deal of care is required in seasoning, since the wood is subject to a large amount of shrinkage and will check if not handled carefully. Where a large amount of curly figure is prominent, it produces some difficulties in working. It is used, however, for carving, furniture and interior work. Quantities of the curly logs are cut into veneers.

JELUTONG *Dyera costulata* (Dyera—after W. T. Thistleton Dyer, English botanist; costulata—with small ribs, probably in reference to the ribbed leaves)

Coming from Malaya, this tree often grows higher than 200 ft. and has a diameter of 5 and 6 ft. It is a fairly light wood, averaging about 30 lbs. per cubic foot, and of soft but firm texture. The wood is of a very plain appearance, off-white color when first manufactured, with no difference between the sapwood and heartwood, but after exposure to the air it has a yellowish tint.

The main value of this wood is in the latex, the greatest portion of which is used in the manufacture of chewing gum. Also, jělutong is used in the making of plywood boxes and cores for plywood. Little if any of the timber is exported.

JONGKONG *Dactylocladus stenostachys* (Dactylo/cladus — finger twig; steno/stachys—narrow spike, e.g. of grain)

Jongkong grows in Borneo, has a cubic weight per foot of about 33 lbs. and is pink in color. It is a particularly interesting wood as it has the same figure as our bird's-eye maple.

THE JUNIPERS

THE FOUR leading species of juniper trees are similar inasmuch as none of them produce any large quantities of usable lumber. The lumber is used for lead-pencil stocks, the making of novelties and, locally, for fence posts and fuel. The four junipers and their leading characteristics follow.

JUNIPER, ALLIGATOR *Juniperus deppeana* (Juniperus—the classical Latin name; deppeana—

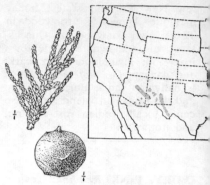

in honor of Ferdinand Deppe, d. 1861, German botanist)

This tree is also known under the name of CHECKERED-BARKED JUNIPER, MOUNTAIN CEDAR and OAK-BARKED CEDAR.

It is native to the deserts in southern New Mexico, Arizona and in southwestern Texas, growing in the higher mountainous elevations from 4,000 to 10,000 ft.

Alligator juniper has a short, large trunk from 2 to 4 ft. in diameter and is different from the other junipers. It has a dark, red-brown bark that varies from 1 to 3 in. thick and is marked in a checkered pattern, resembling alligator hide.

Local Indians use the dry berries to grind into a flour which is used in the preparation of cakes.

JUNIPER, CALIFORNIA *Juniperus californica* (californica—of California)

This wood is also known under the names of CEDAR, BERRIED-CEDAR, JUNIPER and WHITE CEDAR.

California juniper is close to the western juniper and at times it is almost impossible to distinguish it. However, this species is more of a broad, round-top shrub with heavy odd-shaped branches.

244

JUNIPER, ROCKY MOUNTAIN
Juniperus scopulorum (scopulorum —of rocky cliffs or crags)

This juniper is known also under the names of COLORADO JUNIPER, RED CEDAR, ROCKY MT. RED CEDAR and WESTERN JUNIPER.

It is found in the higher mountain regions of western Canada, southward to Oregon and Arizona. It is not quite as tall as the alligator juniper, ranging in height from 20 to 35 ft. It is one of the most desirable woods for use in the manufacture of novelties because of its beautiful color and the closeness of the grain.

JUNIPER, WESTERN *Juniperus occidentalis* (occidentalis—western)

This juniper is often known under the names of SIERRA JUNIPER, WESTERN RED CEDAR and YELLOW CEDAR.

It is native to the Pacific Coast through the states of Washington and Oregon. It grows on rocky soil and canyon sides, in elevations up to 10,000 ft. The berries of this tree mature in two years, are blue-black in color, small in size, about ¼" in diameter and have a tough skin. They have a strong, aromatic odor, sweet to the taste, and are appreciated by both the Indians and the birds.

KABUKALLI *Goupia glabra* (Goupia—after one of the native Guiana names, goupi; glabra—hairless, smooth)

In Brazil and British Guiana, where this wood grows, it is known as CUPIUBA and KABUKALLI, respectively.

It is a large tree, obtaining a height of from 100 to 130 ft., with a comparatively slender trunk (up to 3 ft. in diameter) and branches up to 60 ft. The wood is of a light reddish color which, when aged, loses some of its reddishness and turns more to a brown. When freshly cut, it has a very strong, penetrating odor which is noticeable for quite a distance. Both the odor and the disagreeable taste of the wood diminish with age, though the odor is never entirely absent from the dried wood.

Being a heavy wood, averaging around 50 lbs. per cubic foot, it is used in Brazil and British Guiana for naval construction and wooden buildings. The natives use it in the manufacture of canoes. Until recently, this wood was not exported in any large quantities for commercial use.

KATON *Sandoricum indicum* (Sandoricum—after a Malayan plant name; indicum—of India)

This tree grows in Thailand, where it is known as KAPON, and in Burma, where it is known as THITTO.

It is an evergreen, found in the forests, generally 60 ft. in height. The wood varies considerably in color, the sapwood ranging from a yellowish to a pink color and the heartwood from a grayish-brown to a red resembling mahogany. It is a fairly light wood, 30 to 40 lbs. per cubic foot, of medium texture and generally showing a well-defined stripe.

Katon seasons easily and works with little difficulty. It finishes smoothly and takes a high polish. In the East, where it grows, its main use is for boat building, but it is also a most suitable wood for cabinetwork and furniture making.

KAURI, FIJI *Agathis vitiensis* (Agathis—a ball of thread; vitiensis—from Fiji)

This wood grows in the Fiji Islands, where its native name is NDAKUA NAKANDRE.

It is found in the heavy rain forests on the islands of Vanua Levu and Vanikoro, preferring to grow on hillsides from 1,500 to 3,000 ft. above sea level, but it does grow in lower and higher altitudes than these. The wood can be classified as one of the more valuable of the softwoods. It has a pale yellowish sapwood with a heartwood slightly darker, and it is difficult to tell where one merges into the other. It is a close, even-textured wood of average hardness.

Kauri contains a valuable resin, in collecting which a great many trees of this species are ruined. A large rectangular piece of the bark is removed, some 2 to 3 ft. in size, and this area is warmed by a fire close to the trunk, below the scar, so as to hasten the flow of the resin. Because of this injury the tree frequently dies.

The wood is easy to work with and is used in the manufacture of furniture, high-class joinery work and boat building. It also makes good veneers.

KAURI, NEW ZEALAND *Agathis australis* (australis—southern)

This wood, found only in New Zealand, weighs from 30 to 39 lbs. per cubic foot and possesses lightness and elasticity. It has a pleasant and agreeable odor when worked and has been found to be more durable than pine, one of its uses being for the masts of boats.

KENTUCKY COFFEETREE *Gymnocladus dioicus* (Gymnocladus—naked branch; dioicus—male and female flowers on separate trees)

This tree is also known under a number of different names like AMERICAN COFFEEBEAN, CHICOT or "DEAD TREE," COFFEE NUT, KENTUCKY MAHOGANY, MAHOGANY BEAN and STUMP-TREE.

Kentucky coffeetree grows in western New York and as far west as South Dakota, Oklahoma and southward to Tennessee. The roasted seeds of this tree were long used by early settlers of the country as a substitute for coffee, which explains its name.

The tree is not very attractive. The wood is rather heavy and coarse-grained with the color varying from a light brown to a reddish-brown. It blooms late in the spring and the leaves are the first to drop off in the fall, which is the reason for the name chicot. It is a durable wood and used a great deal for railroad ties and fence posts.

KINGWOOD *Dalbergia cearensis* (Dalbergia—after N. Dalberg, 1735-1820, Swedish physician; cearensis—of Ceara, a state of Brazil)

Emanating in South America,

Upper left, western juniper. Upper right, Kentucky coffeetree. Lower left, Rocky Mountain juniper. Lower right, kauri tree. Note its size in comparison to the three men

Kingwood

this small tree is also known as
VIOLETE.

It weighs about 75 lbs. per cubic
foot and is exported in the form of
logs from 3 to 6 ft. long in diameters from 4 to 8 in., with the sapwood removed.

Kingwood is of a rich, violet-
brown color, shading at times almost to black, and streaked with
varying lighter and darker lines of
golden yellow. It has a bright luster, a fine, uniform texture, very
smooth surface, and stays in place
with little expansion. An unusually
high polish can be obtained. While
this is a beautiful cabinet wood
when first used, it becomes more
so as it is toned with age, the wood
seeming to have a transparent surface and metallic sheen. Examples
of this fine wood can be seen in
furniture of French manufacture.
It is well named, for it is truly the
wood of kings.

It is generally manufactured into
veneers by cutting it across the
heart and used in the manufacture
of fine marquetry work and occasionally in lumber form for articles
of turnery. However, the exporta-
tion of the wood is very limited,
and it is a wood that is quite scarce
in the general market. When available, it is generally in the veneer
form.

KOA *Acacia koa* (Acacia—the
classical Greek name of a thorny
Egyptian tree; koa—the native
name)

Emanating only in the Hawaiian
Islands, koa grows from sea level
and moist soil to the top of vol-
canic mountains. It is from these
high exposed places that the best
figured wood is obtained.

Some of the early history of this
wood in its native country can be
seen in the naming of this tree,
which in Hawaiian is known as
koa-ka—koa meaning soldier, bold
and valiant, ka meaning irregular
in habit. Probably the first part of
the name originated from the fact
that in very early times the Ha-
waiians, renowned for their sea-
faring abilities, used these large
trees for making dugout canoes in
which they made sea trips of great
distances. Ka doubtless comes
from the fact that this tree can
adapt itself to a wide variety of

248

Koa, fiddleback figure

climates and soil conditions.

Koa wood is excellent for musical instruments as it has high resonant qualities. The world-famous Hawaiian ukeleles are always made of koa wood. Also, because of the fiddleback figure and the fine finish it takes, it is an ideal wood, particularly in the veneer form, for use in making fine furniture.

KOKKO *Albizzia lebbeck* (Albizzia, after Filippo del Albizzia, 18th century Italian naturalist; lebbeck —the Arabic common name)

Kokko is common throughout Ceylon and in the Andaman Islands, and in the latter country is the principal wood used in the workshops of the convicts. The wood is a deep brown with a stripe effect and unusually large pores. Kokko, or coco, as it is also known, has not been used in this country in any large quantities, in comparison with other fancy woods.

KUROKAI *Protium decandrum* (Protium—after the sea god Proteus; dec/andrum—ten stamens)

It is also known as the INCENSE TREE.

This species of wood is found throughout the dense forests of British Guiana and also in forests along the Amazon River, and grows with a long, slender trunk often as high as 50 ft., the total height of the tree at times being 90 ft., with an average diameter of 20 in. The heartwood is pinkish-brown in color with variegated darker lines at irregular intervals. It is a moderately hard wood though fairly light, weighing about 35 lbs. per cubic foot.

The wood requires care during the drying period in order to avoid defects, but it works well after being dried.

Considerable quantities of odorous, pale-colored resin or balsam is found in the bark, and this the natives use in medicines and in producing incense, hence the name incense tree.

The wood from British Guiana is similar to the lighter grades of crabwood with the exception that the surface is brighter in color. Locally it is used for the manufacture of furniture and is quite satisfactory, taking a good polish after a careful filling of the pores.

LACEWOOD *Cardwellia sublimis* (Cardwellia—after Cardwell; sublimis—uplifted, exalted)

Lacewood, growing throughout Australia and Europe, is marketed in this country also under the name of SILKY OAK and SELENA.

The logs vary in color from what might be called a shell pink to a light reddish-brown and they have a striking figure, varying from a small lacelike pattern to a large splashlike figure.

Locally it has been used for years in panels and trim work of fine residences and banks, for railings, doors and the like. It is a good wood for use by craftsmen for many types of cabinetwork where a striking and unusual appearance is desired.

Top, lacewood, small figure. Bottom, lacewood, large figure

250

LARCH, EUROPEAN *Larix decidua* (Larix—the classical name of this species; decidua—deciduous, pertaining to the leaves which fall in the autumn)

This species is obtained principally from the Alps and Carpathian Mountains, growing in high altitudes, up as far as the tree line. It is a tall, graceful evergreen, at times reaching a height of 140 ft. and more, though generally averaging 80 to 90 ft., with diameters up to 3 ft.

The heartwood is reddish or brownish, averaging around 35 lbs. per cubic foot. In drying, it requires care so as to prevent the resin content from proving troublesome in working. It is one of the most valuable softwoods used in the United Kingdom and has been used for the planking of boats below the water line, for posts and other outdoor work.

LARCH, WESTERN *Larix occidentalis* (occidentalis—western)

The growth of the western larch extends from Montana through northern Idaho, Washington, Oregon, and southeastern British Columbia. This species is similar to the eastern larch inasmuch as it sheds its needles every fall, but generally it grows on slopes and elevations from 2,000 to 7,000 ft.,

whereas the eastern larch grows in swamps and lowlands.

The bark is of a dull reddish brown, of conspicuous appearance, and a galactan gum is extracted from the wood of which some commercial use is made. The wood

Larch trees drop their needles every fall. Although they're conifers, it isn't correct to call them evergreens

251

closely resembles the Douglas fir, but it is not used for veneers as it is far inferior in quality. It is rather difficult to work this wood with tools and it does not hold paint, but it can be finished natural or stained.

Western larch is mostly used for the cheaper grades of furniture, boxes, various kinds of poles, railroad ties, posts and in the manufacture of fiberboard and craft wrapping paper.

LAUREL, CALIFORNIA *Umbellularia californica* (Umbellularia—refers to the umbrella-shaped flower clusters; californica—of California)

Other names by which this tree is known are: ACACIA BURL, CALIFORNIA OLIVE, MYRTLE, MOUNTAIN LAUREL, PEPPERWOOD and SPICE TREE.

This tree grows on the West Coast of the United States, especially in southern Oregon and northern California. The most beautiful for varied types of figure and coloring is found in Oregon. A rich golden brown and yellowish green in color, the wood has a wide range from light to dark shades and there is a mixture of plain wood, mottle, and cluster burls. It produces a stump and burl figure also, with a scattering of dark purple blotches.

Great care is necessary in the seasoning of the green wood as it will check and warp if not properly handled. However, it is a hard and strong wood, and the burls from Oregon are favored, in the veneer form, by cabinetmakers.

California laurel is an evergreen and is distinguished from others by a strong, aromatic odor when the leaves are crushed. These leaves have been used as a substitute for bay leaves in flavoring meats and soups.

Magnificent, highly figured veneers may be obtained from this wood, and they will take an excellent polish for use in decorative panels and fine furniture. Wood turners also prize this wood for turning bowls, candlesticks and other items.

LEADTREE, GREAT *Leucaena pulverulenta* (Leucaena—to whiten, as the flowers; pulverulenta—powdered, referring to the dusty appearing foliage)

This tree is generally found in the southern part of Texas and in northern Mexico and has many of the characteristics of black locust with the exception that it is considerably softer in texture.

Great leadtree is noted for its flowers which bloom from early spring until summer. They have most delicate colors, shades of red and purple, and a fragrant odor. This, combined with the lacylike pale light green foliage, make it valuable for ornamental purposes. Locally some lumber is produced, but it is not generally offered in the market.

LEMONWOOD *Calycophyllum candidissimum* (Calyco/phyllum—cup/leaf; candidissimum — very bright white)

It is also known as DEGAME SPARS and LANCEWOOD, but is in no way related to our local lemon tree.

This is a small to medium sized tree, from 40 to 65 ft. high and 8 to 20 in. in diameter, growing in Cuba and from southern Mexico through Central America to Colombia and Venezuela. In bloom it

Left, California laurel. Right, typical black locust tree

is beautiful and conspicuous because of the large white calyx lobes. The heartwood is brownish, not sharply demarcated from the thick and nearly colorless sapwood; it has a low luster and is of fine, uniform texture.

Lemonwood is similar in strength, toughness and resilience to hickory. It is without any distinctive odor or taste and is difficult to work. It does not split easily and is not resistant to decay, but holds its place well when manufactured and takes a high, glossy polish.

Locally the wood is used in making agricultural implements, tool handles, various articles of turnery and frames of buildings. Practically all of the timber exported comes from Cuba and in this country its principal use is in the manufacturer of bows by the archery trade.

LIGNUM VITAE *Guaiacum officinale* (Guaiacum—from the Carib Indian name; officinale—pertaining to drugs; gum guaiac, derived from this species is a drug)

Lignum vitae is native to the West Indies, the northern coast of South America and the west coast of Central America. The average size of the logs produced ranges

253

from 4 to 6 ft. in length and from 4 to 24 in. in diameter. The heartwood is of a greenish-black color and upon being exposed to light and air, grows darker. It is the hardest, heaviest and closest-grained wood known and has a density almost equal to iron. The weight is about 83 lbs. per cubic foot with a specific gravity of 1.3. The high resin content of lignum vitae, which runs about 30 per cent of its weight, consists of a natural gum, which combined with its pressure-resisting quality, renders this wood admirably suited for an increasing number of mechanical purposes where the introduction of lubrication is not practical or at all times reliable. Originally it was supposed to contain marvelous medicinal qualities, but little is now employed in medicine.

As lignum vitae has the ability to withstand the great working pressure of 2,000 lbs. per square inch and has resistance to the action of many mild chemicals and acids, it has a limitless variety of uses. Lignum vitae bearings are used in various applications and equipment such as clocks, dishwashing machines, exhaust fans, air conditioning units and underwater use in marine equipment. It is used as rollers in a hundred different places such as awnings, elevator gates, dryer equipment, moving heavy boxes weighing two to four tons. A few of the miscellaneous uses of lignum vitae are: die-cutting blocks, lemon squeezer cups, drainboards for chemicals, thrust blocks for propeller shafts, guides for cables and band saws, the construction of acid tanks, mallets of all kinds, thrust bearings for outboard motors, washers for rotating sprinklers, wheels and casters. The wood turns very well. For drilling, ordinary high-speed twist drills should be used as carpenters' auger bits are not suitable. Holes may be tapped successfully by hand, but external threads are difficult to cut and should be avoided if possible.

Applications of lignum vitae can be found in almost every industry and range from tiny rollers for venetian blinds to propeller shaft bearings in the largest liners.

LIMBA *Terminalia superba* (Terminalia—border or terminus; superba—highest, superb)

Limba, emanating in west Africa, is also known as AFARA, FRAKE, KORINA and OFFRAM.

It is a large tree with wood of a pale yellow to light brown color and of medium texture and hardness. There may be some tendency to split if the lumber is nailed, but the wood stains and takes a good polish. Limba produces good clean timber which is suitable for architectural paneling and general woodworking.

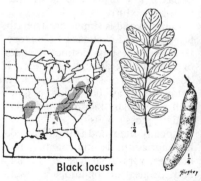

Black locust

LOCUST, BLACK *Robinia pseudoacacia* (Robinia—in honor of Jean Robin, 1550-1629, herbalist to kings of France; pseudo/acacia—false *Acacia*)

Straight-stripe limba, three-piece match

Honeylocust

It is known under a number of names in various states such as ACACIA, FALSE ACACIA, HONEY LOCUST, PEA FLOWER, and WHITE LOCUST. In Great Britain it is often known as ROBINIA as well as acacia, though it does not belong to the true family of acacias.

Black locust, the most prevalent and valuable of the five species of locust found in this country, also grows in the eastern and southeastern part of Canada. It is a small tree with very rough and furrowed bark of an orange-brown color. Black locust is desired for conservation purposes as it is an excellent tree for providing a wind break and conservation of the soil.

The wood is very hard, heavy, stiff and strong and because of its durability when exposed to the ground, locust posts are most highly prized. However, it is a very rapid-growing, short-lived tree which succumbs to the locust borer insect. While it is easily worked by machine tools, it is difficult to work with hand tools, but will take a good finish.

LOLAGBOLA *Pterygopodium oxyphyllum* (Pterygo/podium— winged-foot; oxy/phyllum—sour leaf)

This large, well-shaped tree is found in the equatorial forests of Africa, which includes the Belgian

255

and Portugese territories as well as French and British. It varies in height from 45 to 55 ft., with an average diameter of 30 in., and has a straight trunk. One of the unusual characteristics of the wood is that old trees often shed their bark in long strips. The heartwood is an attractive brown color, striped with reddish lines when cut on the quarter. Sometimes a cross figure is found. After the trees are cut, very rapid removal from the forest and early manufacture into lumber or veneers are necessary as the logs are subject to attack by pinhole borers and other defects.

Lolagbola weighs about 35 lbs. per cubic foot when dried, is fairly soft in texture, and the large amount of resin which the wood contains does not cause serious dulling of cutting edges during manufacture. The lumber works well, and logs are regularly sent to South Africa where they are manufactured into veneers for plywood.

LOVOA *Lovoa klaineana* (Lovoa —after the Lovo River; klaineana —after Klaine, a collector in West Africa)

In the United States this wood is known as TIGERWOOD; outside of the United States it is generally known as AFRICAN WALNUT, and in Africa it is often called ALONAWOOD, BENIN WALNUT, CONGOWOOD, LOVOAWOOD and NIGERIAN GOLDEN WALNUT.

Lovoa is a large tree, growing in Africa, which produces logs up to 48 in. in diameter and 24 ft. long. It has a very attractive bronze shade of yellowish-brown color, occasionally showing dark streaks. When the wood is quarter-sawn or cut, it shows a very pleasing ribbon-stripe figure. With the exception of the name, it does not have much resemblance to the European or American walnut, in most respects being nearer to a mahogany.

The wood seasons well and glues easily. An excellent finish can be

Lovoa, which is also known as tigerwood

obtained by scraping and sanding. After the pores are filled, a fine polish can be produced. It can be rip-sawn easily and cleanly though it is somewhat weaker than our American walnut. Hand turning needs care and sharp tools to avoid tearing, and for the same reason, drills need to be kept sharp or the fibers will tear out at the bottom of the drill hole.

Under normal conditions, plentiful supplies are available in the form of logs, boards and planks. It is a decorative timber, widely used in the making of furniture, in paneling and in veneers. Selected material is occasionally stained and used as a substitute for mahogany, especially faked antique furniture. It is also used for gunstocks and inlaying.

MACA WOOD *Platymiscium,* sp. (Platy/miscium—broad stem, probably in reference to the wide trunk diameter)

This tree grows in northern South America and Central America and is also known as BLEEDING HEART, BRAZILIAN PADOUK, FALSE ROSEWOOD, GRANDADILLO, MACACAHUBA and MEXICAN TULIPWOOD.

It is a rich reddish-brown in color with irregular grain and sometimes shows a stripe. It is a fine wood for borders and decorative work and is used in furniture and musical instruments and for knife handles.

MADRONE, PACIFIC *Arbutus menziesii* (Arbutus—the classical Latin name of *Arbutus unedo,* the strawberry madrone of southern Europe; menziesii—after its discoverer, Archibald Menzies, 1754-

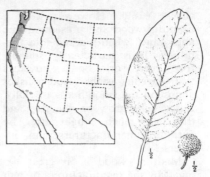

1842, Scotch physician and naturalist)

It goes under several local names, the most generally used is LAUREL, MANZANITA and MADRONE.

Madrone or madroño (the Spanish name) grows along the Pacific Coast from British Columbia southward to central California and obtains its greatest development in the redwood forests of northern California where the trees are sometimes 100 ft. high and 5 to 7 ft. in diameter. It varies greatly in size, dependent upon the quality of the ground, from a small shrub to a tree that spreads its branches wide enough to shade a gathering of around 2,000 men. The branches of a large tree will cover an area from 8,000 to 10,000 square feet. When madrone grows in the open, it has wide limbs like a southern live oak, but in a forest the trunk rises tall and straight to bring the crown into the sunlight and fresh air. It usually grows mixed with other forest trees, but sometimes large stands are encountered by themselves.

The wood is pale, reddish-brown, resembling apple wood in tone but not quite as dark. Its weight is 44 lbs. per cubic foot and the wood is porous with very small pores.

It presents extreme difficulty in seasoning as the wood warps and

257

checks easily. However, it is a beautiful wood and presents a fine appearance when worked into furniture. It is particularly suitable for turned work, bowls, novelties and souvenirs as the wood polishes almost to the smoothness of holly. Large burls grow on the tree and these are much sought after by furniture manufacturers and inlayers.

Madrone wood is in great demand by the manufacturers of gun powder as they find this one of the best sources of charcoal suitable for making gunpowder.

MAGNOLIA, SOUTHERN *Magnolia grandiflora* (Magnolia—in honor of Pierre Magnol, 1638-1715, director of the botanical garden at Montpellier, France; grandi/flora—large-flowered)

It is also known under the name of BAT TREE, BIG LAUREL, BULL-BAY, LAUREL and the SWEET MAGNOLIA, and is the official state tree of Mississippi and Louisiana.

Southern magnolia grows along the Atlantic coastline from central Florida northward to North Carolina and along the Gulf of Mexico from Florida throughout Louisiana and eastern Texas. It is a very shapely tree, growing up to 90 ft. in height and has a large trunk up to 4 ft. in diameter.

There are eight species of magnolia native to the eastern part of the United States, of which this is one, and a part of the 35 species known throughout the world. Magnolias have been traced back long before the coming of man. In the early centuries the Chinese cultivated magnolias for the purpose of preserving the buds, which they used in seasoning rice and also in medicine.

Southern magnolia has thick leaves which are dark green above and silvery color underneath. A fine example of this species grows close to the south portico of the White House in Washington where it was planted by Andrew Jackson in memory of his wife, Rachel.

The southern magnolia tree produces well over half of all the magnolia timber used commercially—for all types of cabinetwork, interior finishes, turnery; a good deal is cut into veneers and is also used for boxes and crates.

MAHOGANY, AFRICAN *Khaya ivorensis* (Khaya—from the native name for this tree, which is Khaye; ivorensis—Latin name for the Ivory Coast)

Several species of mahogany come from the west coast of Africa of which the most important is the

258

African mahogany, highly figured crotch. African mahogany, highly figured swirl

Khaya ivorensis. The mahogany that is exported to Europe is often sold under a dozen different trade names, according to the ports through which the logs are exported. Various types commonly known to the trade are LAGOS and BENIN MAHOGANY from Nigerian ports and HALF-ASSINE and SEKONDI MAHOGANY from the Gold Coast, also GRAND BASSAM from the Ivory Coast.

The tree is large, sometimes extra large, and excellent cuttings both for width and length can be obtained for use as lumber or as veneers. In most cases the trees range from 100 to 150 ft. in height, with a trunk clear of branches up to 90 ft. The diameter varies from 3 to 6 ft. and considerably more at the base, which is usually buttressed. After felling, the logs are frequently squared by natives, using adzes, in order to avoid transporting unnecessary amounts of useless timber for long distances as well as to remove the sapwood to prevent the attacks of ambrosia beetles, which cause pinholes.

Freshly sawn or cut African mahogany varies from a light to deep pink color, which gradually darkens to various shades from a light

259

African mahogany, small bee's-wing mottle   Flat-cut African mahogany veneer

brown to a dark reddish-brown when exposed to air and light. African mahogany is probably the most widely used of the true mahoganies at present, as it is the cheapest and can readily be obtained in all sizes. It is of coarser texture than the New World mahogany and has the disadvantage that it is more likely to warp.

The wood seasons rapidly without any particular attention and is very stable when dry, having less tendency to split than the American or New World mahogany, though it is not quite as strong.

Owing to its interlocked grain,

African mahogany is rather more difficult to work than the Honduras variety; neverthless it is fairly easy to work both with hand and machine tools, though there is a tendency for the grain to pick up when planing. It veneers very well.

African mahogany produces more figured logs than the New World mahogany, and the various types of figures are much more pronounced. It has long had an important established place in the construction of furniture of all classes, boat building, and in the manufacture of high-grade plywood.

This old-time photograph shows half a million dollars' worth of squared African mahogany logs with the New York skyline in the background. The yard was maintained for a number of years by Albert Constantine, Sr., who devoted 60 years to an intensive study of African mahogany, and it was used at a time when the yards of Constantine and Company did not have sufficient room to accommodate the entire requirements of the trade

Native laborers in Haiti rolling mahogany logs at the government lumber mill, which uses economical methods for cutting wood and utilizing the by-products

MAHOGANY, NEW WORLD

THE MAHOGANIES of this hemisphere belong to the genus *Swietenia* (after von Swieten, a Dutch physician), the source of the original or true mahogany. This is the premier cabinet wood of the world. It occurs in southern Florida, the West Indies, Mexico, Central America, Colombia, Venezuela, and the upper Amazonian region. The genus was described by Jacquin in 1760 with a single species, *Swietenia mahagoni* from the Bahamas.

Three South American species of *Swietenia* have been proposed, but each has been based on specimens from a single tree and, for all practical purposes at least, may be considered mere forms of *S. macrophylla*.

Mahogany is the most valuable timber tree in tropical America. Its use by European colonists and explorers dates back at least to the sixteenth century. According to George N. Lamb (*The Mahogany Book*, 2nd ed., pp. 8-10), "the earliest surviving use of Mahogany is that of a rough-hewn cross preserved in the Cathedral of St. Domingo and bearing the legend: 'This is the first sign planted in the center of this field to mark the beginning of this magnificent temple in the year 1514.' The cathedral, completed in 1550, has much carved mahogany woodwork, some of it considered the finest in the world, still in splendid condition after nearly four centuries in the tropics. Mahogany was early established as a ship-building wood and Cortez used it for the construction of ships for further voyages of discovery. . . . The first known European use of mahogany was in the Escorial begun by Philip II of Spain in 1563 and completed in 1584. . . . The earliest use of mahogany known in England was in Nottingham castle built in 1680."

No one knows when mahogany was first introduced into England, but it was probably used in shipbuilding long before it became fashionable for furniture, its identity concealed under the non-distinctive name of cedar. In an account of the trees of Bermuda about 1619 (*The World Displayed*, London, 1760, Vol. 4, Chap. 12), the native cedar is described as "firmer and more durable than any of its kind we are acquainted with and answers in every respect to oak timber. It is therefore used in shipbuilding." Certain rooms in Nottingham castle were wainscoted and floored in 1680 with "Cedar wood," as shown by the original bill for the timber, but contemporary evidence of the hardness and beauty of the woodwork leaves no room for doubt that the wood was mahogany. It was probably to avoid the confusion with other kinds of cedar (*Cedrela* and *Juniperus*) that the English settlers began to use the name mahogany, presumably a term of na-

tive origin. Its first recorded use is as "Mohogeny" in Ogilby's *America,* in 1671. Various spellings were subsequently used—mohogony, mohagany, muhagnee, mehogeny, mehogenny, mahagoni, mahoginy, and mahogany, the last mentioned appearing for the first time about 1724. The French name for mahogany is acajou, and this apparently owes its origin to the early practice of coating the ends of the logs with resin from the acajou or cashew tree (*Anacardium occidentale* L.).

The earliest mention of mahogany ("Mohagony wood") in an English newspaper appears to be in an advertisement in the London Gazette, February 22 to 25, 1702, regarding the sale of the cargoes of two prize ships. The first reference in the statistics of imports filed at the Public Records Office is for the year "Xmas 1699 to Xmas 1700" and pertains to a small lot of "Mohogony wood" from Jamaica. In an authoritative paper on "Early Imports of Mahogany for Furniture" (The Connoisseur, London, October and December 1934), R. W. Symonds says:

"Taking into consideration all the available evidence, I think it is permissible to state that Mahogany was employed in England from

1715 onwards for the making of tables, sometimes of gate-legged construction, but usually with straight round legs terminating in club feet or with the plain cabriole-shaped legs. Tables such as these were made in considerable numbers by many firms of London joiners and cabinet-makers and also by provincial furniture makers who lived in towns where a supply of imported Mahogany was available. Previous to 1715, Mahogany tables were only made sporadically owing to the cabinet-makers not being able to obtain a regular supply of the wood. . . .

"Mahogany overcame the difficulty of making table tops, owing to the large widths of the planks of this wood in comparison to Walnut. It was for this reason that Mahogany became at once popular with cabinet-makers. On its introduction, numerous new types of tables were designed, the construction of which would not have been possible in Walnut. These tables were not only made for the wealthy classes, but large numbers were produced of a plain character for the less well-to-do householder. Evidence in support of this last statement is to be found in the very large quantity of flap and tripod tables of a plain design that have survived. The number of the latter, however, has considerably decreased within recent years owing to the obnoxious habit of the furniture faker of carving up the plain example so that he can pass it off to the unwary collector, at a high rate of profit, as a period piece with the claw-and-ball feet. . . .

"It would appear from the contemporary information, cited from the statistics of imports, Sheraton's *Cabinet Dictionary,* and the *History*

of *Jamaica,* that the first Mahogany to be imported into England in the early eighteenth century was Jamaican and, afterwards, Cuban. In the third quarter of the same century, Honduras Mahogany was imported. The reason for the cessation of any particular variety of Mahogany was because the trees near the coast having been felled, the traders sought another supply which was cheaper, owing to its being more easily procurable. It was not so much a question of seeking wood of fine quality, otherwise exporters would have gone to the trouble and expense of transporting the better quality timber from the interior."

It was during the middle of the 1800's that many of the sailing vessels with their cargoes of West Indian and Central American mahoganies would be consigned directly to the yards of Constantine & Company, at 7th Street and the East River, New York, to await their turn to unload. The accompanying picture, taken on October 19, 1898, of the yards of Constantine & Company on the East River, from 6th to 8th Streets, shows six million feet of mahogany logs.

In the *History of Jamaica,* we note the following: "In felling these trees, the most beautiful part is commonly left behind. The Negro workmen raise a scaffolding, of four or five feet elevation above the ground, and hack off the trunk, which they cut up into balks. The part below, extending to the root, is not only of the largest diameter, but of closer texture than the other parts, most elegantly diversified with shades or clouds, or dotted, like ermine, with black spots; it takes the highest polish, with a singular lustre, so firm as even to reflect objects like a mirror. This part is only to be come at by digging below the spur to the depth of two or three feet and cutting it through; which is so laborious an operation that few attempt it, except they are uncommonly curious in their choice of the wood, or to serve a particular order. Yet I apprehend it might be found to answer the trouble and expense, if sent for a trial to the British market, as it could not fail of being approved of beyond any other wood, or even tortoise-shell which it most resembles."

Sheraton gives an account of Jamaican mahogany in his *Cabinet Dictionary* (1803), and is chiefly concerned with three types, designated as Cuba, Spanish, and Honduras mahogany. Cuba wood is "a kind of Mahogany somewhat harder than Honduras wood, but with no figure in the grain. It is inferior to Spanish wood, though probably the Cuba and Spanish Mahogany are the same, as the island of Cuba is a Spanish colony. . . . That, however, which is generally distinguished by Spanish Mahogany is finer than that called Cuba, which is pale, straight-grained, and some of it only a bastard kind of Mahogany. It is generally used for chair wood, for which some of it will do very well." Regarding the Honduras variety, he says: "From this province is imported the principal kind of Mahogany in use amongst cabinet-makers, which generally bears the name of Honduras Mahogany, and sometimes Bay-wood, from the bay or arm of the sea which runs up to it. The difference between Honduras and Spanish wood is easily perceived by judges, but not by others unskilled in wood."

The comparatively recent discovery of commercial quantities of *Swietenia* in the upper Amazon region is of great importance to the industry, as it opens up a vast, though still undetermined, area of virgin forest containing mahogany.

The known and probable distribution of mahogany in South America is approximately as follows: In Venezuela, it extends from eastern Miranda westward to Calabozo and Guanare, thence around the northern end of Cordillera Mérida to the Lake Maracaibo region, avoiding the dry coastal zone and elevations above 3,000 ft. In Colombia, it is mostly in the upper valleys of the Magdalena and Cauca Rivers. *Swietenia* is also a component of the virgin forests in northwestern Ecuador. In Peru, mahogany occurs east of the divide at elevations of 400 to 4,500 ft. and is in a belt of forest varying in width up to several hundred miles and extending from southern Ecuador through the Ucayali basin to the headwaters of the Tambo and Urubamba Rivers in the south. Eastward across the border in Brazil, there are commercial stands of mahogany in the upper reaches of the Juruá and Purús Rivers, and large quantities of logs are floated down to Manáos for export, either in the round or after manufacture into lumber. There are indications of a separate mahogany timber belt of unknown extent along certain tributaries of the upper Madeira River in eastern Bolivia. Apparently there is no genuine mahogany in any part of the basins of the Rio Negro and Putumayo, or in the lower portions of the Jurua and Purus, or below the falls of the Madeira. The reputed discovery above the waterfalls of the Tapajoz and Xingu Rivers of old Indian canoes made of mahogany implies an extension of the Bolivian belt across Matto Grosso, Brazil. While from the foregoing it appears that only fragmentary knowledge of the range of *Swietenia* in South America exists, enough is known to reassure anyone who fears that the supply of genuine, first-growth mahogany timber is nearing exhaustion.

MAHOGANY, PHILIPPINE

THE PHILIPPINE ISLANDS are the source of a great variety of hardwoods, few of which are imported into the United States. The greatest volume of the latter compose a group of timbers marketed as "Philippine mahogany." However, these are in no way, botanically or otherwise, related to the true or classical mahoganies which belong to the plant family *Meliaceae.* The "Philippine mahoganies" are members of a plant family called *Dipterocarpaceae.*

Philippine mahoganies are quite varied in color and texture and are divided into two classes:

Class I. Red Lauans
    a) Red lauan *(Shorea negrosensis)*
    b) Tangile *(Shorea polysperma)*
    c) Tiaong *(Shorea teysmanniana)*

Class II. White Lauans
    a) Almon *(Shorea eximia)*
    b) White lauan *(Pentacme* spp.)
    c) Bagtikan *(Parashorea* spp.)

In general, all of these woods, as compared with the tropical American and African mahoganies *(Meliaceae),* are of coarser texture. They require a greater amount of sanding to produce a finished surface and are much less stable under atmospheric changes. Color varies from fairly light shades to red and brown. As a rule, these woods are employed in lower quality furniture, doors and cabinetwork. The Philippine mahoganies are available in quartered, sliced and rotary veneers and as lumber.

MAHOGANY, ROSE *Dysoxylon fraseranum* (Dys/o/xylon—hardwood; fraseranum—after Fraser)

This is also known as AUSTRALIAN MAHOGANY and sometimes as PICK WOOD.

Rose mahogany emanates in Malaya and· is fairly heavy, weighing 50 lbs. per cubic foot. It resembles Honduras mahogany in color and is also similar to the strong reddish-brown color of Koko, making it hard to distinguish these two

Logging in the Philippines

Quarter-sliced white lauan (Philippine mahogany), three-piece match

267

woods. The wood has a fragrant rose odor when freshly cut, but it does not in any way resemble the rosewood family.

MAIDOU *Pterocarpus pedatus*
(Ptero/carpus—winged fruit; pedatus—footed)

It is also known as MADOU and MAI TADU and sometimes is mistaken for Burmese padouk.

This tree is found in French Indo-China and resembles amboyna very closely. Maidou varies from a pale straw color to brownish and scarlet shades, has a satiny finish and a ribbon stripe. Only rarely does it come in the form of burls and crotches.

MAKORÉ *Mimusops heckelii*
(Mimusops—monkey face; heckelii —after Heckel)

It is also known as AFRICAN CHERRY, AGANOKWE, BAKU and MAKARU.

Coming from the west coast of Africa, this tree is large and produces logs up to 5 ft. in diameter. It is somewhat similar to close-grained mahogany, but with growth lines and pores more similar to cherry. It is heavy in handling, weighing 40 lbs. per cubic foot. The logs which are exported are short in length, being crosscut and then cut again to make them easier to transport. The wood is dense and hard, firm-textured, heavier than mahogany and while some logs

Maidou burl, two-piece match

Makore, mottle figure. This wood is commonly known as African cherry

268

are straight-grained, others have a very striking mottled figure.

There is a luster to the wood and it glues well but is difficult to work as the timber contains silica which rapidly dulls the tools. It is often cut into veneers as this is much easier than sawing.

MANGGASINORA *Shorea philippinensis* (Shorea—in honor of Lord Teignmouth, John Shore, Governor of Bengal; philippinensis—of the Philippines)

This species is also known as SONORA.

Emanating in the Philippines, this wood has a yellow-white to pale brown color and a texture like almon. It is hard and heavy and the veneer is available in quartered form.

MAÑIO *Podocarpus nubigens* (Podo/carpus—foot fruit; nubi/gens—cloudy race)

This emanates in southern Chile, in the Andes Mountains. It is a tree that would be difficult for one to recognize in the woods as being a conifer or evergreen because it has straight, stiff, leathery leaves and cones which do not look like cones. It is a relation to the yellow wood of south Africa and the podos of east Africa, with similar straight grain, and fine, uniform yellowish wood.

Before drying, the wood twists and warps badly, but after careful seasoning, which can be accomplished without any trouble, it works well and is stable. The average weight is around 35 lbs. per cubic foot.

In South America mañio is used in the manufacture of furniture and general cabinetwork as it has a very pleasing appearance; and because of the well-shaped logs and size of the tree, it could be suitable for the manufacture of veneers. However, very little has been exported to foreign markets because the supply is not too plentiful and the transportation charges would be exceedingly high.

MANSONIA *Mansonia altissima* (Mansonia—after Manson; altissima—of the highest)

It is also known as AFRICAN BLACK WALNUT, APRONO, BÉTÉ and OFUN.

This small tree comes from the Gold and Ivory Coasts of Africa and has a diameter from 16 to 24 in. The heartwood is yellowish-brown to greenish and purplish-brown, but the rich colors, apparent when first manufactured, generally fade when exposed to the light and the wood assumes more of a uniform dark purple brown.

Mansonia dries quickly with little warping and weighs about 37 lbs. per cubic foot. It is similar to walnut, especially when sliced or quarter-sliced, and is usually straight-grained and fine-textured, but it is harder than American walnut. However, its strength properties are about equal to walnut.

The tree is very resistant to decay, but the sapwood may be attacked by pinhole borers. The wood works easily and glues well, finishing nicely. The better-colored timber may be used as an alternative to walnut in high-class furniture and cabinetmaking, interior decoration, piano cases, etc.

MAPLE, JAPANESE *Acer palmatum* (Acer—the classical Latin name of maple; palmatum—shaped like one's palm, a reference to the palmlike nature of the leaf)

In Japan it is known as KAEDE and grows in the forests of Honshushikoku and Kayushu, along with oak, chestnut and beech.

This tree is small, between 30 and 40 ft. in height and with a diameter of 12 in. and upwards. The wood is a pinkish-brown to pale brown in color with no division in appearance between the sapwood and the heartwood. When dried, the wood weighs about 40 lbs. per cubic foot, but it is necessary to dry it slowly, otherwise a large amount of warpage may take place and the shrinkage is quite high. The logs usually are straight-grained or slightly irregular, and occasionally wavy grain is found. It has a fine texture, a lustrous surface and is a hard timber, about equal to our rock maple.

While Japanese maple is a wood that bends very poorly, it has a large use in the furniture industry as it takes a good finish. In addition, it is used in Japan for flooring, some decorative woodwork, and in the manufacture of agricultural equipment.

MAPLE, QUEENSLAND *Flindersia brayleyana* (Flindersia—in honor of the English captain, M. Flinders; brayleyana—probably after Brayley)

This tree is also known as AUSTRALIAN MAPLE, MAPLE SILKWOOD and WARRI, but is not of our maple (Acer) family.

It grows in Queensland and New South Wales in Australia. The color is light red, similar to African mahogany, with a wavy, curly grain, from plain to stripe figure. It has a silken luster but is light in weight though tough and moderately elastic. The bending strength is poor. It has a hard, close grain.

Queensland maple works easily, stains readily and is one of the finest Australian cabinet woods used in making quality furniture, for decorative interiors, boat interiors, for planking and propellers. It is not generally used in this country.

MAPLE, RED *Acer rubrum* (Acer —the classical Latin name of maple; rubrum—red, in reference to the red autumn foliage, the red flowers and red leaf stalks)

It is the state tree of Rhode Island and is known in various states as SCARLET MAPLE, SHOE-PET MAPLE, SOFT MAPLE, SWAMP MAPLE and WATER MAPLE.

This maple, one of the most valuable of the soft maples, grows in about the same states as the sugar maple but as a rule it is found in lowlands, swamps and along river banks. The tree is well named "red" maple. It displays something red all year. In winter the buds, in spring the early flowers and the young leaves, also the seeds, shine in red. The young reddish twigs show a brilliance as the summer comes, and the autumn foliage is the most striking of the red colors. Red maple grows rapidly and is especially desired in landscaping.

The early colonists, before mahogany was imported, used red maple for the greatest number of their furniture pieces.

The wood of the red maple resembles that of the sugar maple, being close-grained, but it is much softer in texture and lacks the figure that the sugar maple has, although it has an attractive plain grain. It is not as costly as hard maple and is generally used in the cheaper furniture and all types of general woodwork. A curl figure is quite common in soft maple, but only once in our history have we ever found a soft maple with very strong bird's-eye figure.

___

MAPLE, SILVER *Acer saccharinum* (saccharinum—sugary or sweet in reference to the sap)

Silver maple belongs to the soft maple group and is very similar to the red maple in respect to its growing conditions and the texture of the wood, but it is easily distinguished from the red maple because of the difference in the leaves, which have five lobes with deep fissures. They have a light green surface and are silvery white on the underside. Silver maple lacks the bright coloring of the red maple in the fall, and the leaves turn to a pale yellow.

___

MAPLE, SUGAR *Acer saccharum* (saccharum—sugary, in reference to the sweet sap from which maple sugar is made)

This species is also known as BLACK MAPLE, HARD MAPLE, ROCK MAPLE, SUGAR-TREE MAPLE, SWEET MAPLE and WHITE MAPLE.

Sugar maple grows throughout most states east of the Rocky Mountains, but the largest quantity is found in the New England states and the states along the Great Lakes. It grows from 70 to 120 ft. tall and from 20 to 38 in. in diameter. Sugar maple is the state tree of Vermont, New York, West Virginia and Wisconsin. It is easily recognized by its leaves, which are five-lobed and pointed. They turn to gorgeous red and yellow colors in the fall. The brilliant orange and red colors of this specie are responsible for making our mountainsides so beautiful in the fall.

The heartwood is a very light tan, sometimes reddish-brown, and the sapwood is really white. It is a heavy, strong wood and has an even texture.

The maple family is divided between hard maple and soft maple. In the United States over 20 different species of maple may be found, such as black, broad-leaved, fig leaf, hard, Oregon, red, rock, river, rough, scarlet, silver, soft and sugar. Of the many species of maple, sugar maple is the most abundant and important of the maples found in the United States.

This maple is named sugar maple because of the delicious maple sugar and maple syrup obtained in the spring by processing the sap from the trees. A tree will produce as many as 12 gallons of sap a year

271

MAPLE LEAVES: 1, sugar; 2, silver; 3, boxelder (*Acer negundo*); 4, black (*nigrum*); 5, sugar (var. *rugelii*); 6, silverleaf; 7, Norway; 8, Florida; 9, boxelder (*californicum*); 10, dwarf; 11, red (var. *drummondii*); 12, vine; 13, sycamore (*pseudoplatanus*) 14, bigleaf; 15, scarlet (var. Sargent); 16, red (var. Tridens); 17, sugar (var. Simosum); 18, red swamp; 19, mountain; 20, cutleaved; 21, field; 22, striped; 23, sugar (*grandidentitum*); 24, sugar (*leucoderme*)

Typical sugar maple tree growing in Knox County, Ind.

Quilted sugar maple, two-piece match

Rotary-cut white (sugar) maple, two-piece match

274

Curly sugar maple

and it takes 35 to 40 gallons of sap to distill one gallon of the pure syrup. The production of this syrup is confined principally to the states of Wisconsin, Vermont and New York and other northern states. The business amounts to many millions of dollars every year.

Various types of figures are obtained in the maple trees, like curly —often called a fiddleback figure because of being used on the backs of violins—bird's-eye maple, maple burl, leaf figure and straight-grained maple. All these are available in the veneer form for craftsmen's use.

As sugar maple has a hard texture, is easy to work and excellent for turning, taking a high polish, the finest dance floors, bowling alleys and bowling pins are made of this wood. It is also used in one of the most vital parts of piano construction, the manufacture of what is called the pin plank—the part into which the pins for the strings of the piano are driven.

MARÍA *Calophyllum brasiliense* (Calo/phyllum—beautiful leaf; brasiliense—of Brazil)

This wood is also known under a number of other names, some of which are: ACA, BARA, BARE, BALSAMARIA, CALABA, CRABWOOD, GACAREUBA, OCUJE, SANTA MARÍA, WILD CALABASH.

Small quantities of this wood have been imported into the United States from time to time, but it has no definite commercial value. The heartwood is brick red to pink in

275

color and when cut into rotary veneers, attractive figures are obtained. This wood requires special attention when kiln-drying. Locally it has been used for furniture, shipbuilding and general construction work.

MĔNGKULANG *Tarrietia simplicifolia* (Tarrietia—probably a personal name; simplici/folia—simple leaved)

This tree grows throughout the forests of Malaya, but it is very limited as the growth averages only one tree in every four or five acres. It obtains a very large size, however, often exceeding 120 ft., and exceptional trees have been recorded as high as 140 ft. with diameters ranging from 18 to 36 in. The wood is coarse-grained and when seasoned properly gives little trouble.

Only small quantities of this wood are exported. It is used locally for various types of furniture, interior cabinetwork and the making of boxes.

MĔRBAU *Intsia bakeri* (Intsia—a native name in Madagascar; bakeri —after J. G. Baker, English botanist of late 19th century)

This large tree grows throughout Malaya, though sparsely, so no large quantities are available. The heartwood is of an attractive dark brown and reddish-brown color and it is of fine texture. Some pores contain a yellow deposit which at times is extracted for use in making a dye.

As mĕrbau is extremely resistant to decay, it is highly valued in the East for house building, construction and bridge work, and is exported in limited quantities only.

It is also used in the manufacture of frames for billiard tables. Selected wood makes very attractive paneling for rooms.

MESUA *Mesua ferrea* (Mesua— after the Arabic physician Mesuach of the 10th century; ferrea—iron in reference to the hard wood)

Native to India, Burma, Ceylon and the Andaman Islands, this wood is called INDIAN ROSE-CHESTNUT and IRONWOOD in India.

The wood is of a bright, rose-red color which darkens upon exposure. It is so hard and heavy, weighing about 70 lbs. per cubic foot, that it is little used because of the difficulties in dragging it. It is very strong and used locally in its native country for gunstocks, tool handles and in the construction of bridges and buildings, but none of it is used commercially in this country.

MONKEY POD *Pithecolobium samán** (Pithec/o/lobium—monkey pod; saman—after a native Central American name, samán)

Other common names for the monkey pod include RAIN TREE, ALGARROBO, SAMÁN and CARRETA.

The monkey pod is commonly distributed as an ornamental plant throughout the tropics and may be found in the Hawaiian Islands in great abundance. It has become naturalized in some areas. Mature trees in the Magdalena River Valley in Colombia may attain heights of 100 ft. or more and reach diameters of 4 to 6 ft. Even though it is one of the most beautiful of neotropical trees, the timber is of little commercial importance. Forest-grown trees are rather scarce and others are too useful for shade. Young trees grow rapidly and pro-

Upper left, red maple. Upper right, silver maple.
Lower left, southern magnolia. Lower right, myrtle

277

duce a light and soft, easily worked, brown wood. However, later growth is slower, and the wood formed is comparatively hard and heavy, very dark in color, fibrous, tough and somewhat refractory. The wood has little resistance to decay. Uses involve manufacture of novelties to some extent, and selected pieces may exhibit an attractive figure. Locally the wood of the monkey pod is employed for dug-out canoes, split posts and some in construction.

The name rain tree is probably derived from the falling liquid excreta of *Cicadeae* insects which inhabit the trees in Central America. Carreta is a Spanish name referring to wagon or cart and probably owes its use to the fact that cross sections of the trunk of *Pithecolobium samán* are employed as wagon wheels in some areas. The monkey pod yields a dark-colored gum of poor quality and the pulp of the pods is said to be edible.

---

* This species may be referred to as *Samanea samán*.

MULBERRY, BLACK *Morus nigra* (Morus—classical Latin name of mulberry, nigra—black)

Black mulberry, weighing about 40 lbs. per cubic foot, grows in the United States and is native to western Asia. It has a brilliant yellow color, becoming a golden, rich brown, and has a firm grain. This is an excellent wood for chair work.

MULBERRY, EAST AFRICAN *Morus lactea*

Locally this tree is also known as KIZULEVULE, MUKIMBU and NYAKATOMA.

The tree generally reaches a height of 60 ft. with diameters from 12 to 18 in. However, the trunk is seldom straight, which prevents obtaining long-length lumber.

When first cut, the wood has a very striking bright yellow heartwood and almost a pure white sapwood. In time, with exposure to light and air, the heartwood continues to darken, going through shades of a golden brown to a warm brown color.

The wood is not durable if exposed to the ground or to the weather, but it is a most satisfactory wood for general cabinetwork, interior woodwork, and wooden articles, its use being limited by the lack of suitable logs.

MUNINGA *Pterocarpus angolensis* (Ptero/carpus—winged fruit; angolensis—from Angola)

It is also known under the names of BLOODWOOD, KEJAAT, KEJATENHOUT, SEALING-WAX TREE and TRANSVAAL TEAK.

The growth of this tree is confined to eastern Transvaal. The heartwood has a wide variation in color from a dark reddish-brown with purple markings to a light uniform brown color. It is of medium weight, averaging 40 lbs. per cubic foot, and the wood has an attractive figure.

There is no difficulty encountered in seasoning, and the wood is free from warpage and shrinkage. It works a little harder than teak, but it glues easily and takes a fine polish.

This is a very popular wood and much in demand in Africa as it is a fine wood for furniture and high-class cabinets. A good example of its use is the railroad station in Johannesburg, which is entirely paneled in this wood, as well as all the furniture in it.

MUSIZI *Maesopsis eminii* (Mae-sopsis—origin unknown; eminii—probably after Emin)

Musizi is also known as AWURU, ESENGE and MUHUNYA.

Growing in east Africa, this tree is generally found on land from which the original trees have been removed, or along the edges of large forests. It reaches heights from 40 to 110 ft., occasionally a little more. The wood is in the lighter class of woods, averaging about 30 lbs. per cubic foot, of a medium to fairly coarse grain, which is generally straight.

The bark is distinctive inasmuch as it is deeply grooved and a dirty white color. The sapwood is whitish and distinctly different from the colored heartwood, which, when first cut, can best be described as greenish-yellow. Upon exposure it darkens through several shades of yellow-brown, sometimes reaching a rich brown.

The wood seasons very easily, without warping or twisting, and works easily with either power or hand tools. After a careful filling of the pores, it will take a fine polish either in varnish or lacquer. It may also be painted.

It can be described as a useful, general-purpose wood for all types of interior work, but not suitable for use outdoors or in wet conditions as it is not resistant to decay. However, this condition can be easily overcome as the wood is particularly receptive to treatment with wood preservatives.

MYRTLE *Umbellularia californica*

This species is also known as ACACIA BURL, CALIFORNIA LAUREL, CALIFORNIA OLIVE, MOUNTAIN LAUREL, PEPPERWOOD and SPICE-TREE.

Myrtle burl cluster, two-piece match

It grows along the west coast of the United States and particularly in southern Oregon and northern California. This is an evergreen tree, distinguished from the others by a strong, aromatic odor when the leaves are crushed. These leaves have been used as a substitute for bay leaves in flavoring meats and soups.

The wood is rich golden brown and yellowish green with a wide range of color from light to dark. It is a mixture of plain wood, mottle and cluster burls. Also, a stump and burl figure will be found with a scattering of dark purple blotches. The myrtle that grows in Oregon is the most beautiful for varied types of figure and coloring.

Great care is necessary in the seasoning of the green wood as it will check and warp if not properly handled. The wood is hard

279

and strong and furnishes a magnificent, highly figured veneer that takes an excellent polish. It is used in decorative panels and furniture and is prized by wood turners for making bowls, candlesticks and other items. Oregon myrtle burl, when manufactured in the veneer form, is a favorite wood of the finest cabinetmakers.

MYRTLE, BEECH *Nothofagus cunninghamii* (Notho/fagus—bastard beech, *Fagus;* cunninghamii—after Cunningham)

This attractive evergreen tree is also known as RED MYRTLE and TASMANIAN MYRTLE.

The growth of beech myrtle is confined to the island of Tasmania and the most southerly part of Victoria. The finest species are found on moist soils in sheltered areas, but it will grow on mountain slopes up to elevations of 3,500 ft. and higher. However, the higher up, the smaller the tree until it becomes just a shrub. In the most desirable conditions trees can be found as high as 100 ft. and 24 in. and more in diameter.

It has lovely coloring, with a range from a light pale color in the sapwood through shades of pinkish-brown to reddish-brown and brown heartwood. Because the lighter-colored wood has a tendency to dry much more quickly than the darker shades of heartwood, considerable care is required in drying. Unless it is first treated with a proper preservative, this wood is unsuitable for use in circumstances that would be favorable for the development of wood rotting as it has a low resistance to decay.

The use of this hardwood is somewhat limited because of the lack of suitable logs, but large use

is made of it in Tasmania for furniture, turning, general interior woodwork, carving and other purposes for which beech is used.

NAINGON *Tarrietia utilis* (Tarrietia—probably a personal name; utilis—useful)

This wood grows in Ghana, Africa, along the Ivory Coast and northward to Sierra Leone and is considered a medium sized tree for this area, generally averaging around 70 ft., occasionally growing to 100 ft., and from 24 to 30 in. in diameter. It often is found in marshy grounds.

A casual glance at the wood shows a resemblance in color to some species of African mahogany, but upon closer examination one finds the texture coarser and the weight a little heavier, averaging around 40 lbs. per cubic foot. When growing, the tree looks somewhat like the mangrove because of the large buttresses, which have a tendency to develop large roots.

The wood contains an unusual amount of resin, which is in sufficient quantity to make polishing difficult at times and presents a problem in making glued joints, but it is not enough to prevent working with tools. The wood is suitable for all lower grades of furniture and parts of interior woodworking.

NÉDUN *Pericopsis mooniana* (Pericopsis—having a round appearance; mooniana — probably after Moon)

Growing in the low forest regions of the island of Ceylon between the sea level and up to 1,000 ft., this tree is becoming increasingly scarce as large sections of this type of forest have been logged to make

Top, a monkey-pod tree growing in a village street, Hawaii.
Lower left, a black oak. Lower right, northern red oak

room for rubber plantations. The tree can be recognized by the unusual pale, pinkish-brown color of its smooth bark. The wood is an attractive warm brown or orange color with darker streaks at regular intervals, all of the colors becoming softer with age. Nédun is fairly heavy, weighing from 50 to 60 lbs. per cubic foot.

Formerly a good deal of the wood was used in cabinetmaking and in the furniture industry, and today a few of the logs are being manufactured into quarter-sliced veneers.

NEPORA *Caryota* sp. (Caryota—pertaining to a walnut, probably a reference to the fruit)

Emanating in Ceylon, India, this wood has a cubic weight per foot of 45 lbs. It is black in color with brown streaks. The wood is used for water conduits and baskets. The leaves, which are very strong, are made into rope, brushes, brooms and other articles.

OAKS

THE BOTANISTS have classified more than 50 species of oaks growing in the United States. They vary a great deal in size, shape and appearance. Some of the woods are extremely valuable commercially and others have little value except for the appearance of the tree. We are going to speak only of a very few of the most important ones. However, these have a number of additional names, like other woods, being known in one state by one name and in another state by a different name.

All of the oaks, regardless of where they grow, are divided into two general groups—the white oaks and the red oaks, the latter some-

times being referred to as the black oaks. Those in the white oak classification have by far the most important commercial value, but there are many more species and trees in the red oak family.

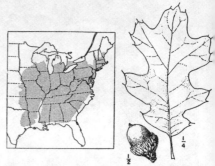

OAK, BLACK *Quercus velutina* (Quercus—the classical Latin name for oak; velutina—velvety, a reference to the downy young leaves)

Black oak, which grows in the eastern part of the United States, is also known as BLACK JACK, BYER'S OAK, JACK OAK, PANBARK OAK, QUERCIPRON OAK and YELLOWBARK, according to the state it grows in.

The name of black oak was given to the tree because of the color of the bark. It is probably the most prevalent of the oaks growing in the eastern section. The acorns take two years to ripen, as do all acorns in the black oak family, as against the one year to ripen in the white oak family. However, this black oak produces one of the poorest quality timbers of the more prevalent oaks. It is used in general construction work and in connection with the manufacture of cheaper furniture.

OAK, BUR *Quercus macrocarpa* (Quercus—the classical Latin name for oak; macro/carpa—large fruit)

In various states this oak is also

That great oaks from little acorns grow is well demonstrated by this exceptional Department of Agriculture photo of a large live oak tree

OAK LEAVES: 1, gray (*Quercus borealis*); 2, gray (*shumardii*); 3, Texas red (*texana*); 4, black (*ellipsoidalis*); 5, black (*velutina*); 6, scarlet (*coccinia*); 7, scarlet (*georgiana*); 8, California black (*kelloggii*); 9, turkey; 10, bear or scrub; 11, red or Spanish (*digitata*); 12, swamp white (*lyrata*); 13, blackjack; 14, mossycup or bur; 15, post (*stellata*); 16, post (var. *margaretta*); 17, white or valley (*lobata*); 18, white (*garryana*); 19, white (*tahensis*); 20, white (*monhana*); 21, chinkapin, yellow or chestnut (*muehlenbergii*) 22, white (*alba*); 23, willow (*phellos*); 24, shingle (*imbricaria*); 25, scarlet or black (*coccinea*); 26, live; 27, water (*nigra*); 28, water (*austrina*); 29, water (*letophylla*); 30, pin (*palustris*); 31, pin (*heterophylla*); 32, pin (*chapmanii*); 33, cow (*michangii*); 34, red or swamp Spanish (*pagodaefolia*); 35, laurel (*laurifolia*); 36, swamp white (*platanoides*)

Top, California live oak. Bottom, Oregon white oak

285

known as Blue Oak, Mossycup, Overcup Oak and Scrub Oak.

This tree grows in southern Canada and throughout the eastern half of the United States, and is the state tree of Illinois. The largest trees are found in rich bottom lands, and the valley of the Wabash River is considered one of the best spots. Bur oak is one of the largest of all oaks but it is not as beautiful and impressive as the white oak.

The leaves are larger than any of the other oaks, 6 to 10 in. long and half the length in width, having five to seven irregularly shaped lobes and a wedged-shaped face. They are dark green on the top and a silvery green on the underside and are on the tree in great profusion. Also, larger acorns are produced by this species than by any other oaks. The kernels have a white meat which is sweet and edible.

Bur oak produces very fine wood. When made into veneers and lumber, it has an appearance very similar to white oak. It is particularly desired in the quarter-sawn form because of the handsome figure.

OAK, CALIFORNIA LIVE *Quercus agrifolia* (agrifolia—probably an error for *aquifolia,* meaning hollyleaf, or *acrifolia,* meaning

sharp-leaved, although literally it means field-leaved)

Originally this oak was known as the Holly-Leaved Oak as the leaves resemble the large evergreen holly. It is also known in California as the Coast Live Oak and the Evergreen Oak.

This tree is found in southern California and northward to San Francisco in the valleys and along the coastal mountains. It is a fairly tall tree, from 55 to 65 ft., and the limbs are crooked, thick and long. The wood warps and checks to a great extent during drying and unfortunately it has little or no commercial value.

OAK, ENGLISH *Quercus robur* (robur—strong)

This oak is often referred to as European Oak or Pollardo.

It varies in color from a light tan to a deep brown with occasional black spots. It produces burls and swirls which are very brittle and fragile, but beautiful work can be obtained with their use. English oak is considered one of the finest woods in use today.

OAK, HOLM *Quercus ilex* (ilex—the genus of the holly, *Ilex*)

Holm oak has long been a na-

Flat-sliced English brown oak,
two-piece match

tive of the countries bordering on the Mediterranean Sea and was first brought into cultivation in England over 300 years ago. It is a large evergreen tree, reaching a height of 70 to 90 ft. The large crown often measures as much in diameter as the height.

The wood is reddish-brown in color, hard and heavy. Because of this heavy density and hardness, it requires extra care in drying to prevent warpage and also care in working with tools to prevent splitting. When manufactured on the quarter, it has a very flashy figure which might be considered too prominent to suit the taste of many.

Little of this timber has been used in industry except in the countries it grows in, where it has been converted into furniture and used for other similar purposes.

OAK, JAPANESE *Quercus mongolica* (mongolica—from Mongolia)

Originating in Japan, this oak is the hardest and heaviest of all the timbers produced there, weighing 40 lbs. per cubic foot. Some of this wood is used in house building, but its principal use is in the making of charcoal.

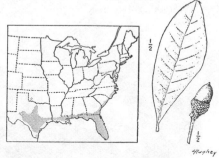

OAK, LIVE *Quercus virginiana* (virginiana—of Virginia)

Live oak grows in the southeastern part of the United States from Virginia and westward along the coast as far as Texas and Mexico. It is short in height, from 45 to 50 ft., and often two or three times as broad as it is high. It is the state tree of Georgia and receives its

287

name of live oak because the leaves remain on the tree the entire year, gradually being replaced by new leaves in about 13 months. The leaves have rounded edges and tips, of a shiny, dark-green color and whitish on the underside. It is one of the most beautiful of the oaks with a short trunk and tremendous spreading limbs.

The wood is tough and heavy. Unfortunately, there is very little commercial value to this wood due to the fact that the trunk is so short it produces little lumber. When available, however, the wood has a very fine figure and will take a high polish. Along the Gulf states it is generally covered with Spanish moss.

For many years the wood has been used in shipbuilding. So-called "knees" are obtained from the section where the large roots join the trunk and are used in shipbuilding. Live oak has a historical connection with our Navy inasmuch as the *Constitution,* commonly known as "Old Ironsides," was made from live oak grown in Georgia.

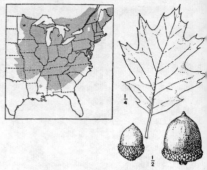

OAK, NORTHERN RED *Quercus rubra* (rubra—red)

Northern red oak is also known as CANADIAN RED OAK, GRAY OAK and RED OAK.

This tree grows across the mid-eastern part of southern Canada and the eastern section of the United States as far south as Alabama and Arkansas, and it is the state tree of New Jersey. It reaches an average height of 65 ft., though a height of as much as 145 ft. has been recorded. It is probably the fastest growing of our native oaks. As a young tree it may add 2 in. to the diameter in a year and 12 in. to the height. It has a short trunk

Rotary-cut northern red oak

288

Flat-cut curly northern red oak

that divides into many heavy branches and is a broad, well-shaped tree. The bark varies from gray to brown in color, and the leaves, from 4 to 9 in. long, are dark green in color. The heartwood, of a light reddish-brown color, is more coarse-grained than the white oak and is considered inferior to the white oak.

The wood is used for many purposes in furniture and flooring and takes a satisfactory finish, though all oaks, because of the open pores, should be filled before finishing or painting.

Our red oak has become one of the most popular North American oaks used in Europe. It was introduced into France and England during the early part of the eighteenth century and today there are many fine buildings of this oak in France, Belgium and Germany.

Currently, it is estimated that there is over 80 billion feet of oak in this country and over 50 per cent of this is the red oak.

OAK, OREGON WHITE *Quercus garryana* (garryana—after Nicholas Garry, secretary of the Hudson Bay Company, who aided David Douglas in his botanical explorations in northwestern United States)

It is also known as GARRY'S OAK, PACIFIC WHITE OAK, PRAIRIE OAK and WESTERN WHITE OAK.

This oak grows in a small, definitely located area from central California northward through Oregon, Washington and British Columbia. The short-length trunk produces a good quality of yellowish-brown heartwood that is strong,

289

hard and fine-grained. There is a large shrinkage in drying, but the wood is easy to work with tools and will take a fine polish. It is used in flooring, all types of cabinet-work and in the manufacture of higher-grade furniture.

OAK, SOUTHERN RED *Quercus falcata* (falcata—sickle-shaped)

Growing from Florida westward to Oklahoma and north through the states of Illinois and New Jersey, this oak is also known as FINGER OAK, HILL RED OAK, SPANISH OAK, SPOTTED OAK and TURKEY RED OAK.

The leaves of this tree are shiny green on the top and a dull green on the bottom, having either three, five or seven sharply pointed lobes. It is a hard and heavy, fairly strong but coarse-grained wood and is difficult to dry as it checks badly. It deteriorates quickly when exposed to the ground. This oak is used in general construction work and will take a fine painted surface providing the wood has first been filled.

OAK, WHITE *Quercus alba* (alba —white)

It is also known as FORKED-LEAF WHITE OAK and STAVE OAK.

White oak is native to the eastern part of Canada and the United States, right to the Gulf states and

Quartered white oak—a good example of the quartered figure

Flat-sliced white oak

south to Florida. It is the state tree of Maryland and Connecticut and is the tree which produces the finest oak lumber and veneers, as well as the largest quantity of lumber.

The heartwood is light tan in color, and in the fall this is the tree that produces such beautiful coloring in red and bright yellow leaves, later turning to a pale brown. These leaves cling to the tree all during the winter. The tree has a large, high, straight trunk and is considered one of the most beautiful of hardwoods. The acorns of the white oak are large, about ¾" long, and edible. The Indians made use of them. They are eaten in a number of different ways—baked in muffins, boiled or roasted. The birds, deer, squirrels and other animals are particularly fond of the acorns, which decreases the chance of germination.

This is one of the heaviest, strongest and hardest of all the oaks. It may be worked easily with any type of tool and when properly finished will take a fine polish. Large quantities of white oak are manufactured into veneers, cut either on the quarter to obtain the flake figure, or what is known as "rift cut" to obtain the fine straight lines very popular in modern furniture. It is a favorite wood for the paneling of fine rooms.

The lumber is largely used in the manufacture of containers for liquids and a good deal is used in the manufacture of barrels for liquors. It is particularly desirable for this purpose as the pores of the wood are filled with a substance (known as tyloses) which does not permit liquids to penetrate.

291

OGEA *Daniellia ogea* (Daniellia—after Samuel Daniell, 1777-1811, English painter; ogea—after the native Nigerian name)

Ogea is also known as DANIELLIA, GUM COPAL and OZIYA.

Ogea originates in west Africa and is generally found in the heavy rain forests of Nigeria. It comes from the same genus of trees which produces the west African gum copal. It is a fairly straight tree and has a smooth bark until the tree ages, when the bark becomes very scaly. The age of this tree can be determined by studying the bark.

The tree produces wood of a pale white or pinkish-brown color without much character and with large pores that produce the lines in the wood. It is of medium weight and strength and does not present any difficulty in working with tools. It takes a good stain, but for a high polish the pores have to be filled first. It is exported only in limited quantities.

OKWEN *Brachystegia spiciformis* (Brachy/stegia—short covering; spiciformis—pointed)

Okwen is a large tree growing in the dense forests in tropical Africa, including Northern Rhodesia and western Africa. It varies greatly in size as some trees are slender and unusual in height and others are much shorter with unusual diameters.

The heartwood has a background of light brown with variable darker brown stripes of irregular width. It is a heavy wood, averaging 47 lbs. per cubic foot, and is hard and resistant to decay. With experienced handling the wood seasons well in the dry kilns and is suitable for all types of interior work and construction. Selected logs will produce a good quality of rotary-cut veneer.

292

OLIVE, EAST AFRICAN *Olea hochstetteri* (Olea—ancient Latin plant name, *oleum,* meaning oil; hochstetteri—after C. F. Hochstetter, a German professor)

This tree, found in the forests of Kenya and also in Abyssinia, reaches a height of 80 ft. or more with diameters around 3 ft. It has an unusually fine texture, heavier than average, around 60 lbs. per cubic foot, and a pleasing brownish, sort of olive color, with attractive markings. The tree bears a small white flower and the fruit is similar to the olives growing on the olive trees in Italy—probably why this tree is so named.

East African olive has unusual strength and is an excellent wood for columns and heavy construction work. Because of its wide variation in color, it is also suitable for paneling, veneering, decorative work and bandings on cabinets.

OLIVE, EUROPEAN *Olea europea* (Olea—Greek name for the olive; europaea—from Europe)

Native to southern Europe and

Olive burl, two-piece match

particularly Italy, this tree somewhat resembles the willow but belongs to the same family as the ash. The wood, which is yellowish-brown in color, streaked with dark brown pigment lines, is hard and heavy, close-grained and slow-growing. Occasionally veneers are available—at high prices—and at times burls and swirls may be obtained.

OLIVILLO *Aextoxicon punctatum* (Aex/toxicon—goat poison; punctatum—dotted)

Emanating in Chile, this is a medium sized tree, similar to red gum or satin walnut, and it grows in stands so thick and close that it kills all of the smaller vegetation.

The wood has a brownish background without much variation in color and is of medium weight and hardness, but with a very fine, even texture and straight grain. Small quantities have been exported in the last ten years to commercial markets where it has been used for miscellaneous work and in the construction of furniture. In Chile it is used for all types of general carpentry, joining and staves for casks.

OMU *Entandrophragma candollei* (Ent/andro/phragma—within the male membrane; candollei—after deCandolle, a family of Swiss botanists)

Growing throughout west Africa, this is a large tree, known as KOSIPO in the French territories, and weighing about 45 lbs. per cubic foot. The heartwood is reddish brown, which darkens upon exposure, and it is especially difficult to season, particularly when kiln-dried.

Selected logs are suitable for furniture, and the heavier species are used in large construction and naval work. The principal interest in this wood is that occasional figured logs will produce a very beautiful veneer, though little of it is available on the market.

OPEPE *Sarcocephalus diderrichii* (Sarco/cephalus—fleshy head; diderrichii—after Diderrich)

This tree grows in southern Nigeria and the Gold Coast in Africa. It is a gray-white to yellowish-pink in color. The heartwood is nearly an orange color and has a pattern somewhat like mahogany.

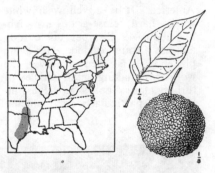

ORANGE, OSAGE *Maclura pomifera* (Maclura—after William Maclure, 1743-1840, American geologist; pom/ifera—apple bearing)

Osage orange grows in the southwestern United States, and the logs obtained are in lengths from 6 to 8 ft. and 12 to 16 in. in diameter. The wood has a greenish yellow color, very close grain somewhat like locust, and is hard and strong. It is seldom cut into lumber or veneers, but when it is, the principal uses are for archery bows and for wheels. It also is used as a dyewood for extracting dyes. Decorative mottles are obtained from selected logs.

293

ORANGE, SOUR *Citrus aurantium* (Citrus—from Greek, citron used for the citron tree, *Citrus medica;* aurantium—orange)

This tree grows in India, southern Europe, Africa and tropical America. It is a yellowish white wood, hard, close-grained, weighing about 49 lbs. per cubic foot, and has a tough surface after being planed. It is used all over the world for making small articles of turnery, fancy boxes, novelties, inlays, and particularly for manicure sticks.

PADOUK, ANDAMAN *Pterocarpus dalbergioides* (Ptero/carpus—winged fruit; dalbergioides—appearing like *Dalbergia*)

Padouk, while emanating from Africa, is secured principally from the Andaman Islands, a group of islands in the Bay of Bengal about 650 miles southeast of Calcutta. Most of the settlements here are penal colonies and a great portion of this timber is logged by convict labor. The padouk tree is one of the most common in these islands. The trees do not grow in groups, but are scattered throughout the forest. They are large, growing to 15 ft. in circumference at the stump and 60 ft. high to the first branch.

Because of the brilliant red color of some of the wood, the name vermilion has been given to it. Among old cabinetmakers it is often referred to as East Indian mahogany and Indian redwood. It comes in both a stripe and a mottled effect. Much use has been made of it by the Pullman Company for trim in dining, smoking

Striped padouk

Florida orange tree with ripened fruit

and sleeping compartments. Craftsmen find it an excellent wood for various small pieces of furniture, turned articles and certain musical instruments.

The padouk from Africa is generally inferior to that described above because of its open grain and softer texture. It is used extensively in the making of dyes. In using this wood one must avoid application of water to the unfinished surface.

PALDAO *Dracontomelum dao* (Draconto—a kind of bird; melum —origin unknown; dao—a native name in the Philippines)

Paldao grows in the East Indies, Indo-China and the Philippines. It has a grayish to reddish-brown color, varied grain effects, usually with irregular stripes and occasionally some very dark stripes. At times a crotch or swirl will develop. It is a fairly hard wood, available in quartered veneers, half-round, and lumber, and is used for architectural woodwork and in furniture.

Semi-figured paldao, two-piece match

PALMS

THE PALM TREE is another of our Biblical woods from which, as we all know, Palm Sunday is named. However, what is not generally realized is that if all species of palms were counted there would be nearly 1,200, classified under the name of *Palmaceae*.

Practically all of them grow in tropical lands and the greatest number have a cylindrical trunk with a crown of leaves, either fan-shaped or featherlike, and having polygamous flowers. The most valuable in commerce are the coconut-palm *(Cocos)* and the date palm *(Phoenix)*.

Some of the others often seen are the Washingtonia palm *(Washingtonia rabusta)*, native to lower California and Mexico; the royal palm *(Roystonea regia)*, native to Cuba and south Florida, which is one of the most striking in appearance, growing to 100 ft. in height with a whitish colored trunk; the fishtail palm *(Caryota urens)*, the most widely known of the nine species from Asia and Australia; the king palm *(Archontophoenis alexandrae)*, native of New South Wales and Queensland; the pygmy-date palm *(Phoenix roebelenin)*, native to Africa and tropical Asia, though also widely grown in Florida for landscaping, and the palm often found in our northern states as potted house plants. Then there is the African oil palm *(Elaeis guineensis)*, native of tropical Africa and the East Indies, which is cultivated commercially for "palm oil" used in cooking, ointments and the making of soap.

Palms have considerable interest to botanists for study, and commercially for the fruit, oil and other products derived from them. However, the palm has little interest to the craftsman because it does not provide wood suitable for working with tools.

PALMETTO, CABBAGE *Sabal palmetto* (Sabal—an unexplained name; palmetto—from the Spanish, palmito, for little palm)

This palm is also known as CAROLINA PALM and SWAMP CABBAGE and is the state tree of Florida and South Carolina.

This tree grows to an average height of 30 to 50 ft., with diame-

ters from 16 to 24 in., and is native to the southeastern United States from North Carolina southward. It obtains its common name from the fact that the leaf bud or "heart" at the top of the trunk is a delicacy with a fine cabbage flavor when cooked as a vegetable would be cooked. The early Florida Indians used it as one of their principal foods and today it is stocked in some stores, precooked, in cans. However, the tree generally dies when the tender bud is cut away.

This is the palm that is used in churches on Palm Sunday and it also has a historical background. The state seal of South Carolina shows the cabbage palmetto, commemorating the fact during the Revolution the South Carolinians built a stockade from logs of the cabbage palm, and in Charleston

Cabbage palmetto

Harbor on Sullivan Island, on June 28, 1776, General William Moultrie defeated the ships of the British.

Cross sections from large trunks of palmetto trees can be polished to make unusually attractive table tops. It is a fairly light and soft wood and locally is used for making fences and telegraph poles.

PARTRIDGE WOOD *Andira inermis* (Andira—from the Brazilian name; inermis—unarmed, without spines)

Emanating in Venezuela and Colombia, this tree averages about 6 ft. in height and 1 to 2 ft. in diameter. The heartwood is deep, purplish-brown or chocolate brown with the positions of the pores marked with a lighter colored line of soft tissues. The wood is named from the figure produced by these soft tissues on plain surfaces as it is somewhat similar to the markings on a partridge wing.

Partridge wood is very heavy, about 75 lbs. per cubic foot, occasionally more, and extremely hard. It has strength and high resistance to rot, which is one of the reasons it is used locally for outdoor construction work. It is suitable principally for turning as it is extremely hard to work, either in wet or dry form, but it takes a very smooth polish. A small quantity of this wood is imported into the United States and used principally for turned work, fancy articles and walking sticks.

PAU d'ARCO *Tabebuia serratifolia* (Tabebuia—a Brazilian plant name; serrati/folia — saw-toothed leaf, referring to the notched margins of the leaflets)

Native to Brazil, this tree is known there as the IRON TREE and IRONWOOD. It is also known as BASTARD, GREENHEART, LIGNUM VITAE and SURINAM, and in the southern part of Brazil as IPÉ.

This tree is described as one of the tallest in the Amazon region, with a height of from 180 to 200 ft. It has a lustrous brown color with a slightly greenish tinge, somewhat resembling a dark greenheart but with a much closer and finer grain. Some of the logs are highly figured with a small broken roe and mottle, and veneers have been obtained which give the appearance of a dark, golden-brown Ceylon satinwood. These have been used for high-class decorative work in both England and America. Other uses of this wood are in general construction and for piling and harbor work.

All of the different varieties have astringent qualities and are reported as of medicinal value.

PAU FERRO *Libidibia sclerocarpa* (Libidibia—probably pleasure bird from *libid ibid;* sclero/carpa—hard fruit)

This wood is native to the Guianas, Brazil and other parts of tropical South America. Its texture resembles African blackwood for smoothness and marblelike appearance. This is another wood known as IRONWOOD. It is a deep, purplish-brown in color, merging almost into a black, and weighs about 69 lbs. per cubic foot.

Locally it is used for building docks, piling, etc., but there is no known use of it commercially in this country.

PAWPAW *Asimina triloba* (Asimina—from the American Indian

Top, the leaves, fruit and flowers of the pawpaw.
Bottom, an orchard of pear trees near Baltimore, Md.

name; tri/loba—three-lobed, referring to the three-parted flower)

This tree grows from western
New York through Nebraska and
southward through the Middle Atlantic states to Texas and Florida.
The fruit resembles a short banana
in shape, from which it receives its
common name.

The wood has little commercial
value except for fuel, and its principal use is for ornamental planting. However, it works well with
tools and where locally obtainable
it offers possibilities to the craftsman for various types of turned
work.

The wood is reddish-brown with
occasional dark streaks and is hard
and heavy. It is often used for
office chairs. A limited amount is
manufactured into veneers for use
in furniture. Pecan wood takes a
lovely polish.

PEAR WOOD *Pyrus communis*
(Pyrus—pear; communis — common)

This is also called PEAR TREE
and grows in the United States,
Germany and France.

The wood is rosy pink in color,
with shadings on a light cream
background. It has a moderate,
leafy grained figure, sometimes
with a mottle figure, and is fine
and close-grained. It is very suitable for reproducing flesh colors.
It is used in mechanical drawing
instruments and rulers, and a great
portion of it in marquetry work.
The most sought-after for veneers
is the pear wood from Europe.

The principal value, however, is
in the very delicious long oval-
shaped nuts it produces. They have
the appearance of a football in
shape and are highly prized as a
delicacy. Today there are tremendous groves of pecans, cultivated
for their nuts, and one of the largest in New Mexico covers more
than 4,000 acres with over 75,000
trees.

Another use for pecan wood is
for the smoking of meats, it being
considered especially desirable for
this purpose.

PECAN WOOD *Carya illinoensis*
(Carya—from the Greek name for
nut; illinoensis—from Illinois)

Pecan is a species of the hickory
tree found in the southern part of
the United States, east of the Mississippi, and is the state tree of
Texas. It was named after the
Algonquin Indian, Peccan. For
many years the Indians believed
that this tree was a part of the
Great Spirit himself.

PEROBA, ROSA *Aspidosperma
peroba* (Aspido/sperma — shield
seed, referring to the waferlike
shape of the seed; peroba—a native
name)

Other names by which this tree
are known are AMARILLO, PALO
and ROSA.

This large tree, with well-formed
trunk, grows in southeastern Brazil
and obtains a height of 125 ft. and
4 or 5 ft. in diameter. The trees
are slender with sparse foliage and
a wrinkled bark, but they stand out

Quarter-sliced rosa peroba

in the landscape clearly because of their majestic appearance. The heartwood is rose-red to yellowish, often variegated or streaked with purple or brown, and the surface becomes brownish-yellow to dark brown upon exposure. It is not sharply demarcated from the sapwood. Being hard and moderately strong, the wood weighs 46 lbs. per cubic foot.

It has a low to medium luster. The odor is not distinctive, but the wood has a very bitter taste. It has good working qualities, with a fine, uniform texture and a grain which runs from straight to very irregular. Rosa peroba is one of the highly important group of Brazilian timbers, comparable in general utility to the oak of the United States. It is used in great abundance in all kinds of building construction.

Other colors of peroba are indicated by their names, as follows: Peroba preta, with conspicuous black streaks; peroba miuda, which is red with darker patches; peroba poca, a white wood; peroba rajada, light red with large black patches; peroba tremida, yellow with lighter patches, almost golden; peroba revesa, having a figure similar to bird's-eye maple. Veneers are available in the peroba species.

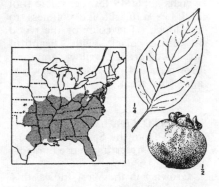

PERSIMMON, COMMON *Diospyros virginiana* (Diospyros — fruit or wheat of the gods; virginiana—of Virginia)

It is also known under the names of BARA-BARA, BOA-WOOD, BUTTERWOOD, CYLIL DATE PLUM, and POSSUM WOOD.

Growing in the southern part of the United States, this wood is known as the ebony of America and has a cubic weight of 59 lbs. per cubic foot. This is usually a small or medium sized tree, but it has obtained heights of 100 ft. and more, with a diameter of 20 to 30 in. The heartwood is black, brown or variegated; when freshly cut, the sapwood is white. The sapwood is strong and tough, of medium to fine texture with fairly straight

301

grain, and finishes very smoothly.

Persimmon sapwood is used for the heads of golf clubs and the manufacture of shuttles, in which form it will withstand 1,000 hours of work without any need of replacement.

PERSIMMON, KAKI *Diospyros kaki* (Diospyros—fruit of the gods; kaki—probably from a native name)

This wood comes from Japan where it is used extensively. It weighs about 49 lbs. per cubic foot and has a marblelike coldness to the touch. The color of the wood is dense black with beautiful streaks of orange, yellow, gray and brown, but it possesses a very disagreeable scent.

PIMENTO *Pimenta officinalis* (Pimenta—from the Spanish pimento; officinalis—referring to use in medicine)

Growing in the West Indies, this wood is firm, hard and close-textured and varies in color from a light salmon to dark salmon. It has a very limited use, practically the entire output being used in making canes.

PINES

BELONGING to the softwood group of the forest trees in the United States, the pines include 35 different species. A brief description is given of a few of them, as well as several important foreign pines.

PINE, CHILEAN *Araucaria araucana* (Araucaria—after the Chilean province of Arauco; araucana—of Arauco)

This species of pine has been known in England for many years under the name of MONKEY PUZZLE.

Growing in a very limited area of southwest Argentina and a small section of Chile, the wood was first discovered many years ago in the province of Arauco, which explains how its scientific name was derived. The height is from 80 to 120 ft. and occasionally trees are found considerably taller than this, with diameters anywhere from 30 to 48 in. An interesting thing about this tree is its seeds, which are large and often number 100 or more in each ripe cone. They are generally about an inch in length. In Chile they are collected for food and when served in roasted form are considered a rare delicacy.

The wood is of a yellowish or gray color and has a tendency to darken slightly with age. It is of fine texture, straight-grained, and like many pines, without any distinctive odor. Chilean pine secretes a valuable resin or gum and it gives up its moisture so slowly and so unevenly in drying that considerable care is necessary.

This wood has been exported for 150 years or more, with considerable quantities going to Great Britain, but as most of the finer trees are in mountainous regions and difficult to get at, only limited amounts are exported today. The tree is often seen in English gardens under the name, as mentioned above, of monkey puzzle.

The wood is suitable for interior work, doors, and was especially used in airplane construction and propellers.

PINE, EASTERN WHITE *Pinus strobus* (Pinus—the classical Latin

Upper left, shortleaf pine. Upper right, longleaf pine.
Lower left, eastern white pine. Lower right, loblolly pine

name; strobus—a Latin word for pine cone)

This tree is also known by other common names such as NORTHERN WHITE PINE, BALSAM PINE and CANADIAN WHITE PINE; in Michigan it is known as CORK PINE, also as SPRUCE PINE and WHITE PINE.

This is the king of all pines in the eastern part of our country and the state tree of Maine. The height of a virgin growth of these trees has been known to reach from 100 to 200 ft., with diameters up to 6 ft. The heartwood is a very light creamy brown, sometimes tan, and tinged with red. It has a dark gray bark that is deeply furrowed in long ridges and bluish-green needles, from 3 to 5 in. long, which grow in bundles of five. The cones are from 5 to 10 in. long and usually curve; they mature at the end of the second season.

It is the favorite wood of carpenters as it works easily and finishes well. It has been used for a long time for patternmaking and for general interior trim.

For over 300 years early Americans used this wood to build their homes, their churches and their mills. The Colonies' flag which was flown in the American Revolution from all the Colonial ships, carried a reproduction of the white pine tree, and the state of Massachusetts in the seventeenth century honored the tree by having its image on a coin.

Many things have reduced the large stand of white pine that was in America at the time of the white man's arrival. As far as can be figured out, the original amount was better than ¾ of a trillion square feet; today's figures indicate that about 15 billion feet have been left growing. White pine in its natural state may have a lifetime of 400 years.

PINE, JACK *Pinus banksiana* (banksiana—after Sir Joseph Banks, 1743-1820, benefactor of one of Cook's voyages to Australia, and naturalist)

This pine is also known as BLACK PINE, GRAY PINE, HUDSON BAY PINE and SCRUB PINE.

Jack pine, considered one of the poorest of the species, grows in eastern Canada, the provinces of Nova Scotia and Quebec, throughout northern New England and northeastern United States, through the Great Lakes states of Indiana, Illinois, Michigan and Wisconsin.

The tree grows to a height of 20 to 65 ft. and the trunks are of a diameter from 6 to 24 in. It may be recognized by the needles, which grow in pairs, only 1 in. long; they are narrow, flat, twisted and sharply pointed, dark gray-green in color. The cones are oblong and curved with thick scales. The tree has a dull, dark red-brown, thin bark with narrow, shallow ridges.

The most important use of this wood is in the manufacture of paper pulp. However, an increasing quantity is being used each year for the manufacture of furniture and plywood and for paneling rooms because of the attractiveness of the knots. It is known as "knotty pine."

Quarter-sawed Liberian pine

PINE, LIBERIAN *Tetraberlinia tubmaniana* (Tetra—Latin, meaning fourth; berlinia—generic name of the Ekop group of the *Leguminoseae* family, or the fourth division; *tubmania*—in honor of William V. S. Tubman, President of the Republic of Liberia)

This is a large, very straight, tall tree with diameters up to 4 ft., the most common diameters being between 2 and 3 ft. It grows along the coastal region of Liberia, and in a number of places it is found in such concentration that large quantities will be available for export to the various wood markets of the world. Leaves, fruit and wood specimens were collected in 1954 by E. W. Fobes of the United States Forest Products Laboratory.

The wood has a pleasing grain with a light to medium reddish brown color. It is a wood of average weight—40 lbs. per cubic foot when oven-dried. It seasons without difficulty and no special care is required in drying other than procedures normally used with hardwoods. It works well with either power or hand tools and can be compared with yellow poplar for planing; in a lathe it does not turn quite as well as American black walnut. However, it shapes much better than American walnut, although not quite as well as Honduras mahogany.

The raw wood has an oily feel but it takes a fine finish. In Denmark it has been sliced into veneers without difficulty and used in the commercial manufacture of furniture. In Liberia it has been used extensively for home building and construction and also in the manufacture of furniture.

PINE, LOBLOLLY *Pinus taeda* (taeda—ancient name of resinous pines)

This is also known as BASSETT PINE, BLACK PINE, FOXTAIL PINE, INDIAN PINE, LONGLEAF PINE,

SWAMP PINE and YELLOW PINE.

Loblolly pine grows in the southeastern part of the United States along the Atlantic coast from Delaware to northern Florida and westward to Texas. It may be recognized by its thin bark, deeply furrowed by long, large scales, and its red-brown color. The needles are pale green, sharp-pointed, 5 to 9 in. long, and three in a bundle. The heartwood is light tan or yellowish-brown. It is a strong, moderately hard wood, used in the manufacture of commercial veneers, boxes, in general construction, and large quantities for paper pulp.

PINE, LODGEPOLE *Pinus contorta* (contorta—contorted or twisted, alluding to the irregular crown of the typical, scrubby shore pine of the coast)

Other common names are BLACK PINE, SCRUB PINE, SHORE PINE, COAST PINE, TAMARACK PINE.

The common name of this tree was given because of its tall, slender, very light poles which were used by Indians of the region in the structure of their lodges. Poles 15 ft. long and 2″ in diameter were selected, set in a circle, the tops bent together and tied, and the frame covered with skins or bark.

Lodgepole pine has often been called a "fire tree"—a very appropriate name—as it profits by severe burning, as some other trees of the United States do. The sealed cones are opened by fire, which softens the resin; and after the fire has passed, the seeds are liberated to wing their flight wherever the wind carries them. The passing fire may be severe enough to kill the parent tree without destroying or bringing down the cones. The seeds soon fall on the bared soil where they germinate by thousands. More than one hundred thousand small seedling trees may occupy a single acre. Most lodgepole pines never reach large size.

The tree is one of the slowest in growing; possibly 3 feet is the limit. It is very tall and slender. A hundred years will scarcely produce a saw log of the smallest size. The wood is about the same weight as eastern pine, light in color, rather weak and brittle. The wood is characterized by numerous small knots.

Lodgepole pine has long and widely been used as ranch timber, serving as poles and rails in fences and for sheds, barns, corrals, pens and small bridges.

If fires cease among the western mountains, with more efficient methods of patrol and stricter enforcement of laws against starting fires, the spread of lodgepole pine will come to a standstill and existing forests will grow old without much extension of their borders.

PINE, LONGLEAF *Pinus palustris* (palustris—of the marsh)

This species is also known as FLORIDA PINE, GEORGIA HARD PINE, NORTH CAROLINA PITCH PINE, TEXAS LONGLEAVED PINE and TURPENTINE PINE.

This pine grows in the southeastern states, extending westward to Alabama (of which state it is the official tree), Mississippi, Louisiana and Texas. It bears one of the longest needles—6 to 20 in.—of a dark green color, shiny, flexible, growing three in a cluster. They drop off every two years. The tree obtains its name from these very long needles. The bark is of an orange-brown color, slightly marked into broad scales. The brownish cones also are long—5 to 10 in.— and grow in clusters of several cones.

This tree has no heartwood until it is about 18 years old; then the heartwood is light orange, yellow and red, while the sapwood is practically white.

Longleaf pine provides large quantities of turpentine, rosin and pine oil, which is used in the manufacture of cosmetics and perfumes. The wood is used in the manufacture of pulpwood and craft paper and also for railroad ties, piles, heavy construction work and shipbuilding.

years or more. It has a short trunk and often is no higher than 8 or 10 ft., twisted and crooked. At times it may reach 50 ft. and is from 10 to 24 in. in diameter. The tree grows in mountainous areas at elevations of 5,000 feet and upwards and is found in the western part of the country from Wyoming through Colorado and into northern Mexico and Texas. It is the state tree of Nevada and New Mexico.

This tree is mostly prized for its pine nuts, which are delicious and edible. These nuts are generally baked shortly after being gathered to retain their rich flavor. They are the most valuable product of the tree, and the annual crops of nuts range from one million to as high as eight million pounds.

As the tree is very knotty, because of the many limbs, the wood is generally used locally for general construction and in the manufacture of charcoal. It is a favorite wood for telephone poles.

PINE, PINYON *Pinus edulis* (edulis—edible, referring to the large edible seeds commonly called Indian nuts, pine nuts or piñones)

This species is also known as NUT PINE, PITCH PINE and SCRUB PINE.

This is a very slow-growing tree and its life span may reach 350

PINE, PONDEROSA *Pinus ponderosa* (ponderosa—ponderous or heavy, in reference to the heavy timber)

This species is also known as BIG PINE, BIRD'S-EYE PINE, KNOTTY PINE, LODGEPOLE PINE, OREGON

307

The ponderosa pine—a typical stand, bark and needles

PINE, PITCH PINE, POLE PINE and PRICKLY PINE.

Ponderosa pine is the state tree of Montana.

It grows along the extreme western part of the continent from Alaska down through California and through most of the Rocky Mountains, up to elevations of 10,000 and 12,000 ft. It is one of the most beautiful pines, with diameters up to 7 ft. It may be recognized because of the thick, scaly, irregular bark of a pale brown or grayish color. The needles generally are in bundles of three, from 5 to 10 in. long with a gray-green to deep yellow-green color.

The town of Flagstaff, Arizona, was so named because of this tree. On the Fourth of July in 1876, lumberjacks selected one of the tallest trees and as it grew, stripped it of all its branches to fly the American flag from its top. It is said that this is the only American wood whose name has been under consideration by the U. S. Supreme Court. It issued a ruling in 1934 preventing the sale of the wood as California white pine. It is estimated that over 185 billion feet are growing, over 3 billion feet being logged annually.

Sometimes a bird's-eye figure, the same as seen in maple, is found in this pine. It provides a large quantity of lumber for cabinetwork, general millwork, sash, doors and moldings, and it is used as knotty pine for interior trim. Also it is used for miscellaneous purposes such as various types of poles, fence posts and paper pulp.

Upper left, pinyon pine. Upper right, singleleaf pinyon pine.
Lower left, slash pine. Lower right, plane tree growing on the
campus of Vassar College, Poughkeepsie, N. Y.

PINE, SCOTCH *Pinus sylvestris* (sylvestris—of the woods)

This pine emanates in Europe, particularly Great Britain, and is generally known abroad as RED WOOD.

It weighs about 26 lbs. per cubic foot, is even and straight in grain, tough and elastic. It is easily worked and is famous for use as heavy timbering and in general construction work.

PINE, RED *Pinus resinosa* (resinosa—resinous)

This pine at times is also known under the name of NORWAY PINE. It acquired this name because originally large quantities of these trees were located in the village of Norway, Maine.

The average red pine grows to a height of 65 to 80 ft. with diameters of 2 to 3 ft. and it is estimated there are over a quarter million acres of red pine in Minnesota. 'United States figures show that there are a little less than 3 billion board feet, most of it in the northeast with the balance divided between Wisconsin, Michigan and Minnesota. Red pine is the state tree of Minnesota.

This pine is a light, close-grained wood of average softness and produces better lumber for building purposes than the eastern pine because of its extra weight and strength. It is an excellent tree for piling because it has a high penetration with creosote.

The early colonists found that this wood was best suited for the deckings, masts and spars of their sailing boats. Today there is a great demand for the red pine logs for building summer log cabins.

PINE, SHORTLEAF *Pinus echinata* (echinata—spiny, describing the cones)

This species of pine is also known as CAROLINA PINE, NORTHERN CAROLINA PINE, PITCH PINE and YELLOW PINE.

It is the official state tree of Arkansas and grows from New York southward to most of the southeastern states as far as Florida, and the eastern sections of Oklahoma, Texas and Arkansas. It is recognized by the blue-green, slender needles, 3 to 5 in. long, in bundles of two that remain on the tree from two to five years. The cones are a dull brown, only 1 to 2 in. long, and of prickly egg shape.

The name *echinata* was given to this pine in 1768 by Philip Miller, the British botanist, as coming from the Latin word for hedgehog, probably suggested by the green cones and needles. Before the days of the steamship, it was one of the most prized woods in ship construction and was used for the masts in all naval vessels of the United States and Great Britain. Early in the 1700's the wood was proclaimed by Great Britain as the property of the British Crown for the masts of the Royal Navy.

It is now used in building construction and interior trim as knotty pine. It is so rapid in growing that it is being used in increasing quantities for paper pulp.

PINE, SLASH *Pinus elliottii* (elliottii—after its discoverer, Stephen Elliott, 1771-1830, botanist and banker of South Carolina)

This species of pine is also known as MEADOW PINE, SALT WATER PINE, SPRUCE PINE, SHE PITCH PINE and SWAMP PINE.

Growing in lowlands and swamps, called "slashes," from which it is named, this pine is found in the southeastern states from the Atlantic seaboard to Mississippi and Louisiana. The needles are dark lustrous green, 8 to 12 in. long, two or three in a bundle, growing in clusters at the end of the twigs. The cones are a glossy brown, egg-shaped, 3 to 6 in. long, with short spines at the end of each scale of the cone, which is a distinguishing feature of the slash pine.

This is the pine largely used along roadsides and for home planting because of its fine appearance. It also outranks all others in the production of pine oils, resins, etc.

Sugar pine is a genuine white pine, readily identified by clusters of five slender needles

---

PINE, SUGAR *Pinus lambertiana* (lambertiana—in honor of Aylmer

Bourke Lambert, 1761-1842, English specialist in pines)

It is also known under other various names such as BIG PINE,

311

GIGANTIC PINE, GREAT SUGAR
PINE and SHADE PINE.

This tree grows in the regions of
southern Oregon to lower California and Mexico, generally at higher
altitudes. It reaches a height of up
to 150 ft. and is from 4 to 8 ft. in
diameter, though species have been
found as high as 240 ft. and diameters up to 18 ft. Sugar pine
has been described as the finest of
all pines for size and is similar in
color to the eastern and western
pines, although of a little lighter
shade.

PINE, WESTERN WHITE *Pinus monticola* (monticola — of the mountains)

This species is also known as
IDAHO WHITE PINE, MOUNTAIN
PINE, WHITE PINE and SILVER
PINE.

This is the pine of the northwest
and is similar in character to the
wood of the eastern pine but very
different in appearance. This wood
grows from the southern region of
British Columbia southward along
the Cascade Mountains and the
Sierra Nevadas, through Washington and Oregon to central California, and it is also the state tree of
Idaho.

The wood is very light cream to
light reddish-brown in color, dark-

Bark and needles of Western white pine

ening somewhat upon exposure. Its
chief characteristic is its knots.

Western white pine has a re-
markable resistance to weather,
growing both in very dry lands and
in moist lands, in temperature anywhere from 25 degrees below zero
to 100 degrees above. It is a long-
lived tree, sometimes up to 500
years, and it is estimated that over
16 billion board feet of this pine
exists in the United States today
with more than two thirds of it
growing in Idaho.

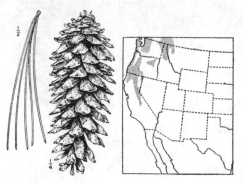

312

This pine was discovered around 1830 by a Scotch plant explorer, Davis Douglas, who sent some of the seeds to England. However, it was many years before this tree was cultivated, and more of it can be found in Ireland and Scotland than in England.

The wood is used for the same purpose as the eastern white pine, particularly for interior trim in the lumber form, but it is also available in veneers for the manufacture of plywood.

PINYON, SINGLELEAF *Pinus monophylla* (mono/phylla — one leaf, in allusion to the solitary needles)

This is the state tree of Nevada and grows in parts of Idaho, western Utah, Nevada and parts of Arizona and southern California. Singleleaf pinyon is one of the hardiest of trees, going undamaged through long periods without any moisture and subject to changes in temperature from well below zero to over 120 degrees.

The Indians have received the greatest benefit from these trees as the nuts which they produce are still an important part of their food. They have a period of feasting and dancing at the time of harvesting the nuts. Each Indian may gather as many as 35 bushels of nuts a year. Much of the ill feeling and

the resultant bloodshed was due to the destruction of this tree by the white man in the southwestern part of our country.

This wood has little commercial value with the exception that it is preferred for the manufacture of charcoal and is used for firewood.

¼ x

PLANE, EUROPEAN *Platanus acerifolia* (Platanus—from the classical Latin name for the oriental plane tree; acerifolia—with leaves like maple, *Acer*)

Of the various kinds of plane tree, the London plane tree as cultivated in Great Britain is one of the most common. It is a rapidly growing tree and apparently thrives well in the dusty and smoky air of large cities.

The wood is of very fine texture, with a straight grain, and when cut across the heart resembles beech with the exception that it is a little grayer in color. It averages about 40 lbs. per cubic foot and unless the lumber is quarter-sawn, requires considerable care in drying to prevent warpage. However, it has good strength and is an easy

313

wood to work. At times the quartered wood has been sold as a substitute for lacewood. The wood is used in inlaying and also in cabinetmaking.

PODO *Podocarpus gracilior* (Podo/carpus—foot fruit; gracilior—slender)

In east Africa this wood is known as MUSENGERA WOOD.

Podo is a large evergreen tree growing in several countries of east Africa including Kenya, Uganda, Abyssinia and parts of Transvaal and Tanganyika territories.

The wood varies in color from a pale yellow to a pale brown and often there is no difference in appearance between the heartwood and the sapwood. It is of fine, uniform texture with a straight grain and weighs a little more than 30 lbs. per cubic foot.

Podo is similar in strength to other foreign softwoods and while slightly harder, does not have the strength of those woods to sustain heavy loads. It is a good all-around wood for the cheap unseen parts of furniture, as drawer bottoms and shelves, and also would be suitable for cutting into veneers for the making of plywood.

POON *Calophyllum tomentosum* (Calo/phyllum—beautiful leaf; tomentosum—hairy)

This large tree, sometimes reaching a height of 150 ft., with diameters up to 48 in., is found in the heavy evergreen rain forests on the western side of the peninsula of India, in various altitudes up to 5,000 ft. It is also found on the island of Ceylon.

Because of the color, at first glance one would think the wood similar to mahogany or more like

the andiroba from South America with its darker wavy streaks of reddish-brown lines. With care the wood may be properly seasoned despite its tendency to warp, which is more marked in wood that has great irregularity of grain. However, it works well with saws sharpened and set properly to prevent burning in sawing. The wood possesses fine strength for its weight of approximately 35 lbs. per cubic foot and is much sought after in the East for the masts and spars of boats.

Choice logs have been converted successfully into attractive veneers. The extracted oil from the seeds of these trees is used for burning lamps.

POPLAR, BALSAM *Populus balsamifera* (Populus—the classical Latin name for the poplar; balsamifera—balsam bearing)

This wood is also known under the names of BALSAM, BALM-OF-GILEAD POPLAR and TACAMAHAC and is one of the thirteen species of COTTONWOOD.

This tree may be found almost across the entire northern part of the United States from the Atlantic Coast to the Rocky Mountains, and also in Canada and Alaska. It is the state tree of Wyoming.

Its leaves tremble in the breeze like those of the aspen, but the difference is easily noticed because of the pale green, lustrous leaves, the underside of which is a bright, rusty brown. It is a tall, straight tree which grows up to 100 ft. in height and with a diameter of 2 to 3 ft.

Great care has to be taken in drying this wood or it will warp badly. One of the principal uses is for making boxes and crates as the wood is light in weight, strong, nails easily without splitting and its appearance is suitable for stenciling or printing. Other uses are for butter and lard pails, matches, excelsior and rough lumber work.

According to records, standing timber in the United States is over 500 million feet, and each year a little over 12 million board feet is cut. The wood itself is light grayish and straight-grained. It always seeks wet, moist land. In the West it is one of the principal woods used for shade in city streets.

POPLAR, YELLOW *Liriodendron tulipifera*

This tree is also called CANARY WOOD and CANOE WOOD and the lumber is known as POPLAR, TULIPTREE and WHITEWOOD.

It grows throughout the eastern part of the United States, preferring damp locations and being found along the banks of streams. It is also found in southern Ontario. It is the state tree of three states: Indiana, Kentucky, and Tennessee. It grows singly, out in the open, generally 100 ft. or less in height, but it has been known to reach 200 ft. with a trunk of 8 to 10 ft. in diameter. About three quarters of the remaining first growth of timber is in the southeastern Appalachians. With good reason, it is regarded as one of the most valuable hardwood trees in the eastern United States.

The flowers are very sweet and the mature tree will yield as much as 7 or 8 lbs. of nectar a year, from which the bees produce up to 4 lbs. of one of the most strongly flavored honeys.

The heartwood is a yellowish or grayish color, occasionally with a slight greenish cast or dark streaks. It sometimes turns to a dark purple or blue color. The second growth of this timber has a very, thick, white sapwood.

Yellow poplar is manufactured into veneers, furniture and musical instruments and is used in general cabinetwork such as sash, doors and shelving and for painted interior trim. It is a wood used in the hat industry for hat blocks because it does not absorb the moisture present during the steaming process. In the veneer form, this wood is generally used for crossbanding and backs, and the soft yellow poplar growing in the mountain regions is considered the most desirable wood for crossbanding.

It works very easily with all kinds of tools, being suitable also for carving. It is an excellent wood for painting.

PRIMAVERA *Tabebuia donnell-smithii* (Tabebuia—a native name; donnell-smithii—after Donnell-Smith, a botanist)

Primavera is found growing along the west coast of Mexico and Nicaragua in rich, damp soil. However,

Striped primavera with mild figure

trees which grow in the uplands are stronger and produce a more beautiful figure.

Although it resembles white mahogany and is often erroneously referred to as "white mahogany," it does not come from the botanical classification which produces the true mahogany *(Swietenia)*. It perhaps is a good name, however, as it is similar in all respects to mahogany except for the color. When first cut, it is a pale yellow or cream color which darkens with exposure to air and light, changing to a yellowish-rose color, resembling Ceylon satinwood, with streaks of red, orange and brown. The principal defect is that many of the logs contain small pinholes caused by insects.

One of the little-known facts about this tree is that the sap of these trees in the tropics rises and falls with the phases of the moon instead of in the spring and winter as it does in temperate zones. This has an important effect upon the value and marketability of the timber—according to when it was felled. It should be cut in the "dark of the moon." The reason for this is that when the sap is down and the logs are cut, little of it exudes from the ends of the log, whereas if the trees are felled when the moon is on the increase there will be a large amount of sap in the trees and greater quantities will exude from the ends of the cut logs, attracting quantities of insects and causing damage to the trees before they are taken to the mill and converted into timber or veneers.

Primavera averages about 35 to 38 lbs. per cubic foot, works easily and finishes nicely and is very suitable for craftsmen, either in the thin lumber or veneer form, for producing individual effects.

While primavera is well known in the United States, it is seldom ever mentioned in the United Kingdom, being little used there.

PURPLEHEART *Peltogyne paniculata* and other species (Peltogyne —with the female organs shield-shaped; paniculata—referring to the flower cluster)

Purpleheart is also known as AMARANTH and VIOLET WOOD. Locally, in British Guiana, it is called SUCUPIRA.

This tree obtains a top height of 125 ft. with diameters up to 4 ft. It is a well-formed tree covered with smooth grayish-black bark, and often clear of branches up to 50 ft. The heartwood is a dull brown in color, but when freshly cut it turns deep purple upon exposure to air. It is used in the lumber form, one of its biggest uses being for making butts of billiard cues. When cut into ⅛₈" veneer, it is used for decorative work and in general cabinetmaking.

PYINKADO *Xylia xylocarpa* (Xylia—wood; xylocarpa—woody fruit)

Pyinkado grows in India and Burma and is known as the IRON WOOD OF BURMA.

The wood is reddish-brown in color, hard and heavy, weighing about 70 to 81 lbs. per cubic foot, and is very strong and rigid. Its pores are filled with a thick, glutinous, oily substance which gives a sticky feeling to the touch and is still noticeable after a great many years of exposure to the weather. As the logs are too heavy to float, it makes transportation not only difficult but very costly.

When the tree is freshly cut, it works with some difficulty, but after long exposure it becomes practically impossible for any woodworking tool to work it. Locally, the chief use of the wood is for the Burma railways. It is an excellent wood for paving blocks, having been successfully used for this purpose in Rangoon.

QUEBRACHO *Schinopsis* spp. (Schinopsis—having the appearance of *Schinus*)

Native to Argentina, this wood is also known there as BREAK-AXE, IRONWOOD and RED LIGNUM VITAE. It is a heavy wood, weighing about 70 to 80 lbs. per cubic foot.

A fine example of figured purpleheart

QUEENSLAND WALNUT *Endiandra palmerstoni* (En/di/andra— in two stamens; palmerstoni—after Palmerston)

This wood is also known as AUSTRALIAN LAUREL, AUSTRALIAN WALNUT, ORIENTAL WALNUT and ORIENTAL WOOD.

It grows only along the coast of Queensland in Australia and is a rich, decorative wood resembling in color the American and European walnut. While it is not related to the genuine walnut, it is a beautiful and striking wood.

In this country the greatest quantity is manufactured into veneers and originally was called oriental walnut, being so named by the ones who imported it so that others might not learn of the origin and true identity. Throughout the United Kingdom it is known as Australian or Queensland walnut.

The color varies from a pinkish-gray to brown with a figure somewhat like walnut but with much darker stripes. It is a fairly heavy wood, averaging around 45 lbs. per cubic foot, has a highly figured grain and has a most objectionable odor when freshly sawn. This, however, is not apparent after manufacture and drying into veneers.

The wood is difficult to season, requiring great care to prevent warpage and shrinkage when used in the solid wood. It also splits easily and is difficult to work with hand or power tools. When the wood is completely dry, the amount of silica in it quickly dulls knives and teeth of machine tools. For this reason the wood is much more suitable when used in the veneer form. However, it turns and polishes well, being firm and hard.

The wood is said to have more than 50 times greater insulating resistance to electric current than most other woods so it is particularly desirable in work that involves electrical appliances.

This is one of the very popular woods in Australia, where it is used in cabinetwork, in the manufacture of pianos and, as just mentioned, in various types of electrical equipment because of its insulating value.

Quarter-sliced oriental wood or Queensland walnut, mottle figure, two-piece match

Upper left, balsam poplar. Upper right, an excellent specimen of yellow poplar or tuliptree growing in the Bronx Botanical Gardens, New York. Bottom, young rubber trees grafted on older ones in a plantation in Malaya. The Federation of Malaya produces about half of the world's natural rubber

319

RANIA *Alseodaphne semecarpifolia* (Alseodaphne—grove laurel; semecarpifolia—naked with leaflike fruits)

The growth of this tree in its natural state is strictly limited to two places, western Ghats in India and what is known as the dry zone in the northern part of the island of Ceylon, in which place it grows on the mountainsides up to an elevation of 4,000 or 5,000 ft.

The wood, which has a very pleasing brownish appearance, is moderately heavy, averaging 45 to 60 lbs. per cubic foot, and hard, and in Ceylon is considered one of the best timbers. It is unusual that it is so little-known in other countries.

While the wood is more or less straight-grained, some of the logs produce a very beautiful broken mottle figure that should find a good market in the furniture centers of the world if more of it was exported. In Ceylon it is used for the finest cabinetwork, in furniture manufacture and house construction and decoration.

REDBUD, EASTERN *Cercis canadensis* (Cercis—the classical Greek name of *Cercis siliquastrum,* of southern Europe and western Asia; canadensis—of Canada, erroneous as the center of distribution is more southern)

Eastern redbud, the state tree of Oklahoma, is a small tree, growing from Connecticut to northern Florida and westward to the Mississippi, from 20 to 30 ft. in height and from 12 to 18 in. in diameter. A large number of these trees may be found on the grounds of Mt. Vernon, in Virginia, planted by George Washington and Thomas Jefferson.

This is a strong, hard wood of a brownish color, variegated with darker streaks. One of the chief values is for ornamentation, but in some southern sections of the country the blossoms and buds are eaten in salads, and fritters are made from the young pods. In Mexico, fried redbud flowers are a delicacy and the bark of the redbud is used in medicine. Refer to the chapter on Woods of the Bible for the legend of the redbud tree.

There is little value to the lumber it produces, but it has been used in some degree for small cabinetwork and turning.

REDWOOD *Sequoia sempervirens* (Sequoia—after the Cherokee Indian, Sequoyah, 1770?-1843; semper/virens—always green) Stephen Endlicher, well-known Austrian botanist, in 1947 gave the botanical name to this tree.

Redwood trees grow along or near the coast of California in a narrow strip not more than 35 miles

Redwood burl

'Midst some of nature's oldest and
largest living wonders—redwood trees in California

wide and about 500 miles long, extending from 100 miles south of San Francisco to a little above the Oregon border. Single acres of redwood have been found that contained over 1 million board feet of lumber. Redwood is the state tree of California.

A record size redwood tree that was felled 7 ft. above the ground had a diameter of 26 ft., was 261 ft. to the lowest branch, and measured 380 ft. in height. When sawed into lumber, it produced 344,000 board feet.

One of the loftiest redwoods now living is in the Humboldt State National Park in California—364 ft. in height and still growing. However, the size of these trees is not an accurate determination of their age. A giant Sequoia that was felled had a diameter of 27 ft. but was only 1,244 years old, whereas another of only 11½ ft. in diameter was over 2,000 years old. The availability to sunlight, condition of the soil and amount of water determine to a great extent the size of the trees. The Indians considered these trees immortal because of their long life.

The heartwood is usually a uniform deep reddish brown. The wood is without resin canals and has no distinctive odor, taste or feel. Typical redwood is moderately light in weight, averaging 20

The General Sherman Bigtree in the Sequoia National Park, California lbs. per cubic foot, and is moderately hard.

Over half of the redwood lumber produced is used in the form of planks, dimension boards, joists and posts. A large part of this material goes into framing for houses and industrial buildings, bridge trestles and other heavy construction. Some of the finer boards, and particularly the burls, are cut into veneers and used for decorative work on fine furniture.

ROSEWOOD, BRAZILIAN *Dalbergia* spp. (Dalbergia—after the Swedish physician, N. Dalberg, 1735-1820)

This species is also known as JACARANDA and PALISANDER WOOD.

Coming from the ports of Bahia and Rio, in Brazil, this rosewood is one of the most beautiful of cabinet woods. At one time many of the finest pianos were made of Brazilian rosewood and some may still be seen today. The wood has been popular for well over 100 years. A great amount of rosewood was used during the Empire Period in the early days of Queen Victoria's reign.

There is a wide variation in color from almost a cream to a light brown with streaks of jet black, and some pieces of lumber will contain a number of variegated irregular streaks which form a stripe pattern. Some of the wood, when manufactured into veneers and cut on the quarter, produces a straight stripe and other logs, cut half round, produce wild effects and wider sheets. The lumber may be obtained in squares of 1 x 1 in., 2 x 2 in. and other thicknesses, which are excellent for turning purposes.

Rosewood has a very fragrant odor when cut and even when it is burned, and it is said that from this odor the name of Brazilian rosewood was derived.

One can obtain an exceedingly smooth and highly polished surface with the use of this wood. It is employed in the veneer form for decorative and inlay effects in cabinetwork.

Brazilian rosewood

ROSEWOOD, HONDURAS *Dalbergia stevensonii* (stevensonii—after Stevenson)

The rosewood of British Honduras has been exported for over a century, the first record being a shipment of 188 pieces in 1841. It is a tree which obtains a height of 50 to 100 ft. and the trunk, which is often fluted, commonly forks at about 20 or 25 ft. from the ground.

Growing in damp places in Central America and concentrated for the most part along rivers, it is lighter in color than the Brazilian wood, more pinkish-brown or purplish, with darker and lighter bands. When freshly cut, the bark and sapwood have a distinctive odor, suggesting stored apples, and the taste is slightly bitter.

Straight-stripe East Indian rosewood, two-piece match

It is a coarse-textured wood, hard and heavy, weighing from 60 to 70 lbs. per cubic foot when thoroughly dried. It does not take a high natural polish very well. The supplies are fairly scarce, but when available the wood is used in cabinetwork and marquetry, but it is chiefly employed for the bars of the marimbas and xylophones manufactured in the United States.

ROSEWOOD, INDIAN *Dalbergia latifolia* (Dalbergia—after the Swedish physician, N. Dalberg, 1735-1820; lati/folia—broadleaved)

Emanating in India and Ceylon, this wood, after teak, is considered one of the most valuable that India produces. The logs are mostly cut on the quarter to obtain a straight stripe effect. The color runs from a very light yellow or light rose, with light and dark streaks, to logs that are almost black in color. The wood weighs about 53 lbs. per cubic foot and experiments show that it has an unusual quality of not shrinking either way of the grain, retaining exact measurements after being cut. It is therefore very useful where definite measurements must be secured.

In India it is one of the most important woods used in the manufacture of furniture, and in this country and throughout Europe, quantities of this rosewood have been used for a number of years in the lumber form and in veneers for fine cabinetwork and paneling.

ROSEWOOD, MADAGASCAR
Dalbergia greveana

This wood comes from the forests of Madagascar and is often named FRENCH ROSEWOOD and also MADAGASCAR PALISANDER.

It is a very hard wood, light rose-pink and sometimes of darker shades, with pronounced lines of a darker shade of red. It is generally available in veneers in the quartered-cut form.

RUBBER TREE *Hevea brasiliensis*

Other names are PARÁ RUBBER TREE in England, ÁRBOL DE CAUCHO in Venezuela and SERINGA in Peru.

This is the principal rubber tree. On occasion it grows to a height of over 100 ft., with a well-developed trunk more than 12 ft. in circumference. The usual height on plantations is from 60 to 80 ft. The structure of what is popularly known as the bark is of considerable importance in this tree because it contains the latex vessels which are the chief source of the world's rubber supply. The trunk of the tree may be divided roughly into an inner portion of wood and an outer portion of bark. The tree originally grew in the Amazon Valley.

The *brasiliensis* tree produces the purest and best para rubber. At one time there was no other source except in the Amazon Valley, but as long ago as 1834 Thomas Hancock, the English discoverer of vulcanization and a rubber manufacturer, called attention to the possibility of growing it in the East. The *hevea* trees were established in Ceylon and many are now growing in plantations in Malaya and the Dutch East Indies. Smaller amounts are grown in India, Sarawak, French Indo-China, Thailand as well as parts of Africa. The tree thrives on many types of soils with the exception of swampy, undrained, exposed land. It grows better in altitudes under 2,000 ft. than over.

Hevea brasiliensis is the most important genus of the *Euphorbiaceae* as its latex is the source of nearly all the world's supply of rubber. Twelve species grow in the Amazon basin, but only the *hevea brasiliensis* is cultivated on plantations. Some trees in Brazil at times obtain heights from 100 to 125 ft. They have a large cylindrical trunk, with or without buttresses.

Hevea wood is pale brown in color, light in weight, medium coarse-textured and brittle. It stains easily and is perishable when exposed to a humid climate, so has few if any commercial uses.

The plantations are thinned out, leaving about 90 trees per acre. Most trees on an estate yield 4 to 5 lbs. of rubber per year, but a few yield as much as 30 lbs., sometimes growing alongside others which yield only 2 lbs. The trees are ready for tapping for latex when about 5 years old, but the yield of latex and the quality of rubber obtained is not as good as when the trees are a few years older. Tapping is a delicate and important operation, consisting of the removal or the shaving of the bark with a sharp knife. For perfect tapping it is necessary to cut within 1/25" of the wood, an operation requiring practice.

During Christopher Columbus' second visit to South America, he was astonished to see native Indians amusing themselves with a heavy black ball made from a vegetable gum. Later explorers were equally impressed by these balls and a historian of the time reported that they rebounded so much that they appeared alive. Three centuries elapsed before the material was brought into commercial use in Europe and then it was not marketed for its elastic properties but to rub out lead-pencil marks, hence the name India rubber or rubber.

SABICU *Lysiloma latisiliqua* (Lysiloma—to loose the border, in reference to the separation of the pods at the borders at maturity; lati/siliqua—broad pods)

Sabicu grows in the West Indies and the wood is generally exported as square logs from 8 to 10 ft. and longer, with widths of 12 to 30 in. and occasionally larger. The wood is a dull brown color but has a bright luster. A large number of the logs are highly figured, containing not only straight and broken roe but a mottle. Fine examples of crotches are also produced.

The wood seasons slowly, does not split and shrinks but little during this process. It stands exposure to weather like teak, not being affected in any degree and not requiring the protection of paint or varnish. It is a hard, strong, tough wood with exceedingly close, smooth, firm grain, weighing 60 lbs. per cubic foot. In this connection it is said to have a peculiarity similar to greenheart in that the wood shows no sign of yielding as additional weight is added when tested for crushing force, but suddenly at a certain point it gives way, leaving nothing but a mass of shapeless fibers.

This wood works well in the timber form and was used extensively for many years in the works of the Adam brothers, Sheraton and others of that period. It is most attractive when used in conjunction with satinwood, developing a mellow tone which improves with years of exposure. In fact, much of the wood used by these cabinetmakers which was considered mahogany has been later found upon examination to be sabicu.

SANTA MARÍA *Calophyllum brasiliense* var. *rekoi*

Growing all through Central and South America, this species of wood is also known as HARI, LECHE MARÍA and PALO MARÍA.

The wood is of pinkish color to a deep red, usually developing a dark stripe and bearing a resemblance to mahogany. It has to season very slowly, and the greatest danger in splitting is towards the end of the seasoning period. It is a fairly heavy wood, weighing around 45 lbs. per cubic foot, and moderately hard.

Santa María is easy to work with and is generally produced in veneers for drawer bottoms. In the countries where it grows, it is used for carpentry, bridge work, boat building and bridges.

SAPELE *Entandrophragma cylindricum* (Ent/andro/phragma—within the male membrane; cylindricum—cylindrical)

This species is also known as ABOUDIKROU, SAPELE MAHOGANY, SIPO and TIAMA.

Sapele grows in Nigeria and along the African Ivory Coast. It is a large tree and logs often come as much as 72 in. in diameter though the usual range in the market is from 30 to 36 in. The color of the wood is a dark reddish-brown with a very strong stripe and at times the grain is very irregular. This irregularity causes the plum pudding and blister figures so highly prized in the veneer field.

The wood is very fine in texture and care has to be taken in the seasoning as it warps badly. Sometimes it is mistaken for African mahogany and used as such; however, it is harder and heavier, weighing from 35 to 40 lbs. per cubic foot, and the stripe is much more pronounced. Sapele is superior to either African or American mahogany in strength and is somewhat similar to the strength of our American oak.

Sapele is used for interior paneling and also in general furniture work.

SAPODILLA *Achras zapota* (Achras—ancient Greek name for ancestor of the common pear; zapota —from the Mexican Indian name, sapote)

Sapodilla is an evergreen tree growing throughout British Honduras, Guatemala, Venezuela and down into Brazil and also found in the West Indies. This tree is known for its remarkably long life and it provides three separate products. One is a very tasty fruit that it bears, similar in appearance to plums, and it is reported that this sapodilla plum is considered one of the best of the tropical American fruits.

Secondly, the bark of this tree, reddish-brown in color, contains a large amount of latex which ranges from a white to a purple color. This is gathered and used commercially as a basis for chewing gum. This latex is the most valuable product of the tree and large plantations have been planted for this purpose alone.

Thirdly, the tree is useful in that the wood is fine-textured, heavy, averaging 65 lbs. per cubic foot, and produces straight-grained wood which turns well and is used, amongst other purposes, in the manufacture of tool handles. A very fine polish can be obtained with this wood.

SASSAFRAS *Sassafras albidum* (Sassafras—a Spanish name, possibly of American Indian origin; albidum—whitish)

This species is also known as

CINNAMON-WOOD and RED SASSAFRAS.

This tree grows in an area from Massachusetts to Iowa and Kansas, and south to Florida and Texas. In the northern limit of its range it is generally small, often of brush size, but further south it becomes a tree which sometimes exceeds 100 ft. in height and 3 or 4 ft. in diameter. The best development of the species is in Arkansas and Missouri.

This wood bears a considerable resemblance to ash in color and in grain, but is lighter in weight, about 31 lbs. per cubic foot, and has a slightly aromatic scent. It is inclined to check in drying and is lower in strength than ash, but is very durable when exposed to dampness.

The tree has had a peculiar history. It was once supposed to possess miraculous healing powers and people believed that it would renew the youth of the human race. Bedsteads made of sassafras were supposed to drive away certain nightly visitors which disturbed slumber, and the belief was that a bed made of sassafras would help the individual sleep more soundly.

The production of sassafras oil is perhaps the largest industry dependent upon this tree. Roots are grubbed by the ton and are subjected to distillation. The oil obtained is used in flavoring medicines and candies, and also used in perfuming soap. The early settlers used to dye their homespun articles with the orange color obtained from the bark.

Another product of the sassafras is tea made from the flowers or bark of the roots. It is relished in the early spring and is popular in most regions where the tree is known. This bark is tied in small bundles and retailed in drug stores and groceries in various parts of the country.

Most of the sassafras manufactured by sawmills is used in furniture and listed as ash, generally losing its name.

SATINAY *Syncarpia hillii* (Syn/carpia—fused fruits; hillii—after Hill)

The growth of this large tree is confined to Fraser Island, off the coast of Queensland in Australia. It is a hard wood, averaging 50 lbs. per cubic foot, and at times the logs produce a fiddleback figure for which there is an active demand in fine cabinetwork. The heartwood is very attractive, of a pleasing reddish color like that of tropical mahogany.

It is used for interior paneling, but to prevent deterioration in quality, the stock must first have a considerable period of air-drying before it is kiln-dried.

SATINÉ *Brosimum paraense* (Brosimum—edible; paraense—from Para, a Brazilian state)

This wood is also known as MUIRATIRANGA, SATINA and principally as SATINÉ RUBANNE.

Emanating in South America, the wood has a rich red coloring, is of medium texture, is an easy wood to work with and takes a fine polish.

SATINWOOD, BRAZILIAN *Euxylophora paraensis* (Euxylophora—true bearer of wood; paraensis—from Para, a Brazilian state)

Also known as PAU AMARILLO

Brazilian satinwood, two-piece match

and SATINA, this wood from Brazil at times is used as a substitute for Ceylon and San Domingo mahogany. However, it is of coarser grain and the figure and mottle are lacking. It has a rich, bright, warm golden yellow color and can be obtained in good widths and lengths.

SATINWOOD, EAST INDIAN
Chloroxylon swietenia (Chlor/oxylon—yellowish-green wood; swietenia—after Baron Gerald von Swieten, 1700-1772, Dutch physician and founder of the Vienna botanical garden)

This satinwood grows in Ceylon and India, and an important trade has been carried on with the island of Ceylon for a great many years. Logs running in size from 12 to 30 in. and of good lengths, from 5 to 20 ft. and longer, are obtained.

Nearly all of the timber is more or less figured, the plain log being an exception. The figure ranges from a plain light- and dark-colored stripe to the finest mottle (a very fine sized mottle being especially desirable in the inlay and furniture trade) and what is known as a bee's-wing mottle. It varies considerably in color from a light, bright yellow to a dark brown. As a rule, the lighter and brighter colors are the most sought after. In the form of veneer, the wood has long been used for furniture and by marquetry manufacturers. Entire suites have been made of satinwood veneer. In the solid form it is usually confined to brush and mirror backs.

In India the wood has been used for many purposes, including wharf piling and agricultural implements. The well-known bridge at Peradeniya in Ceylon was constructed almost entirely of satinwood. It contained a single arch of over a 200-ft. span, but this bridge was taken down some years ago.

In this country the wood commands a high price, based upon the indication of the figure, size and soundness of the log. The big problem in the handling of these logs

Ceylon satinwood, mottle figure

is what are known as cup shapes and gum rings. They may be seen upon careful examination on the butt ends—thin lines following the annual growth. Defects of this kind at times can render almost worthless an otherwise valuable tree when manufactured. On one occasion it is reported that one log was sold at a price of $5,000 for the purpose of converting it into veneers.

A peculiarity of the wood is that while it burns in an open fireplace very well and with a fragrant restful odor, inducing slumber in many who sit before it, the smoke of this satinwood will kill canary birds.

SATINWOOD, WEST INDIES *Zanthoxylum flavum* (Zanth/oxylum—yellow wood; flavum—yellow)

Coming from the West Indies, this is the finest satinwood known. not only for quality but also for color. The best wood comes from Santo Domingo. However, the supplies have become so exhausted that no logs have been imported into this country for many years.

The logs that used to come in ranged from 6 to 22 in. in diameter and were generally manufactured into oblong pieces with square edges. The average probably ranged from about 8 to 10 in. Logs could not be kept for long before manufacturing as they split badly, but when once manufactured, this wood splits less than the East Indian satinwood.

This satinwood has a strong and pleasant scent, sometimes associated with that of coconut oil. It is this satinwood that you find on old pieces of furniture—the Sheratons and Hepplewhites. The wood is a lovely golden yellow and has a bright sheen like satin, an effect

which cannot be equaled by any other wood or obtained by artificial means. Pieces that were made 100 to 150 years ago have matured to a lovely tint that even the old masters did not realize would result. The finest furniture was sometimes made with West Indian satinwood combined with mahogany.

Nearly all of this wood was converted into veneers for highly decorative work, and prize veneers from good logs commanded high prices, sometimes as high as $1 per square foot for the log.

SEN *Kalopanax ricinifolium* (Kalo/panax—beautiful *Panax*; ricinifolium—with castor, *Ricinus,* leaves)

Growing in the mountainous districts of central Japan, this tree is also known as CASTOR ARABIA.

The heartwood is a pale greenish-brown color, somewhat like our native ash, and it is of medium hardness and weight. The lumber seasons easily but with a high shrinkage. When the wood is dry, it always presents danger of warping and shrinking or swelling with the change of moisture content. Notwithstanding this, it is widely used in Japan for such purposes as chests, furniture, passenger coaches, baseball bats. It has the advantage of working well with all types of tools. When converted into veneer, it is used for the manufacture of plywood, and quantities of the plywood have been exported to various countries.

SEQUOIA, GIANT *Sequoia gigantea* (Sequoia—after Sequoyah, or George Guess, 1770?-1843, American Indian inventor of the Cherokee alphabet; gigantea—gigantic)

This tree is also known under

Scene in giant sequoia forest

the names of BIGTREE, MAMMOUTH-TREE and the SEQUOIA.

The sequoia grows in higher altitudes than the redwood and is limited more or less to some thirty groves, varying from a few trees to over a thousand. These are located only in the Sierra Nevada Moun-

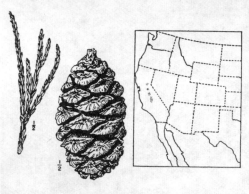

tains of California, in the Sequoia National Forest and in the Tahoe National Forest. These trees are the oldest and largest of all living things, the largest sequoia and largest tree in the world being in the Sequoia National Park. It has a diameter at the base of 36½ ft., and 18½-ft. diameter 100 ft. above the ground, with a total height of 273 ft. Its bark is 4 ft. thick. If the tree were converted into lumber, it would provide over 600,000 board feet. It is estimated to be somewhere between 3,000 and 4,000 years old.

The wood is a dull, purplish red-brown when exposed to the light, similar but lighter in color than redwood.

There is very little use for this wood inasmuch as the supply is so limited, plans having been made to preserve these trees for posterity.

SERVICEBERRY, DOWNY *Amelanchier arborea* (Amelanchier—

the common name of a European species; arborea—treelike)

This tree, which grows in the eastern part of Canada and through all of the eastern states west of the Mississippi in this country, is known under a number of different names in the various states, as CURRANT TREE, JUNE-BERRY, MAY-CHERRY, SERVICEBERRY, SHADBERRY, SUGAR PLUM and WILD INDIAN PEAR. In addition to these names, the wood is also marketed under the name of LANCE-WOOD.

Downy serviceberry is a small, attractively shaped tree and an excellent one for landscaping. The tree blossoms in the early spring, when the shad travels upstream, which is why the tree is sometimes referred to as shad-berry or shad-bush. The small, mealy, black berry, which ripens in June or July, according to where the tree is located, is sweet, edible and a favorite with the birds. This tree is generally found along brooks or bordering on the edge of woods.

The wood is very hard, heavy and close-grained but has excellent bending qualities. Because of its toughness and flexibility, it is used in the manufacture of fly rods. It is easy to work with all types of tools and takes a fine finish. Outside of the manufacture of fly rods, large quantities of it are used for making all types of handles and various turned work.

SISSOO *Dalbergia sissoo* (Dalbergia —after N. Dalberg, Swedish physician; sissoo—a native name)

Sissoo is often called the SHISHAM WOOD of British India. It is an extremely hard-textured wood, rich brown in color, often having a pronounced stripe and attractive mottle figure which is caused by deeper shades of gold and brown.

SMOKETREE, AMERICAN *Cotinus obovatus* (Cotinus—from the Greek for oleaster or wild olive, although the origin is confused; obovatus—the shape of the leaf is ob-ovate)

This tree is referred to in the Bible as CHITTAM WOOD or SMOKETREE.

The tree is rare in this country, even more so in Europe, and is found in the eastern United States, in parts of Tennessee, northern Georgia, southwestern Missouri and the northern part of Arkansas. Smoketree is small in size and is a bright, clear, rich orange color with thin, nearly white sapwood. It is so named probably because the small yellow and purplish flowers, which appear in clusters, have the look of a puff of smoke or a thin film spreading over the foliage when they turn to a rosy haze.

Commercially, the wood is rare and the only use that is made of the tree is for obtaining a dye from the rich orange heartwood. In localities where the tree is grown, it is used for fence posts because of its high durability in contact with the soil.

If desired, it can be used in the lumber form for craftwork, but should always be finished in its natural color so as to preserve the beautiful coloring, which would be altered by most finishing materials.

SNAKEWOOD *Piratinera guianensis* (Piratinera—sea pirate; guianensis—from Guiana)

Commonly known as snakewood, doubtless because of its markings, this wood is likewise known to some as LEOPARD WOOD, LETTERWOOD and SPECKLED WOOD.

It is native to British Guiana and South America and has a deep bright red color, darkening upon exposure. The wood turns very well though it does not slice well. It takes a high polish and is available in $\frac{1}{24}$" sawn veneers and also in 1 x 1 in. squares.

Snakewood is prized for the handles of fine parasols, violin bows and umbrellas, and for the butts of choice fishing poles. A cane made of snakewood is considered the aristocrat of canes.

Snakewood

American smoketree in full bloom

SOURWOOD *Oxydendrum arboreum* (Oxy/dendrum—sour tree; arboreum—treelike)

This species also is known as ARROW-WOOD, ELK TREE, LILY OF THE VALLEY TREE, SORREL GUM, SORREL TREE and TITI TREE.

These trees are found along the coast from New Jersey down to Florida and westward from Kentucky to Louisiana. The greatest value of this tree is its handsome foliage and it is planted for decoration in landscaping. It has little value commercially. The wood is heavy, hard, strong and close-grained, making it fairly difficult to work with tools, except for turning purposes.

Certain extracts from the sap of this tree are used in medicine for the treatment of fevers. Outside of this, sourwood is only of ornamental value.

SPRUCE, BLACK HILLS *Picea glauca* var. *densata* or *Picea glauca* (Picea—the ancient Latin name from *pix* or *picis,* meaning pitch; glauca—a blue-green covering; densata—dense or compact, probably referring to the crowded needles)

Locally, in South Dakota where this tree emanates, it is often called WHITE SPRUCE.

French explorers were the first white men to visit the little known Black Hills in the land of South Dakota. The Black Hills spruce is now the state tree of South Dakota. This spruce varies from the eastern variety of white spruce in that it is a much slower growing tree and the foliage is a very bright green.

SPRUCE, BLUE *Picea pungens* (pungens—sharp-pointed, referring to the needles)

Locally it is often known as COLORADO SPRUCE and SILVER SPRUCE.

This spruce is called the pride of the Rocky Mountains and it is the state tree of Colorado and Utah. It is a very hardy tree and grows in mountainous elevations up to 11,000 ft., sometimes in pure stands. It is one of the slowest growing spruces, having a height of no more than 10 to 20 in. after five years and only 3 to 8 ft. after ten years' growth.

Blue spruce was first discovered on Pike's Peak in the middle 1800's. It is one of the most widely used trees for landscaping because of the silver-blue color and symmetrical shape. The wood is soft and weak and its only value commercially is in landscaping.

SPRUCE, ENGELMANN *Picea engelmannii* (engelmannii — after George Engelmann, 1809-1884, German-born physician and botanist of St. Louis, who was the first to identify and clarify this spruce species about the year 1862)

This spruce grows in the high mountains of the West at elevations from 4,000 to 12,000 ft., ranging from British Columbia southward through the western states into Arizona, Colorado and New Mexico. The trunk is straight

335

and is identified by the bark—a dark, purplish brown with small, overlapping scales. The deep blue-green needles are about 1 in. long, soft, flexible, four-angled, and with a tendency to curve forward.

Some of this spruce has been used in aircraft glider work because of its extreme lightness, combined with strength. Quantities have been used in construction work and sheathing. It also makes some of the finest quality paper.

Typical stand of Engelmann spruce trees, bark and needles

½   ½

Top, Sitka spruce. Lower left, blue spruce, "the pride of the Rocky Mountains." Lower right, white spruce

SPRUCE, SITKA *Picea sitchensis* (sitchensis—of Sitka Island in southeastern Alaska)

This species is also known as SEQUOIA SILVER SPRUCE, SILVER SPRUCE, WESTERN SPRUCE and WEST COAST SPRUCE.

Sitka spruce grows along the Pacific coast from Alaska to northern California. It is found in a very narrow strip at elevations up to 3,000 ft. and never more than 50 miles inland from the coast. It is the largest species of spruce, ranging to 150 ft. or more in height with diameters up to 7 ft. The largest tree known at present is one growing in the state of Washington with a recorded height of 240 ft. and 14 ft. in diameter. Most of the trees in dense forests grow from 40 to 70 ft. high.

ADIRONDACK SPRUCE, BLUE SPRUCE and SKUNK SPRUCE.

The wood is light pink to tan and it darkens to light brown upon exposure. The needles stand at right angles to the tree and are stiff, pointed, and grow all around it.

Some Sitka is used for making musical instruments, but the white spruce is preferred for this purpose. Sitka spruce is one of the favorites for making high-quality paper.

SPRUCE, WHITE *Picea glauca* (glauca—blue-green in reference to the foliage)

This species is also known as

The white spruce trees grow across Canada from Newfoundland to Alaska and southward into British Columbia, Montana, Minnesota, Wisconsin and Michigan, up through the northeastern states and upper New York State. It is a tree of many branches, drooping downward from the trunk and then turning up to form a beautifully shaped tree, tapering to a long, sharp crown. Its needles are dark blue-green and if injured give off an unpleasant odor that has resulted in the tree being called a cat spruce or skunk spruce. The needles are four-angled, sharp-pointed, and grow in great profusion along the twigs.

White spruce is one of the most sought-after woods for the manufacture of paper pulp because of the extra long, fine quality of the fibers. It is also a wood that piano manufacturers buy for making the best sounding boards. In addition, the wood is used for many of the usual purposes as interior finishing and furniture as well as for the manufacture of lightweight oars and canoe paddles.

STINKWOOD *Ocotea bullata* (Ocotea—a Guayana plant name; bullata—inflated)

This species is also known as STINKHOUT, CAPE LAUREL and UMNUKANE in South Africa.

Stinkwood is closely related botanically to East African camphorwood *(Ocotea usambarensis)* but the tree and wood are appreciably different in their commercial aspects. The tree is from 60 to 80 ft. high with a clean, straight bole from 3 to 5 ft. in diameter. The species occurs in the Union of South Africa, predominantly in the forested country of the Cape Peninsula northward to Natal and eastern Transvaal.

The wood varies in color from an even straw shade through various shades of gray-brown to almost black. The straw-colored wood does not appreciably darken on exposure, but the brown wood darkens noticeably under oil and exposure. The wood is moderately hard and heavy to very heavy, varying in specific gravity according to color. Light-colored portions have an average specific gravity of 0.67; black portions may have an average specific gravity of 0.80.

The dark portions of the wood air-season and kiln-season rather poorly with a marked tendency to distort and honeycomb. The light-colored wood dries more rapidly with much less degrade.

The wood is stronger in proportion to its specific gravity than East African camphorwood. Stinkwood compares favorably with domestic hardwoods of similar specific gravity. The seasoned wood of stinkwood may be compared to that of rock elm *(Ulmus thomasii)* of somewhat greater specific gravity.

The shrinkage of the wood is exceptionally great, being 8.0 per cent tangentially and 4.2 per cent radially. These values are in the order of those for blue gum *(Eucalyptus globulus)* and are associated with the tendency of the wood to distort and collapse in drying.

The wood works well with hand and machine tools, but is hard and severe on the tools. The best surface appears to be obtained by scraping and an excellent finish is easily secured in this manner. Smooth surfaces can also be obtained by sanding.

In spite of its drawbacks, stinkwood is reported to be one of the most prized furniture woods in Africa and is largely used for furniture, paneling, framing and high-class millwork. Supplies of the wood are becoming increasingly scarce and it brings a greater price than any other furniture wood. There are no reports of this species being exported from Africa.

STRAWBERRY TREE *Arbutus unedo* (Arbutus—the classical Latin name of this species; unedo—Latin name for the fruit of this tree)

The original home of the strawberry tree was in southwestern France along the Mediterranean region and in Ireland. It is still fairly abundant in the Killarney and Kerry districts. In England it is cultivated as an ornamental tree because of the fine appearance when in full bloom or flowering in the late autumn. A small tree, it seldom grows higher than 25 ft. It produces fruits which are orange-red to a bright scarlet color, round in shape and rough on the outside with tiny grains.

The wood is available only in small sizes. However, it is of fine texture, fairly hard and weighs about 45 lbs. per cubic foot. Sometimes the figure is so irregular as to give it almost the appearance of burl, and veneers cut from this tree at times are hard to distinguish from the madrona burls that grow on the Pacific coast. It is very closely related to these *(Arbutus menziesii),* but these trees will grow three or four times the height of the strawberry tree.

The wood seasons satisfactorily and works with little difficulty though it has a tendency at times to check. This species makes very attractive veneers for fine cabinet-making.

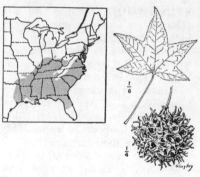

SWEETGUM *Liquidambar styraciflua* (Liquid/ambar—liquid amber in reference to the fragrant resin; styraciflua—old generic name meaning styrax or storax, an allusion to the production of medicinal storax from *L. orientalis* of western Asia)

This wood is also known under the names of ALLIGATOR-TREE, ALLIGATOR WOOD (because of the warty excrescences on the bark of some of the trees) HAZEL PINE, INCENSE TREE, LIQUIDAMBAR, SATIN WALNUT and STAR-LEAVED GUM. Sweetgum is sold on the market as RED GUM or SAPGUM.

Sweetgum, or red gum, grows in the United States and extends from Connecticut to Texas and as far northwest of the Alleghenies as Missouri and Illinois. It reaches the largest size in the lower Mississippi region. The largest examples exceed a height of 120 ft. and a diameter of 4 ft., but logs from

Figured sweetgum or redgum, to use a common market term

340

Sweetgum tree of medium size growing in New Jersey

20 to 34 in. are the usual size. It grows well on land which is never covered with water, but it needs plenty of moisture.

This tree does not belong to the same group as black gum and tupelo, which are in the dogwood family, but is in the witch hazel family.

Green red gum is so heavy that it scarcely floats. The trees are often girdled and left standing for a year to partly season them. It is only moderately strong and stiff and is a poor competitor of hickory, ash, maple and oak for strength and elasticity. The wood weighs about 37 lbs. per cubic foot; a large percentage of it is figured; and the tree has green seed balls, more commonly known as burrs, that hang by long threadlike stems for about two years.

The description "red" does not refer to the color of the wood, but originally referred to the color of the autumn leaves. The resin, which is sometimes used in France and probably elsewhere to perfume gloves, has a pleasant odor, and therefore the name "sweetgum" was derived.

The wood is often painted or stained to look like oak, cherry, maple or mahogany, and this species of gum is used more in the veneer form than any other species.

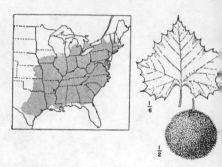

SYCAMORE, AMERICAN *Platanus occidentalis* (Platanus—the classical Latin name for the Oriental plane tree; occidentalis—western)

This species is also known under various names such as AMERICAN PLANETREE, BUTTONBALL, BUTTONWOOD, PLANE-TREE and WATER BEECH. It is also called the GHOST TREE of the woods because of its white bark, which is mottled with various shades of green and brown.

American sycamore grows singly or in scattered groups from southern Maine westward to Nebraska and southward to eastern Texas and northern Florida. It is a very large tree, up to 120 ft. high, with wide-spreading branches and a large trunk. The best species are found on flatlands where there is a good supply of ground water and along the edges of streams, lakes and swamps.

The heartwood is reddish-brown or flesh brown in color and it is

Rotary-cut American sycamore

342

Upper left, downy serviceberry. Upper right, three sassafras trees growing in New York State. Lower left, sycamore tree in early spring, showing pattern of the branches. Lower right, tamarack moderately heavy, averaging 34 lbs. per cubic foot. Large shrinkage is encountered in drying, and the wood is inclined to warp, being somewhat difficult to season. Sycamore wood does not impart taste, odor or stain to a substance that comes in contact with it.

The principal use of this wood is in the manufacture of lumber and veneer for decorative surfaces, but it is also used for railroad ties, fence posts and fuel. Because of its toughness, it is the favorite wood for butchers' blocks.

TAMARACK *Larix laricina* (Larix —the classical name of the European larch; laricina—like a larch)

This tree is also known as HACKMATACK, JUNIPER and LARCH.

The tamarack is an eastern wood found all through eastern Pennsylvania, southeast from Maine to Maryland and into Minnesota. It generally grows in swampy locations. The limbs, which start close to the ground, are horizontal and curved slightly upwards. The needles give a feathery appearance and are bright green in color. They grow in clusters all along the small branches, about 1 in. in length. In the fall they turn yellowish or brown and then drop off.

The heartwood is yellowish to brown in color. The timber is generally used for rough construction such as railroad ties, flagpoles, telephone poles and some paper pulp. Boat builders use the lower portion of the trunk and the larger roots to cut out "ship knees" used in keels of wooden hulls.

TAMBOOTIE *Spirostachys africanus*

This tree grows in the forests of Zululand and Transvaal in eastern Africa. The logs secured from this species are from 6 to 8 ft. long, seldom averaging more than 12 in. in diameter. The wood is dark brown with black streaks that create beautiful markings. It is a hard wood, averaging about 65 lbs. per cubic foot, and has a very pleasant scent, sweeter than that of sandalwood. This pleasant odor will last a long time after the wood is cut. A piece of furniture made of it can scent a large room for a long time.

Because of the limited quantities —and the defectiveness of the tree —it is a rare wood, therefore much sought after for small fancy articles and high-grade furniture. Although the wood seasons easily, it is fairly difficult to work, but not quite so difficult as other woods of the same hardness, due to the unusual oily nature of the wood.

TAMO *Fraxinus mandshurica* (Fraxinus—classical Latin name for ash; mandshurica—of Manchuria)

This is also known as JAPANESE ASH.

This tree grows in the mountainous regions of Japan and is only gotten out with great difficulty. Oftentimes the logs are carried and dragged out by human labor. The first export shipments were made from Japan about 1908, records seem to indicate, and since then it has been exported in steadily increasing amounts.

The wood varies in color from a light straw yellow to a bright brown, with intermediate shadings, and the color is permanent. It does not dim with age and retains depth and richness in the finished product. The figured logs are eagerly sought in this country. The prize figure is known as "peanut" because of the resemblance to this

Tamo with so-called "peanut" figure

nut. The wood, either in the veneer or lumber form, is easily glued and makes a hard, flat surface.

A peculiarity of the wood is that half of the tree is figured and the other half is plain. The trees are therefore split in the forests and the plain half generally is left because it has little commercial value.

Craftsmen find this wood particularly fine for producing bizarre effects in matching for table tops and small articles of furniture.

TAWA *Beilschmiedia tawa* (Beilschmiedia—after Beilschmied; tawa —a native name)

The growth of tawa is confined to the northeastern area of South Island and all of North Island, both of New Zealand. The average size tree is from 60 to 70 ft. with diameters from 9 to 18 in. It grows at sea level and up to altitudes of no more than 1,000 ft.

This species comes from the family of trees known as *Lauraccae* from which such timbers as aromatic camphorwood, Queensland walnut, black stinkwood and greenheart are obtained. It is an attractive wood, even-colored, yellowish to grayish-brown with occasionally streaks of darker brown. It is medium heavy, averaging around 40 lbs. per cubic foot, with strength in proportion to the weight, of fine texture and a good straight grain.

A considerable amount of this wood is used in New Zealand for decorative woodwork, interior trim and furniture. A good quantity is also used in the manufacture of staves in the cooperage industry. Selected logs are converted into rotary-cut veneers from which attractive plywood may be manufactured. Because of the distance of New Zealand from many of the major wood markets and the high cost of transportation, not too much of this wood is used elsewhere.

TAWENNA *Cryptocarya membranacea* (Crypto/carya—hidden nut; membranacea — parchment-like,

probably a reference to the leaves)

This tree grows only in the rain forests of Ceylon, along the coast, up to elevations of around 2,500 ft. The wood, when freshly cut, is a dull yellow color, but with exposure often turns to a dark reddish-brown. It is a moderately heavy wood, weighing about 45 lbs. per cubic foot, and of fine texture and straight grain. The small pores are partially filled with a chalklike white deposit and the wood is easy to work with sharp tools.

In Ceylon it is used in heavy construction such as bridges, but a limited quantity is produced in sliced-veneer form, which gives a very attractive appearance.

TEAK *Tectona grandis* (Tectona—after a Malayan plant name, tekku; grandis—great or large)

Teak grows in India, Burma, Thailand and Java and often obtains a height of from 70 to 100 ft. or more, with a circumference of 5 to 12 ft. Samples of one of the largest logs secured weighed over 12 tons.

Because of its tremendous weight and the difficulty in getting it out of the forest, an original method is used in forestry. The trees to be felled are first girdled—that is, cut completely around from the bark into the heartwood. In this condition the trees soon die and in three years they become light enough to float down the river; otherwise the wood would be so heavy it would sink. Transportation to streams is carried on with the aid of elephants and buffaloes. A good-sized, well-trained elephant will cost several thousand dollars and because of the great difficulty and labor, an elephant may handle only 30 to 40 teak trees a year. Local firms engaged in this work will employ several thousand elephants to carry on the work of transportation. Today it takes from two to eight years for a log to arrive after cutting, because of the girdling process and the labor of getting the trees out of the woods.

Teak wood varies in color from a yellow or strawlike color to a rich deep brown when first cut and darkens with exposure to the air. Some wood will have streaks almost black in color. It has an oily surface and when first cut, feels very sticky to the hand.

There is little shrinkage in drying and the wood is moderately hard (comparable to oak), strong, of straight grain and easily worked. It may come in a straight stripe to an occasional mottle, which is much sought after in the cabinet trade.

Teak has a peculiar scent of its own which, while agreeable to some, is unpleasant to others and is not unlike that of old shoe leather. Occasionally parcels of teak have a much stronger and more unpleasant odor than the majority of the wood.

The teak tree has the largest leaves of any tree, running from 10 to 20 in. in length and 7 to 14 in. wide, of an oblong shape. They are so rough that the natives use them as an abrasive, just as a modern

Flat-cut teak with mild figure

Teak, mottle figure

worker uses sandpaper, because they have a peculiar tough and coarse surface. Few people know of this interesting fact.

An immense quantity of teak goes into shipbuilding, as for decks of liners and warships. Also, a good percentage of this wood is used in the paneling of fine homes and offices and in the construction of all types of furniture. It is obtainable by the craftsmen in both the lumber and the veneer form.

THUYA BURL *Tetraclinis articulata* (Tetra/clinis—four slopes or angles; articulata—jointed)

Thuya, which grows along the Mediterranean in northern Africa, is also found on the island of Malta and has been planted in Cyprus. It is always used in the burl form, the burls growing underneath the ground and having to be dug out. The cause of burls is still a subject of scientific study and speculation, and craftsmen often make inquiry

347

Thuya burl

as to the knowledge and full history of these.

The wood has a figure and color similar to our American redwood burls and is very similar to Amboyna burl with the exception that it is considerably harder. It is yellowish-brown in color with various shades of red, and can be identified by its aromatic scent. It is much more suitable to work with in the veneer form than the redwood burl, due to a better and more solid texture. Thuya wood was one of the woods used in the earlier known cabinetwork. During the time of the Roman Empire it was greatly sought after for fine tables.

TOTARA *Podocarpus totara* (Podo/carpus—foot fruit; totara—a native name)

Totara is principally found only in the islands of New Zealand. The largest trees recorded have been a little in excess of 150 ft. in height and as much as 5 and 6 ft. in diameter, though the great majority of these trees are considerably smaller than this. It is a tree that prefers dry valleys but occasionally

may be found on the sides of mountains, up to an altitude of 2,500 ft.

The wood has a very uniform coloring of a dull pinkish- or reddish-brown, is of medium weight, around 35 lbs. per cubic foot, and has an unusually fine, uniform texture with a straight grain. The heartwood is quite resistant to decay, which makes it suitable for many purposes. It works very easily and because of its fine, even texture it is a good wood for cutting into veneer for the manufacture of furniture and plywood. In New Zealand large quantities are used in the planking of boats, building of barges and pontoons, the making of vats, and in exterior work.

TULIPWOOD *Dalbergia variabilis* (Dalbergia—after N. Dalberg, Swedish physician; variabilis—variable)

Emanating in Brazil, this timber is exported from the port of Bahia in the form of round logs. Most of these are under 6 ft., although occasionally longer ones are found, and the diameters are from 2 to 12 in. without sapwood.

It is a beautiful wood when freshly manufactured, but in time gradually fades and loses some of its original attractiveness. It is irregularly striped, the prevailing colors being yellow, red rose and violet. It also has a mild fragrant scent when worked. The wood is heavy, averaging about 60 lbs. per cubic foot, strong and hard, and is not particularly easy to work, being inclined to splinter, but it takes a high natural polish.

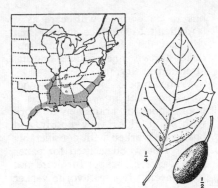

TUPELO, WATER *Nyssa aquatica* (Nyssa—a water nymph; aquatica—of the water)

This species is known under quite a number of different names, some of the most prominent being: BAY POPLAR, GUM, GRAY GUM, HAZEL PINE, OLIVETREE, PAW PAW GUM, SOUR GUM, SWAMP TUPELO, SWAMP GUM, TUPELO, TUPELO GUM, WHITE GUM and YELLOW GUM.

This tupelo grows in a long, narrow belt around 100 miles wide, running down from southern Illinois through the Mississippi Valley to Texas, across the Gulf states and up along the Atlantic coast as far north as Virginia. The wood is named from the fact that it grows best in fresh water swamps, along the edges of lakes and streams. Generally it is a fairly small tree—50 to 75 ft. in height with an average diameter of around 2½ ft.

The heartwood is a light brownish-gray to a yellowish-brown and sometimes nearly white in color. The bark is roughened by small scales, furrowed longitudinally, and of a dark brown color. This wood

Rotary-cut water tupelo

has to be worked with care as it is difficult to produce lumber that will stay flat. It has a natural tendency to twist and requires unusual attention in drying.

Water tupelo is a weak wood, soft and light in weight. It is a poor wood for craftsmen to work with as it glues very poorly and has to be worked with considerable care. This wood is used for paper pulp, caskets, cheaper furniture and for veneers. It is a favorite veneer for the manufacture of tobacco or cigar boxes, tupelo being used as a core with a thin veneer of cedar on either side.

TURPENTINE *Syncarpia procera* (Syn/carpia—fused fruits; procera —high)

The growth of this large tree is confined to the coastal districts and the Blue Mountains of New South Wales. The wood in appearance and characteristics is very closely related to the red satiné. The sapwood is pale pink and the heartwood a color like brown mahogany. The wood is heavy, averaging 60 lbs. per cubic foot, and is considered about 100 percent harder than oak.

An important feature in handling this lumber is that it has to be air-dried well before it is kiln-dried, otherwise a state of collapse will take place. Its most valuable characteristic is probably its resistance to attack by marine life. It will stand, without ill effects, many years of life in salt water and is resistant against all decay, especially when the logs are used as piling with the bark still attached.

Turpentine wood is used principally for heavy construction and beams so it is not of particular importance that it does not work well with hand tools and also rather

poorly with power tools, since it rapidly dulls the edges of saw teeth and cutters.

UTILE *Entandrophragma utile* (Ent/andro/phragma—within the male membrane; utile—useful.

In Ghana the wood is usually known as CEDAR or UTILE, while in Uganda it is known as MUFUMBI. It also has been called SIPO.

Utile grows along a large part of west Africa, extending inland to Uganda. It is an unusually large tree and logs are exported at times with diameters of 6 ft. The wood weighs about 35 to 45 lbs. per cubic foot and closely resembles sapele except that it is a little darker in color and the cedar scent which is noticeable in sapele is missing. Also it is not as plentiful as sapele.

Utile requires considerable care in seasoning as it has a strong tendency to warp and twist. It is not a particularly difficult wood to work with, but being harder and having a more irregular grain, is more difficult to work than mahogany.

This wood is suitable for the manufacture of furniture and interior fittings. It has a limited use in boat building and also is a satisfactory wood for converting into veneers.

WALNUT, BLACK *Juglans nigra* (Juglans—the classical Latin name for walnut, meaning Jupiter's nut; nigra—black)

Black walnut has long been considered one of the most desirable woods of this country, not only because of the beautiful wood of various figures that the tree produces, but also for the food value in the black walnuts—a delicacy

American black walnut, plain half-round figure

Sliced black walnut, cross figure with wild heart

Plain sliced black walnut with narrow heart

used in candies, bread and ice cream.

The bark of the tree is dark and deeply grooved. This bark, in addition to the husks of the nuts, is used in manufacturing a yellow dye. The leaves of the black walnut are as long as 1 and 2 ft. and have many narrow, sharp, slender-pointed leaflets, as many as 15 to 23.

After being seasoned, the wood shrinks and expands very little and is a good wood for craftsmen to use. The wood saws, planes and finishes excellently. It has long been used for gunstocks, being superior to all other woods because it keeps its shape, is fairly light in weight and helps take up the recoil better than any other wood. In the veneer form the figures obtained are butts, crotches, burls, fiddle-back, leaf and straight stripe.

WALNUT, CIRCASSIAN or EUROPEAN *Juglans regia* (regia—royal)

This walnut is obtained from Circassia in the Caucasus at the Black Sea and is the original of all species of European walnut. The wood, which was prized by the Romans and Greeks for its fine nuts, was heavily planted and the species extended to other European countries. The difference in the color and texture between Italian, French, English, Spanish and Circassian walnut is due to the varied climate and the different soils it grows in, which affect the color and marking of the wood. It resembles most closely our American black walnut, but it has a closer grain with distinct color shadings from a light brown to dark, with occasional black streaks in some of the logs.

The walnut from England is naturally limited in quantity because of the size of the British Isles, but it has long been used in its native country. The color and texture vary considerably and the wood is somewhat harder and considerably darker than the French walnut. In the seventeenth century a portion of the finer furniture was made of this wood, but because of the early supremacy of the English oak, it was only in later years that it was used more extensively.

Circassian walnut

352

Top, an unusually fine black walnut tree growing in California.
Bottom, black willow growing at Kennebunkport, Me.

The major portion of French walnut is consumed in the French market and only a relatively smaller portion is exported to the United States and other countries for special cabinetwork, interior paneling and trim. This wood is known by its light color of gray or grayish-brown. Architects occasionally specify French walnut for their finest work. This walnut works and handles very much like our own American walnut.

WALNUT, HINDS *Juglans hindsii* (hindsii—after Richard B. Hinds, English botanist aboard the ship *Sulphur* in a voyage around the world, 1836-1842)

It is also known as CALIFORNIA WALNUT, but there is considerable confusion as to the exact species of *Juglans* that produces this walnut.

This is a fast-growing walnut, found in the southern Oregon and northern California coastal areas. It has an ivy grain, prominent light stripes and sometimes resembles Circassian walnut. Hinds walnut is seldom available in the lumber form and only small quantities are manufactured into veneers.

WALNUT, JAPANESE *Juglans cordiformis* (cordi/formis—heart-shaped)

In Japan this species is known as KURUMI and is one of that country's more valuable hardwoods.

The tree grows in quantities in the forests of Hokkaido from 50 to 65 ft. high with diameters of around 24 to 30 in. This walnut is rather similar in appearance to the European and American walnut with the exception that the overall color is of a golden hue instead of brownish or grayish. It weighs between 35 and 40 lbs. per cubic foot.

It possesses the same characteristics of seasoning well, is free from warpage and stays in place with a minimum of shrinkage and expansion after the proper seasoning. The wood works easily and smoothly with sharp tools.

This Japanese walnut was brought into Great Britain some time in the 1860s, but the climate did not lend to good growth. An interesting fact is that in Japan the kernels of this nut are used as a food.

WALNUT, MANCHURIAN *Juglans mandshurica* (mandshurica—of Manchuria)

Growing in Korea, this walnut resembles the European species but is generally milder and straighter in grain. The wood weighs about 32 lbs. per cubic foot and the trees are small in girth, providing only narrow widths. As a result, it has very little value commercially.

WALNUT, NEW GUINEA *Dracontomelum mangiferum* (Draconto—a kind of bird; melum—origin unknown; mang—the mango, a tropical fruit; iferum—to bear)

This is a tall tree, growing in New Guinea and the Philippines, which often reaches a height of 125 ft. and with diameters of 30 in. The color is similar to paldao and it runs very heavily to a contrasting stripe and some mottled figure. Being a rather hard cabinet wood, very much like paldao, it is often mistaken for it. The average weight is 45 lbs. per cubic foot.

The lumber can be dried without difficulty and may be worked easily with hand and power tools. When cut on the quarter, it produces very attractive veneers which command a good price and it is used in architectural front panels and in furniture.

WALNUT, SOUTH AMERICAN

WALNUT of different kinds grows in Ecuador, in Peru on the western Andean slopes and in Argentina. These trees are of the *Juglans* species and vary slightly from each other, but in most ways the wood is similar to the American walnut.

WALNUT OF ARGENTINA *Juglans australia.* These trees seldom grow more than 60 ft. in height and generally are considerably shorter, but have a very thick trunk, at times more than 3 ft. in diameter. They grow in fair-sized quantities in Salta, Estero and Jujuy. The wood is very similar to American walnut for color and general characteristics with the exception that it is lighter in weight. All other properties of seasoning, workability and stability are the same as the American species.

Walnut also grows in the Cordilleras of Colombia and one species produces a rich brown wood of a beautiful satiny luster, similar in many ways to Spanish cedar, which explains why it is commonly known as Cedro, Negro and occasionally as Cedro Nogal.

WALNUT OF PERU *Juglans neotropica.* This tree often obtains a height of from 45 to 60 ft. and a diameter up to 36 in., occasionally more, with a straight, well-formed trunk, at times 20 to 30 ft. above the ground before the first branches occur. The tree grows in sandy valleys at elevations from 5,000 to 8,000 ft.

While possessing many of the fine characteristics of our American walnut, this wood is little known because of the inaccessibility of the countryside where it grows. One way is to raft the logs through hazardous rapids, involving great danger, to the town of Iquitos. A safer and more tedious method is to transport small lots over the western Andean range on pack mules to the town of Celendin—a six-day trip—and then by road and railroad to the nearest port on the Pacific Ocean.

A product of the fruit, leaves and bark is used for dyeing. The lumber locally is used for cabinetmaking, furniture manufacture and musical instruments. It is highly prized for these purposes.

WANDOO *Eucalyptus redunca* (Eu/calyptus—true cover; redunca—curved backwards)

Wandoo grows in an area of some 10,000 square miles throughout western Australia, the trees reaching a height of 110 ft. or more with a diameter of some 30 in. It is one of the twelve or more eucalyptus which are classed as red gums.

The wood is plain-colored, of fine, dense texture, the color varying from a rich reddish-brown to a light yellow-brown color, the color darkening after exposure to air and light. Wandoo is heavy and hard, weighing about 70 lbs. per cubic foot, and is seldom exported from Australia because its extreme hardness and weight limit its usefulness in most industries.

This wood is very difficult to work with hand tools, but power tools do a satisfactory job. It is not a wood that is used in fine cabinetmaking. The large timbers are generally used for decking, wharves, girders, joists and bridge timbers.

It is also a good wood for railroad ties because of its high resistance to decay and some have been reported as being in good condition after serving for 35 years or more.

WELI-PENNA *Anisophyllea cinnamomoides* (Aniso/phyllea—unequal leaves; cinnamomoides—like *Cinnamomum*)

This wood emanates from the lowlands of Ceylon and produces a dark, heavy wood, about 50 lbs. per cubic foot, very similar in color and grain to the silver grain of oak. It is a very attractive wood in appearance, and veneers are generally cut on the quarter to show the grain. Only very limited quantities of this timber are exported.

WHITEBEAM *Sorbus aria* (Sorbus —classical Latin name; aria—goodness)

This tree grows in Great Britain and throughout the larger portion of Europe. It is a slow-growing tree, rarely obtaining a height of more than 70 ft. and a diameter of 1 to 2 ft. It is a handsome tree, valuable for decorative purposes, and produces very nice timber.

The heartwood is pinkish-brown, and the pinkish-gray shades have mild markings. It is moderately hard and heavy, about 43 lbs. per cubic foot, of fine texture and straight grain. This wood seasons well, providing the seasoning is done slowly. It is a good wood for carving and turning and suitable for all types of tool handles and heads of mallets.

WILLOW *Salix* (Salix—the classical Latin name)

The well-known species are CRACK WILLOW, CRICKET BAT

WILLOW and WHITE WILLOW.

No group of trees grows in a wider range of territory than the willows. They range all the way from the polar regions to tropical countries. There are many species, some of which are more or less shrubs, while others have the dimensions of large trees.

Willow is a straight-grained, white-colored wood and upon exposure it deepens to a pale brownish color. It is soft, light in weight, but extremely tough for its weight. In England this wood is highly prized for the manufacture of bats for playing cricket, which explains why it has names which refer to this use. It is also preferred at times for the manufacture of artificial limbs.

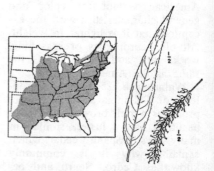

WILLOW, BLACK *Salix nigra* (nigra—black)

This tree grows through practically the entire eastern half of the United States from Canada to the Gulf, with the exception of Florida. Black willow is recognized by the long, narrow leaves, pointed at the tip. The top surface is a bright green and the under surface has a hairy appearance and is a little lighter in color. It is considered the most valuable commercially of over 100 different types of willows

356

that may be found in the United States.

The wood is generally grayish-brown with dark streaks, but at other times it is light reddish-brown. Working this wood with tools is very difficult. It is of even texture, lightweight but strong, and manufacturers of artificial limbs prefer to use this rather than other woods. Quantities of it are also used in the manufacture of paper pulp and excelsior.

WOMARA *Swartzia leiocalycina* (Swartzia—after Olaf Swartz, 1760-1817, Swedish botanist; leio/calycina—smooth floral leaves)

This large tree grows in British Guiana and is one of the 70 species of the genus *Swartzia*, all of which may be found in tropical America. The tree grows tall and may have a clear trunk up to 60 ft., with a total height at times of 110 ft. or more. There is a large amount of almost pure white sapwood, but the heartwood is in sharp contrast, shading from purple to a dark brown and at times containing a dark green stripe.

The wood is extremely heavy and hard, the weight varying anywhere from 60 to 80 lbs. per cubic foot. In logging, it is advisable to have as little time elapse as possible after the tree is felled before it is sawed into lumber, otherwise there is a great tendency for the wood to split.

A considerable amount of this wood is used in British Guiana for cabinetwork, fancy articles, furniture, inlays, archery bows, etc., and this is very unusual because the wood is most difficult to work, either with hand or power tools. The one exception is that it is an excellent wood for turning on the lathe.

YELLOW STERCULIA *Sterculia oblonga* (Sterculia—from the Latin *Stercus*, referring to the odor of some of these trees and meaning manure; oblonga—oblong)

This species is known as OKOKO in Benin and grows on the west coast of Africa.

The color of this wood is a pleasing yellow with lighter markings, and the wood is hard and heavy, averaging around 55 lbs. per cubic foot. When freshly cut, the wood has a most unpleasant odor, but this disappears almost entirely as it is dried. It dries well when done slowly and it can be worked without trouble with either power or hand tools.

Until recent years this wood was used almost exclusively in the countries in which it grows, but it has lately been exported to Great Britain and other commercial markets in limited quantities.

YEMERI *Vochysia hondurensis* (Vochysia—native name of the plant; hondurensis—from Honduras)

This wood, called QUARUBA in San Juan, grows in southern Mexico and south through British Honduras, preferring moist soils.

It is a slender tree, often 130 ft.

357

in height, and seldom more than 3 ft. in diameter. The heartwood is a pale, pinkish-brown color; it is of straight grain, without any distinctive odor or taste, and light in weight—some 25 to 30 lbs. per cubic foot.

The wood is hard to season as it has strong tendencies to warp and also has a high shrinkage. It has to be converted fairly quickly after felling, for it will deteriorate rapidly in the forest from attacks by termites and pinhole borers. The manufactured lumber will work fairly easily with either hand or power tools, but quickly takes the edge off them. It is a good all-around, useful timber, suitable for general carpentry work and particularly where the surface is to be painted.

YEW WOOD *Taxus baccata* (Taxus —the classical Latin name; baccata —berrylike, in reference to the red-covered seed)

Yew is one of the very few evergreen trees native to Great Britain, but it also grows in many parts of Europe, Asia, Persia, north Africa and in sections of the Himalaya mountain ranges.

The tree is small, from 20 to 60 ft. in height, with a short trunk. At times it is as much as 3 ft. in diameter. The sapwood is white and the heartwood, when first cut, will vary from a bright tan to brown or purple but with exposure to air and light it assumes a uniform, warm brown color.

It is a heavy wood for a softwood species, tough, hard and strong, and its fine texture will produce a highly polished surface. At times the tree produces burls which are highly prized when manufactured

Yew wood, two-piece match

358

into veneers. They equal the markings and coloring of thuya wood.

For many centuries this wood was used in the manufacture of archery bows and before firearms were invented there was not sufficient yew in some countries to produce the bows required. Today yew is occasionally used in small cabinetwork and in creating unusual pieces of furniture.

YUBA *Castanospermum australe* (Castano/spermum—chestnut-seeded; australe—southern)

Emanating in Australia, this species is also known as BEAN WOOD, BLACK BEAN and MORETON BAY CHESTNUT, inasmuch as the tree was first discovered in Moreton Bay near Brisbane, Australia.

The tree is large, reaching a height of over 110 ft. and with diameters up to 3 ft. The wood is attractive in appearance, brown or olive-green in color, deepening nearly to a black, with streaks of lighter shades, like a blending of chestnut and teak. Occasionally it will be highly figured. It is coarse-textured and fairly hard and heavy, weighing 48 lbs. per cubic foot. It has somewhat the feeling of teak to the touch but not as pronounced.

When properly seasoned, it is an excellent wood to work with and is one that is highly prized because of its high electrical insulation properties. The difficulty experienced in the handling and manufacturing of this wood is due to the fact that so many logs contain gum spots, distributed throughout the tree. When it is manufactured, much of the veneer is of little value, as only a small percentage of the log will be found absolutely clear and free of this gum.

A fine polish can be secured on this wood. In this country it has been used principally in the veneer form for high-grade paneling and for furniture, although in small quantities.

ZEBRANO *Cynometra*

This wood is also known as

Zebrano or zebra wood

ZEBRA WOOD and ZINGANA and is so named because of its similarity to the markings of a zebra with its blackish longitudinal stripes on a light background. The name, however, may be misleading for there are a number of different species of wood emanating from South America and Africa which are known as zebra. The zebra illustrated herewith, known throughout this country as zebra, is from the west coast of Africa. It could be better named to distinguish it from the other species known as zebra wood.

The trees grow to large size and due to their practical inaccessibility, the handling, which is done by native labor, is extremely hazardous and costly. The bark averages a foot in thickness and is always trimmed at the place of felling. It may be used where diamond matching is desired because of its pronounced lines. Oftentimes it is used for borders on furniture because of the striking effect.

APPENDIX

terms commonly used in referring to wood

AIR-DRIED Removing moisture from green wood by exposing to the air, usually in a yard without artificial heat.

BARK A nontechnical term used to cover all the tissues outside the xylem cylinder— the outer layer of a tree, comprising the inner bark, or thin inner living part (*see* Phloem) and the outer bark, or corky layer composed of dry, dead tissue (Rhytidome).

BUTT DIAMETER The larger cross-sectional measurement of a log, at the end toward the original base of the tree.

CAMBIUM (vascular cambium) The actively dividing layer of cells that lies between, and gives rise to, secondary xylem and phloem or, in other words, the layer of tissue just beneath the bark from which the new wood and bark cells of each year's growth develop.

CELL A chamber or compartment at some time containing a protoplast; a general term for the minute units of wood structure. It includes fibers, vessel segments and other elements of diverse structure and functions.

CELL WALL The limiting membrane of a cell.

CELLULOSE The carbohydrate that is the principal constituent of wood and forms the framework of the cells.

CHECK A separation of the wood, usually extending across the rings of annual growth and commonly resulting from stresses set up in the wood during seasoning.

CLOSE-GRAINED WOOD Wood with narrow and inconspicuous annual rings. The term is sometimes used to designate wood having small and closely spaced pores but in this sense the term "fine-textured" is more correctly used.

COARSE-GRAINED WOOD Wood with wide and conspicuous annual rings; that is, rings in which there is considerable difference between springwood and summerwood. The term is sometimes used to designate wood with large pores such as oak, ash, chestnut and walnut, but in this sense the term "coarse-textured" is more accurate.

COLLAPSE The flattening of single cells or row of cells in hard wood during the drying or pressure treatment of wood, characterized externally by a caved-in or corrugated appearance.

CROSS-BREAK A separation of the wood cells across the grain. Such breaks may be due to internal strain resulting from unequal longitudinal shrinkage or to external forces.

CUP The distortion in a board that deviates flatwise from a straight line across the width of the board.

DENSITY The weight of a body per unit volume. When expressed in the c.g.s. (centimeter-gram-second) system, it is numerically equal to the specific gravity of the same substance.

DRY ROT A term loosely applied to any dry, crumbly rot, but especially to that which, in an advanced stage, permits the wood to be crushed easily to a dry powder. The term is actually a misnomer, since all wood-rotting fungi require considerable moisture for growth.

ELEMENT A general term used for an individual cell.

EPIDERMIS The outermost layer of cells on the primary plant body; often with strongly thickened and cuticularized outer walls; sometimes consisting of more than one layer of cells.

FIBER A general term of convenience in wood anatomy for any long, narrow cell of wood or bast other than vessels and parenchyma.

FIGURE The pattern produced in a wood surface by irregular coloration and by annual growth rings. Rays, knots and such deviations from the regular grain as interlocked and wavy grain also contribute to the design of figure.

GREEN Freshly sawed lumber, or lumber that has received no intentional drying; unseasoned. The term does not apply to lumber that may have become completely wet through waterlogging.

GROWTH LAYER A layer of wood or bark produced apparently during one growing period; frequently, especially in woods of the temperate zones, divisible into early and late wood or bark.

HARDWOOD The botanical group of trees that are broad-leaved and bear flowers. The term has no actual reference to the hardness of the wood. The botanical name for hardwoods is Angiosperm. (When "hard wood" has been used in this book as two words, it means that the wood is hard without respect to whether it is botanically a "hardwood" or a "softwood".)

HEARTWOOD The inner layers of wood, extending from the pith to the sapwood, which in the growing tree have ceased to contain living cells and in which the reserve materials (e.g., starch) have been removed or converted into heartwood substances. Heartwood may be infiltrated with gums, resins and other materials which usually make it darker and more decay-resistant than sapwood.

KILN A heated chamber for drying wood. There are two types of kilns: the compartment kiln which keeps the same temperature and relative humidity throughout any given time, and the progressive kiln which provides drying conditions that increase in severity from entrance to exit.

KILN-DRIED Oven-dried.

LAMINATED WOOD A "piece" of wood built up of plies or layers that have been joined, either with glue or mechanical fastenings. The term is most frequently applied where the plies are too thick to be classified as veneer and when the grain of all plies is parallel.

LIGNIN A principal constituent of wood, second in quantity to cellulose. It encrusts the cell walls and cements the cells together.

LONGITUDINAL Generally, the direction along the length of the grain of wood; axial.

MERISTEM A tissue capable of active cell division, thereby adding new cells to the plant body.

MERISTEM, APICAL The meristem at the growing point of shoots and roots.

MOISTURE CONTENT OF WOOD The weight of the water contained in the wood, usually expressed in percentage of the weight of the oven-dry wood.

NAVAL STORES A term applied to the oils, resins, tars and pitches derived from oleoresin contained in, exuded by, or extracted from trees, chiefly of pine species (genus *Pinus*) or from the wood of such trees.

OLD GROWTH Timber growing in, or harvested from, a mature, naturally established forest. When the trees have grown most or all of their individual lives in active competition with their companions for sunlight and moisture, this timber is usually straight and relatively free of knots.

PARENCHYMA Tissue composed of cells that are typically brick-shaped or isodiametric, and primarily concerned with the storage and distribution of food materials.

PERFORATION, VESSEL An opening from one vessel member to another.

PHLOEM The principal food-conducting tissue of the vascular plants.

PIT A recess in the secondary wall of a cell.

PITH The small soft core occurring in the structural center of a tree, consisting chiefly of parenchyma or soft tissue.

PLYWOOD An assembly made of layers (plies) of veneer, or of veneer in combination with a solid core, joined with an adhesive. The grain of adjoining plies is usually laid at right angles, and almost always an odd number of plies are used to obtain balanced construction.

PORE A term of convenience for the cross section of a vessel.

RADIAL Coincident with a radius, from the axis of the tree or log to the circumference. A radial section is a lengthwise section in a plane that extends from pith to bark.

RATE OF GROWTH The speed at which a tree increases in size. This may be measured radially in the trunk, or in the lumber cut from the trunk, or in the dimension of the crown or other tree part. One unit of measure in wood is in number of annual growth rings per inch.

RAY A ribbonlike aggregate of cells formed by the cambium and extending radially in the xylem and phloem.

RAYS Strips of cells extending radially within a tree and varying in height from a few cells in some species to 4 in. or more in oak (*Quercus*). The rays serve primarily to store food and transport food horizontally in the tree.

RESIN CANAL An intercellular canal containing resin.

RING, ANNUAL In wood and bark, a growth layer of one year as seen in cross section.

RING, ANNUAL GROWTH The growth layer added in a single growing year.

RIPPLE MARKS Fine horizontal striations visible on the tangential longitudinal surfaces of certain woods, due to the storied arrangement of the rays or of the axial elements or of both.

SAP All the fluids in a tree except special secretions and excretions, such as oleoresin.

SAPWOOD The portion of the wood that in the living tree contains living cells and reserve materials. The layers of wood next to the bark, usually lighter in color than the heartwood and actively involved in the life processes of the tree. Under most conditions sapwood is more susceptible to decay than heartwood. It is also more permeable to liquids. Sapwood is not essentially weaker or stronger than heartwood of the same species.

SEASONING Removing moisture from green wood in order to improve its serviceability.

SECOND GROWTH Timber that has grown after the removal by any means of all, or a large portion, of the previous stand.

SHRINKAGE When drying or seasoning, timber gives up moisture to the atmosphere and shrinks in size. The amount of shrinkage differs from one timber to another. Within the same piece of timber, the shrinkage varies in different directions and this may cause cracks.

SILICA The chemical compound silicon dioxide which is present in some woods. It imparts a hardness to the wood and dulls the cutting edges of tools used in machining.

SOFTWOOD The botanical group of trees that have needle or scalelike leaves and are evergreen for the most part—cypress, larch and tamarack being exceptions. The term has no reference to the actual hardness of the wood (see note under Hardwood). Softwoods are often referred to as conifers and botanically they are called gymnosperms.

SPECIFIC GRAVITY The ratio of the weight of a body to the weight of an equal volume of water at some standard temperature.

SPRINGWOOD The portion of the annual growth ring that is formed during the early part of the season's growth. It is usually less dense and weaker mechanically than summerwood.

STAIN A discoloration in wood that may be caused by such diverse agencies as micro-organisms, metal or chemicals. The term also applies to materials used to color wood.

STORIED A term applied to the axial cells and rays in wood when these are arranged in horizontal series on tangential surfaces.

SUMMERWOOD The portion of the annual growth · ring that is formed during the latter part of the yearly growth period. It is usually more dense and stronger mechanically than springwood.

TIMBER STANDING Timber still on the stump.

TRACHEARY ELEMENTS The principal water-conducting elements of the xylem, mostly vessel members and tracheids.

TRACHEID An imperforate wood cell with bordered pits.

TWIST A distortion caused by the turning or winding of the edge of a board so that the four corners of any face are no longer in the same plane.

VENEER Thin sheets of wood from 1/100 to ¼ in. thick.
  Rotary cut — veneer cut in a continuous strip by rotating a log against the edge of a knife, in a veneer lathe.
  Sawed—Veneer produced by sawing.
  Sliced—Veneer sliced off by moving a log, bolt or flitch against a large knife.

VESSEL An axial series of cells that have coalesced to form an articulated tubelike structure of indeterminate length. A union of wood cells which have open ends and are set one above the other, forming continuous tubes. The openings of the vessels on the surface of a piece of wood are usually referred to as pores.

VESSEL MEMBER OR ELEMENT One of the cellular components of a vessel.

VIRGIN GROWTH The original growth of matured trees.

WARP Any variation from a true or plane surface. Warp includes bow, crook, cup and twist or any combination thereof.

WOOD The principal strengthening and water-conducting tissue of stems and roots.

WOOD, COMPRESSION Reaction wood formed typically on the lower sides of branches and leaning or crooked stems of coniferous trees and characterized anatomically by heavily lignified tracheids that are rounded in transverse section and bear spiral cell-wall checks; zones of compression wood are typically denser and darker than the surrounding tissue.

WOOD, DIFFUSE-POROUS Wood in which the pores are of fairly uniform or only gradually changing size and distribution throughout a growth ring.

WOOD, EARLY The less dense, larger-celled, first-formed part of a growth ring.

WOOD, LATE The denser, smaller-celled, later-formed part of a growth ring.

WOOD, NON-PORED Wood devoid of pores or vessels; characteristic of conifers.

WOOD, PORED Wood with vessels; typical of woody flowering plants as opposed to conifers.

WOOD PRESERVATIVE Any substance that for a reasonable length of time will prevent the action of wood-destroying fungi, borers of various kinds and similar destructive life when the wood has been properly coated or impregnated.

WOOD, REACTION Wood with more or less distinctive anatomical characters, formed typically in parts of leaning or crooked stems and in branches and tending to restore the original position, if this has been disturbed.

WOOD, RING-POROUS Wood in which the pores of the early wood are distinctly larger than those of the late wood and form a well-defined zone or ring (cf. Wood, diffuse-porous).

WOOD, TENSION Reaction wood formed typically on the upper sides of branches and leaning or crooked stems of dicotyledonous trees and characterized anatomically by lack of cell-wall lignification and often by the presence of an internal gelatinous layer in the fibers.

WORKABILITY The degree of ease and smoothness of cut obtainable with hand or machine tools.

bibliography

Audas, J. W. 1952. Native trees of Australia. Whitcombe and Tombs Pty. Melbourne

Benson, L. 1957. Plant classification, D. C. Heath. Boston

Boas, I. H. 1947. The commercial timbers of Australia. Government Printer. Melbourne

Bond, C. W. 1950. Colonial timbers (British). Isaac Pitman and Sons. London

British Standards Institution. 1955. British standard nomenclature of commercial timbers. B. S. 881 and 589. British Standards Institution. London

Brown, H. P., Panshin, A. J., and Forsaith, C. C. 1949. Textbook of wood technology. Vol. 1. McGraw-Hill. New York

Burkill, I. H. 1935. A dictionary of the economic products of the Malay Peninsula. Crown Agents for the Colonies. London

Dallimore, W., and Jackson, A. B. 1948. A handbook of the Coniferae. Edward Arnold and Co. London

Dalziel, J. M. 1937. The useful plants of west tropical Africa. Crown Agents for the Colonies. London

Hill, A. F. 1952. Economic botany. McGraw-Hill. New York

Howard, A. L. 1951. A manual of the timbers of the world. Macmillan. London

Jane, F. W. 1956. The structure of wood. Macmillan. New York

Lawrence, G. H. M. 1951. Taxonomy of vascular plants. Macmillan. New York

Little, E. L. 1953. Check list of native and naturalized trees of the United States. Agriculture Handbook No. 41. Washington

Meyer, H. 1933-1936. Buch der Holznamen (Book of wood names). Schaper, M. and Schaper, H. Hannover

Moldenke, H. N., and Moldenke, A. L. 1952. Plants of the Bible. Chronica Botanica Co. Waltham, Mass.

Muenscher, W. C. 1944. Poisonous plants of the United States. Macmillan. New York

Pearson, R. S., and Brown, H. P. 1932. Commercial timbers of India. Central Publication Branch. Government of India. Calcutta.

Penick, S. B. and Co. 1952. Price list and manual. New York

Record, S. J., and Hess, R. W. 1943. Timbers of the New World. Yale University Press. New Haven

Reyes, L. J. 1938. Philippine woods. Department of Agriculture and Commerce. Commonwealth of the Philippines. Technical Bulletin 7. Manilla

Spalt, H. A., and Stern, W. L. 1956. Survey of African woods. (A series still in publication). Tropical Woods 105 et seq.

Stern, W. L. 1957. Guide to institutional wood collections. Tropical Woods 106:1-29

A NOTE ABOUT THE TWO INDEXES

WOOD INDEX

This index includes the names of all the woods referred to in the text, indexed under the noun, not adjective—i.e. Spruce, blue. In addition to the approved common name, whenever the wood is often known by other names, these are also given.

Immediately following most of the scientific (botanical) names in the text is an explanation as to why this particular name has been selected . . . who named it, if that is known, or if the person was a recognized authority in his field . . . and what the name means when translated. This is, to our knowledge, the first time this has ever been done.

Scientific names are set in *italics*. Numbers in the index followed by an asterisk * refer to pages giving a detailed description of a wood. If the number and asterisk (161*) follow a name set in *italics,* this indicates an explanation of the derivation of the name of the wood.

GENERAL INDEX

Listed alphabetically are special items of interest referred to in the text, such as the country from which the wood comes (other than the United States), the special products made from each of the woods, the most durable woods, workability of woods, rare woods, those that finish well, odor and taste of woods, exceptionally tall trees, heavier than average woods, woods that are used as substitutes for other woods, figure in woods, poisonous woods.

This cross-indexing makes available at a glance much of the information contained in this volume. For example, if you want to know what woods come from Formosa, India or Turkey, by referring to the listing of the country in the General Index, you will find after each country the page numbers where these woods are discussed. If you want to know the favorite wood used for making baseball bats, archery equipment, artificial limbs or toothpicks, the index directs you.

wood index

369

370

374

general index

377

Cabinetwork, high-grade 167, 221, 224, 231, 248, 278, 280, 290, 308, 323, 324, 328, 340, 354
Cable guides 254
Cacao butter 157
Calycanthine 118
Calycanthus fertilis 118
Cambium 23, 32, 34
Camerouns 180, 197
Camphor 100, 101
Canada 100, 104, 174, 176, 190, 199, 226, 231, 233, 238, 240, 245, 255, 288, 290, 304, 330, 338, 356
Canary, smoke poison 330
Candles 152
Candlesticks 190, 252, 280
Canes 172, 298, 302, 333
Canoe paddles 338
Canoes 170, 173, 190, 204, 215, 225, 245, 278
Cardwell 250
Carolina allspice 118
Carpathian Mountains 224, 250
Carpentry, general 200, 215, 218, 358
Carpentry, rough 214
Carving, wood for 197, 200, 210, 215, 243, 280, 315, 356
Cascara sagrada 101
Cassia pulp 101
Castor bean 118
Castor oil 118
Cedar chests 205
Cedar-like scent 196, 204, 206
Cedars of Lebanon National Park 86
Cells 24, 38, 39, 75
Cellulose, amount in wood 24, 38; structure 38
Cements 215, 226
Central America 99, 106, 186, 196, 202, 228, 230, 252, 253, 257, 262, 278, 324, 326
Ceylon 106, 109, 172, 184, 219, 221, 249, 276, 280, 282, 314, 320, 324, 329, 346, 356
Chair work 174, 178
Chairs 224, 278; office 300
Cheese containers 179
Chemical drainboards 254
Cherry, bounce 210; cider 208; rum 208
Chessmen 211
Chestnut blight 211
Chestnut, wormy 101, 211
Chewing gum 152, 244, 327
Chile 100, 269, 293, 302
China 100, 102, 106, 110, 112 113, 119, 168, 200, 211
Chippendale furniture 150
Chocolate 100, 110
Christmas trees 154, 226

Chromosomes 26
Church altars 157, 200
Church paneling 172
Cinchonine 102
Cinnamon, Biblical 90; commercial 102
Circassia 352
Clock bearings 254
Cloth, white bark 173
Clothing boxes, mothproof 85
Cloves 102
Coca-Cola 104
Cocaine 102
Cocoa 100
Cocoa butter 100
Coconut 111
Coffee substitute 156
Coffins 182, 350
Cogs, machinery 238
Colombia 102, 109, 121, 186, 196, 252, 262, 265, 276, 298, 355
Color 82, 84
Columns, heavy 292
Combs 197
Conduits, water 282
Conifers See Softwoods
Constantine, Albert, Sr. 229
Constantine, Thomas 150
Constantine & Co. 56, 59, 150, 264
Constantine
   measurement 63
   Wood-O-Rama 136, 137
   woodworking awards 1958, 150
Cordus, Valerius 212
Cork products 212
Corsica 197
Cosmetics 307
Costa Rica 109, 211
Craft wrapping paper 252, 307
Crates 189, 195, 202, 218, 258
Cricket bats 356
Cromwellian furniture 139
Cross, Crucifixion 91
Cross figure 256
Cross figure with wild heart 351
Crossbanding 315
Cross-fire figure 240
Crotch figures 76, 179, 182, 230, 259, 296, 326, 352
Cuba, 99, 121, 170, 252
Cullen 221
Cunningham 280
Cupboards 194
Curare 104
Curly figure 76, 243, 271, 275
Cyprus 347

Dalberg, N. 246, 323, 324, 332, 348
Dance floors 275
Daniell, Samuel 292
deCandolle 46, 293

Decay-resistant wood 269, 276, 292, 298, 348, 350, 356
del Albizzi, Filippo 168, 249
Dendrochronology 24
Density, corkbark 155; ironwood 154
   lignum vitae 254
Deppe, Ferdinand 244
Diderrich 293
Die cutting blocks 254
Digitalis 120
Dimension boards 323
Dock construction 230, 298
Dominican Republic 121
Donnell-Smith 315
Doors 167, 189, 194, 250, 302, 308, 315
Douglas, David 289, 313
Dowels 190
Doyle & Scribner measurement 63
Drugs from trees 98-108
Drums 171
Drying equipment, plant 134
Dutch elm disease 156, 223
Dutch Guiana 189
Dyer, W. T. Thistleton 244
Dyes 38, 84, 229, 276, 296, 328, 333, 352, 355
Dyewood 153, 156, 200, 293

East Indies 172, 212, 221, 296
Ecuador 102, 265, 325, 355
Egypt 108, 114
Elasticity of wood 247, 270
Electrical equipment 155, 318
Electrical insulation 155, 318, 359
Elephants haul teak 346
Elliott, Stephen 311
Elm disease 156, 223
Emin 279
End wood 63
Endlicher, Stephen 320
Engelmann, George 335
England 110, 174, 224, 231, 232, 238, 251, 286, 287, 289, 298, 302, 310, 313, 318, 339, 352, 356, 358
English ivy 119
Engraving blocks 153, 210, 238
Engravings 219
Europe 100, 110, 111-114, 166, 170, 212, 215, 232, 238, 240, 241, 250, 289, 292, 294, 310, 352, 356, 358
Excelsior 152, 179, 214, 357

Farm implements 184, 232, 236, 238
Faux satine crotch 182
Fence posts 154, 194, 204, 244, 246, 251, 278, 298, 308, 333, 344
Fences 184, 204
Ferns, tropical tree 125

381